December 1994

British Bus Publishing

1995 Stagecoach Bus Handbook

The 1995 Stagecoach Bus Handbook is the second edition of the special Bus Handbook series which contains the various fleets of Stagecoach Holdings, both within the United Kingdom and overseas.

Although this book has been produced with the encouragement of, and in co-operation with Stagecoach management, it is not an official Stagecoach fleet list and the vehicles included are subject to variation, particularly as substantial new vehicle deliveries lead to older vehicles being 'cascaded' to other subsidiaries. Some vehicles listed are no longer in regular use on service but are retained for special purposes or preserved by the company. The services operated and the allocation of vehicles to subsidiary companies are subject to variation at any time, although accurate at the time of going to print. The contents are correct to December 1994, and include the fleets of Cleveland, Hull and Hartlepool Transport.

Principal Editors: David Donati and Bill Potter

Acknowledgements:
We are grateful to Keith Grimes, Mark Jameson, John Jones, Colin Lloyd,
Brian Pritchard, Steve Sanderson, the PSV Circle and the Management and officials of Stagecoach
Holdings and their operating companies for their kind assistance and
co-operation in the compilation of this book.
To keep up to date with the fleets we recommend *Buses*, published monthly by Ian Allan Ltd.

The front cover photo is kindly supplied by Stagecoach International
The rear cover photographs are by Stagecoach International and Bill Potter

ISBN 1 897990 22 7
Published by *British Bus Publishing*
The Vyne, 16 St Margarets Drive, Wellington,
Telford, Shropshire, TF1 3PH
© British Bus Publishing, December 1994

Contents

In tandem with the 1983 coach service expansion, a number of school contracts had been secured. These were operated primarily with second-hand Bristol Lodekkas and, by the mid 1980s, Stagecoach was the largest operator of that type, with a fleet of over 20. One of these, 653 HGM335E, has been retained in the Bluebird fleet for special duties. It is seen here at the Scottish Vintage Bus Museum open day at Whitburn. *Phillip Stephenson*

Stagecoach has chosen the Volvo B6 and Dennis Dart for its new mid-size single deck vehicles as part of the major investment. Recently delivered to Fife Scottish is B6 671, M671SSX, seen at the attractive village of Dysart on the Fife coast. *Bill Potter*

Stagecoach

The Stagecoach Group is the largest private sector operator of buses in the United Kingdom. This Bus Handbook details the latest fleets of constituent companies, both in Britain and overseas in Africa, Hong Kong and New Zealand.

Stagecoach can trace its roots back to a small self-drive caravan and caravanette rental business which was formed in Perth in 1976. Trading as Gloagtrotter (later GT Coaches), the business expanded a couple of years later to include minibus private hire under the original partnership of Ann Gloag, now Managing Director of Stagecoach Holdings, and her husband, Robin. Her brother, Brian Souter, now Executive Chairman (an accountant by profession), joined the fledgling organisation in 1980 just prior to its starting regular long distance services at which time the Stagecoach name was adopted, at the suggestion of Ann's other brother, David. This move into regular services was made possible by coach deregulation, introduced in the 1980 Transport Act.

Stagecoach was born out of deregulation and privatisation. The freedom of deregulation and the opportunities of privatisation have facilitated the rapid growth of Stagecoach.

The first service began in October 1980, an overnight run from Dundee to London. Subsequently further legs were added that brought in Aberdeen and Glasgow to form a network of coach services. Soon a network of express services was developed that operated throughout Scotland and ran south of the border to London via Manchester and Birmingham. The quality of vehicle provided on these services quickly improved, exotic foreign double deck coaches becoming the norm from 1982 onwards in marked contrast to the traditional single deck coaches used by their main competitor - The Scottish Bus Group.

In 1983 Mrs Gloag's husband left the business and set up his own company trading as Highwayman Coaches at Errol near Perth. In tandem with the coach service expansion, a number of school contracts had been secured. These were operated primarily with second hand Bristol Lodekkas and, by the mid 1980s, Stagecoach was the largest operator of that type, with a fleet of over 20. In December 1980 Stagecoach took its first step into regular bus service operation when the Perth to Errol route of A & C McLennan of Spittalfield was taken over. It was this route which five years later was to see the start of the 'Provincial Routemaster Revival' which was started by Stagecoach when it introduced Routemasters between Perth and Errol in the spring of 1985. In the early 1980s a number of other Scottish coach operations were absorbed into Stagecoach including Adamson & Low of Edinburgh and Bennetts of Kilwinning in Ayrshire, although both were

In December 1980 Stagecoach took its first step into regular bus service operation when the Perth to Errol route of A & C McLennan of Spittalfield was taken over. One of McLennan's former vehicles, DGS625, has been re-acquired for special duties. A first generation Leyland Tiger PS1/2 it features a body built by McLennan. The large depot site at Spittalfield played an important part in the early expansion of Stagecoach. *Phillip Stephenson*

subsequently disposed of. After a period of consolidation, a further expansion into local bus services was achieved when, in November 1985, the remaining business of McLennan's of Spittalfield was purchased. This gave the Stagecoach company a significant presence in the Tayside region, and most importantly McLennans extensive workings and engineering facilities at Spittalfield which were needed to maintain the ever-growing express coach fleet.

The 1985 Transport Act resulted in the deregulation of bus services outside of London. As the implementation of the Act drew near, the Stagecoach company prepared its plans for a major expansion in the bus market. A new company was formed called Magicbus, and on 26th October 1986 it commenced operating a number of services in Glasgow. The vehicles utilised were primarily Routemasters formerly with London Buses or Northern General and these vehicles brought back conductor operation to the city along with the Routemasters of Kelvin and Clydeside. At the same time there was some expansion of services in Tayside, Stagecoach taking over a number of rural routes not registered commercially by Strathtay Scottish, including the routes north of Perth to Aberfeldy and Pitlochry.

With established operations in Tayside and Glasgow, and an extensive network of express services, the Stagecoach team considered for the first time acquiring operators outside its native Scotland, and took an interest in the pending privatisation of National Bus Company's subsidiaries. An unsuccessful bid for City of Oxford did not deter the directors who turned their attention to Hampshire Bus. A new holding company, Skipburn Limited, was formed by directors Brian Souter and Ann Gloag together with their uncle Fraser McColl and the General Manager of Hampshire Bus. Skipburn was successful in purchasing Hampshire Bus together with Pilgrim Coaches on 2nd April 1987. The new owners did not waste time in rationalising their new acquisition, with Pilgrim Coaches closing down on 26th April 1987. During the summer two properties in Southampton were disposed of and, by 3rd October, the Southampton area operations had been sold to Southern Vectis who formed a new company, trading as Solent Blue Line, to operate the routes. The residual Hampshire Bus operation continues as part of the Stagecoach South company with depots at Andover, Basingstoke and Winchester.

In 1987 Derek Scott joined the board as Finance Director, and has subsequently paid a key role in shaping the growth of the group. While still digesting Hampshire Bus, the Stagecoach board turned its attention to the acquisition of a second NBC subsidiary. This time Cumberland was the target and, following a successful offer, Stagecoach took control of Cumberland Motor Services on 23rd July 1987. The Cumberland operations were based at Whitehaven with depots in Carlisle, Penrith, Keswick, Workington and Millom. The new owners quickly recast the Carlisle city network and introduced crew-operated Routemasters to that city. The Cumberland company acquired a number of its competitors during 1988 including Yeowart's of Whitehaven and Kirkpatrick of Brigham, near Cockermouth.

By November 1987 Fraser McColl had returned to Canada but further expansion of the group was still being sought. Under the NBC privatisation rules only three subsidiaries could be acquired by any purchaser. However, Hampshire Bus and Pilgrim Coaches had been classed as one unit, Cumberland a second and, therefore, Stagecoach was able to acquire United Counties. The area of operation encompassed Bedford, Corby, Huntingdon, Kettering and Northampton and was the group's first presence in the Midlands. As with Cumberland, it was not long before the potential of Routemasters was realised and the Corby and Bedford networks received a fleet of these vehicles soon after the Stagecoach acquisition.

During 1988 Ewan Brown joined the board of directors in a non-executive capacity. Being a Merchant Banker by profession, and a former director of the Scottish Bus Group, he brought valuable skills and knowledge to the management team.

Up to this point the Stagecoach Group had acquired three NBC companies. All were operating a typical mix of National Bus Company standard vehicles which primarily consisted of Leyland Nationals and Leopards, and Bristol VRTs. Additionally, the fleet in Scotland was mainly secondhand Routemasters and Bristol Lodekkas together with Volvo B58 and Neoplan coaches for the express network. Vehicles in Scotland were in the now standard Stagecoach livery of white with blue, red and mustard (later to become orange) stripes and it was decided that in order to provide flexibility and enable vehicles to be transferred between fleets, all vehicles in the group would be painted in this corporate style. Very quickly the new livery began to appear on all three English fleets.

New vehicle purchases had to be made in order that the bus companies could maintain and develop their business into the 1990s and early purchases of Alexander-bodied Mercedes 709 minibuses and Leyland Olympians were to be a portent of large numbers of vehicles of these types in years to come. The importance of investing in new vehicles, and its consequent increase in patronage and reduction of maintenance costs, has continued to the present.

The most significant event of 1988 was the private placing of a quantity of Stagecoach shares with institutional investors. This raised £5 million and set the financial scene for Stagecoach to develop into a major force within the bus industry. It was also a sign of things to come, that is the Stock Market floatation five years later.

1989 saw the first Stagecoach acquisition overseas when, in March of that year, it purchased a 51% share in United Transport Malawi Limited from United Transport International. The vehicles operated in Africa are somewhat strange to British eyes with large numbers of ERF Trailblazer and Leyland Victory single deckers, all built to meet the rough African conditions where much mileage is run on dirt roads. Stagecoach did, however, introduce double decker operation to the Malawi fleet with Daimler CVG6 double deckers previously operated in Hong Kong by the Kowloon Motor Bus Company. Several of these, together with a Bristol FLF, are now withdrawn as the company has taken delivery of Dennis Dragons. City services and long distance express routes are operated from four depots based in Blantyre (Makata Road), Chichiri, Lilongwe and Mzuzu.

Having ventured into Africa, Stagecoach soon returned to the acquisition trail in England. East Midland Motor Services had been sold to its management by NBC, but in April 1989 the management decided to sell its entire share holding, Stagecoach being the purchaser. The operation was conducted under East Midland, Mansfield & District, and Rainworth Travel names in the East Midland area, and in addition there were two Frontrunner operations, one based in Essex and the other in north west Derbyshire and eastern Greater Manchester. The

Frontrunner South East operation was quickly sold on to Ensign Bus of Purfleet while the Derbyshire/Manchester operation was absorbed by Ribble. This left the East Midland management to concentrate in its own territory and soon its coaching operations were consolidated into Rainworth Travel which was renamed Midland Travel. The bus operations are based on Worksop, Chesterfield and Mansfield and, as with other acquisitions, former London Routemasters were again tried, this time in Mansfield where Routemaster operation lasted until 1991. In May 1993 the Midland Travel coaching operation was sold to Skills of Nottingham.

Only a matter of days after the East Midland acquisition, a further company was acquired from its management. Ribble Motor Services Limited, based in the north west of England, had been bought by its management team and had subsequently purchased, from United Transport, the Bee Line Buzz Company - a large minibus operation based in Manchester, together with the Zippy minibus operation based in Preston.

Having added two major bus companies in North West England to one it already owned, Stagecoach embarked upon a reorganisation and rationalisation of its interests in the area. The Barrow-in-Furness municipal undertaking had been in financial difficulties for some time, following heavy competition with Ribble, and its services and depot were acquired in May 1989. For operational control reasons, and to align with the county boundaries, Ribble's South Cumbrian and Lake District operations were transferred to Cumberland Motor Services which also took control in Barrow. This concentrated Cumberland into the county of Cumbria and Ribble into Lancashire and Greater Manchester. In September of 1989 Ribble sold its Bee Line Buzz subsidiary and some of its own Ribble Manchester operations to the Drawlane Group though it retained the Preston-based Zippy minibuses, a name now used for all Ribble minibus operations. Having lost depots at Barrow, Ulverston and Kendal to Cumberland and the Manchester operation passing to Drawlane, Ribble was left to concentrate on the central area which consists of the old Lancashire towns of Blackburn, Bolton, Chorley, Clitheroe, Fleetwood, Lancaster, Morecambe and Preston, the largest expansion being at Bolton.

Despite the activity in England there were still changes taking place in Scotland during 1989. On 19th June new bus services in and around the cities of Perth and Dundee were introduced, primarily in competition with Strathtay Scottish, whose managing director, Neil Renilson was recruited by the group at the same time. This new network was branded Perth Panther and, over a prolonged period of competition, in which both operators used Routemasters on Perth City services, resulted in Strathtay closing their Crieff depot and operations in 1991 and their Perth depot and operations in the summer of 1993.

Perhaps the most surprising development of 1989 was the decision by Stagecoach to sell the express coach operations that had been the genesis of the company. On 4th August 1989 the company announced the sale of its express network to National Express who re-branded the operation as Caledonian Express. With this sale Stagecoach clearly indicated that it was to concentrate on local bus operations in future. The Scottish operations saw further expansion when Inverness Traction was purchased from receivership in November. Inverness Traction had been competing with Highland Scottish on town services in Inverness since 1987. Stagecoach placed this Inverness operation under the Magicbus and Perth Panther management, and renamed the Magicbus company Stagecoach Scotland Ltd as the holding company for its Glasgow, Tayside and Inverness operations. All of these operations were carving out their market through head to head competition with established state-owned operators, whereas in England established operators had been purchased, and competitive pressures were the other way round.

The south coast of England was not neglected either. In August 1989 the management of Southdown decided to sell out to Stagecoach. This brought a sixth former NBC subsidiary into the fold and Stagecoach then acquired, in October, the operations of Portsmouth City Bus from Southampton City Bus. In December 1989 Hastings and District was added when the management sold the company which it had bought from NBC.

In 1990 there was expansion overseas with the purchase of Gray Coach Lines of Toronto, Canada. This brought to the Stagecoach Group an extensive network of express coach services throughout eastern Canada together with Niagara Falls sightseeing tours and the Toronto City/Airport express coach service. The venture proved to be unsuccessful in financial terms and the Group's interest in Gray Coach Lines was sold in December 1992, but not before a number of Stagecoach Scotland Bristol FLFs had been transferred for sightseeing tour work.

One result of the large expansion on the south coast of England was an inquiry by the Monopolies and Mergers Commission that subsequently instructed Stagecoach to divest themselves of Portsmouth City Bus, and this operation was subsequently sold to Transit Holdings in January 1991. The South of England subsidiaries that remained were then restructured and consolidated in April 1992 when a new company, Stagecoach South Limited, was given overall control of Hastings Buses, Southdown and Hampshire Bus. As part of the reorganisation Southdown was split into two operating companies, Sussex Coastline Buses and South Coast Buses, the latter also taking in Hastings Buses. The Southdown name was discontinued, and South Coast Buses operates at Eastbourne and Hastings with Coastline Buses trading from Chichester, Havant and Worthing.

Following on from the privatisation of NBC the Government decided to extend privatisation to the Scottish Bus Group. It was decreed that only two companies could be acquired by any one purchaser and Stagecoach completed its quota with the purchase of Bluebird Northern and Fife Scottish during the first half of 1991. Bluebird is based in Aberdeen and also has depots at Ballater, Elgin, Fyvie, Macduff, Peterhead and Stonehaven, together with several outstations. Bluebird was acquired in March and its archaic legal company name of Northern Scottish Omnibuses Ltd was quickly changed to Bluebird Buses Ltd. Bluebird was placed under common management with Stagecoach Scotland Ltd and its fleet renumbered into a single series.

By July of 1991 the Fife company was also under the Stagecoach umbrella. In line with the company name operations are concentrated in the Kingdom of Fife with depots at Aberhill (Methil), Cowdenbeath, Dunfermline, Glenrothes, Kirkcaldy and St Andrews. In the autumn of 1991 Stagecoach Scotland further expanded when it took over the remaining Inverness and Easter Ross area operations from Highland, adding some 30 extra buses to the Inverness Traction Fleet, plus the former Highland depot at Tain. With two former SBG companies now under its wing, plus the Perth and Inverness operations, Stagecoach had established a strong presence on the eastern side of Scotland. In line with Stagecoach policy the corporate colours started to appear on the newly-acquired fleets and fleet renewal commenced in line with group policy, primarily involving Alexander-bodied Mercedes minibuses and Leyland Olympians. There were also transfers north of the border of vehicles from the English companies which resulted in some unfamiliar types of vehicles being introduced into Scotland, especially ECW-bodied Bristol VRTs. The VRT had been despised by SBG with all its examples being exchanged for NBC-owned Bristol FLFs.

November 1991 saw further expansion in Africa. British Electric Traction (BET) had decided to divest themselves of local bus operations throughout the world and Stagecoach saw potential in acquiring its Kenya operations. As a result of the deal Stagecoach now has a 75% share of Kenya Bus Services (Nairobi), and a 51% share in Kenya Bus Services (Mombassa). The remaining share holdings are held by the local city councils and both operations are maintained under a franchising arrangements. As in Malawi the ERF Trailblazer and Leyland Victory tend to dominate the fleets though there are a number of unusual vehicles including some manufactured by Isuzu in Japan.

There is one company in the Stagecoach Group which plays a large part in the UK transport system as a whole, but operates no buses! National Transport Tokens was formed in the 1970s to manufacture and distribute concessionary travel tokens to various bodies, mostly local authorities. The aluminium tokens produced by National Transport Tokens are accepted by a variety of operators in lieu of cash fares, including bus companies, taxi firms and rail services. Stagecoach bought a controlling interest in the company in March 1992 and its headquarters were moved from Manchester to Preston. Late in 1992 Brian Cox, Managing Director of Stagecoach South, and Barry Hinkley, Managing Director of Cumberland joined the main board.

It came as a significant surprise in April 1992 when Stagecoach decided to sell another of its initial operations. Having disposed of the express network the deal was now to sell the Glasgow-based Magicbus operation to Kelvin Central Buses. The vehicles transferred included some newly-delivered Dennis Darts and a substantial number of Bristol VRTs and Routemasters, and Glasgow depot was also acquired by Kelvin. The Magicbus name and Stagecoach livery continued in use with Kelvin Central until 1993 as part of the deal.

1992 also saw further expansion of the southern fleet when Stagecoach acquired Alder Valley's operations based at depots in Aldershot, Alton and Hindhead. Alder Valley had been through a particularly disturbed time having had a number of owners since privatisation from NBC, suffering from subsequent fragmentation. The Alder Valley operation acquired by Stagecoach was placed under the Stagecoach South umbrella and is operated under the brand name Hants & Surrey.

Having seen the deregulation and privatisation process in the United Kingdom the New Zealand Government decided to embark on a similar course of action. In October 1992 the Wellington City Transport undertaking was privatised and Stagecoach was the successful bidder. There are three companies involved: Wellington City Transport, with a depot at Karori and an outstation at Kilbirnie; Cityline Auckland based at Papakura and Cityline Hutt Valley with depots at Lower Hutt and Stokes Valley. With its new undertaking, Stagecoach now has experience of operating MAN and Hino vehicles but more interestingly, is now operating electric traction. The Wellington City Transport fleet contains over seventy Volvo trolleybuses while Wellington City Transport's share in Harbour City Cable Car Limited has resulted in Stagecoach having an operating interest in this funicular railway.

Overseas developments in 1992 were not confined to Africa and New Zealand. For some time Stagecoach had held a stake in Speedybus Enterprises Limited of Hong Kong, whose primary functions were to sell advertising space on double deckers it supplied to Chinese municipal bus companies, and to import vehicles to China through Hong Kong. Speedybus also supplied Hong Kong double deckers to Stagecoach Malawi. In 1992 Stagecoach Hong Kong Ltd was formed to operate bus services in Hong Kong, and to gain an operating base in the colony. (Speedybus was primarily a bus dealer and bus advertising contractor rather than an operator and was disposed of in early 1994). In 1994 the company commenced operating services on two commuter routes with five Volvo B10Ms. These vehicles are almost the same as the Stagecoach standard Alexander PS-bodied Volvo B10Ms except that they are fitted with air conditioning to cope with the humid Hong Kong climate.

In the spring of 1992 Lancaster City Council expressed an intention to sell its municipal bus undertaking, much of the network operated comprised joint services with Ribble. As Ribble already had a substantial presence in Lancaster and the surrounding area, Stagecoach was not expected to be a bidder for the operation. However, in order to protect its services, Ribble registered many of Lancaster City's routes and subsequently the City Council decided to liquidate their undertaking, selling the depot and some twelve buses to Ribble. As a result of this acquisition Ribble was able to close its own, smaller, depot in Morecambe and move into the former council depot in Heysham.

Expansion in the south of England continued in 1993 when the management of East Kent sold their company. This is yet another former NBC subsidiary that was purchased by a management team. Again the new acquisition had been placed under the control of Stagecoach South and it now trades under the Stagecoach East Kent name. The East Kent purchase brought with it depots at Ashford, Canterbury, Thanet (Westwood), Dover, Folkestone and Herne Bay and contained a typical mix of former NBC vehicles with Leyland Nationals, Bristol VRs and Olympians together with a substantial number of minibuses. In addition it contained several Metrobus and Scania products. In 1994 East Kent purchased four Dennis low-floor vehicles with Berkhof bodies for the Canterbury Park and Ride service, these being the first such vehicles in the Stagecoach Group.

While the Government has not legislated for the privatisation of municipal bus companies, a number of councils took the opportunity to sell before the end of 1993 to allow the income from the sale to be used on other projects. Grimsby Cleethorpes Transport was jointly owned by the Boroughs of Grimsby and Cleethorpes and the two councils decided to sell the undertaking to Stagecoach as a result of a competitive tendering process. The deal was completed in October 1993 and has now brought the Stagecoach livery to South Humberside. The vehicles acquired are of a typical municipal nature and included substantial numbers of Dennis Dominators and Lances. The last of the five Lances delivered in 1993 was painted into Stagecoach livery before delivery. Grimsby Cleethorpes is managed as part of the East Midland company.

The 1000th new bus to join Stagecoach was handed over to Ann Gloag and Brian Souter on the opening day of Coach & Bus '93; this was a Volvo B6 destined for United Counties. Stagecoach has been the largest UK purchaser of new buses in recent years, and has invested heavily in renewing its fleet and offering passengers modern, comfortable vehicles. The order for new vehicles for delivery in 1995 is the largest annual order for buses in the UK since privatisation began in the 1980s. Purchasing

Late 1993 saw the 1000th new vehicle added to the Stagecoach group. This Volvo B6 with Alexander bodywork destined for United Counties is seen here being received by Ann Gloag (managing director, Stagecoach Holdings) from Ian Galloway (managing director, Alexanders) in the presence of Brian Souter (executive chairman, Stagecoach Holdings) and Bill Cameron (Alexanders). *Bill Potter*

policy continues to be based on Volvo double and single deck chassis together with Mercedes minibuses, though Dennis have supplied the Dart and Javelin in significant numbers. Alexander are the preferred bus body builder with Plaxton as the coach body supplier, although some vehicles have been bodied by Northern Counties.

December 1993 saw a further major acquisition by Stagecoach Holdings. Western Travel Ltd was formed on the privatisation of the Cheltenham and Gloucester company from NBC. Cheltenham and Gloucester operates in both the cities mentioned in its title together with services in Swindon and the Cotswolds based on Stroud. Western Travel itself went on the acquisition trail as part of the NBC privatisation process and acquired the Midland Red South company which brought with it operations in Leamington Spa, Nuneaton, Rugby, Stratford-upon-Avon and Warwick. Western Travel had also secured the eastern part of the National Welsh operation trading as Red & White, adding operations around the Red & White historical base of Monmouthshire and the eastern valleys of South Wales. A further 650 vehicles were added to the Stagecoach Group with this purchase, the first being painted into corporate colours during December 1993, under the Stagecoach West name.

1993 also saw the company become listed on the London Stock Exchange. The successful 1993 share flotation attracted much publicity and the proceeds have given the group access to considerable additional funds with which to expand. Some 80% of Stagecoach UK employees are now shareholders.

1994 has seen the bus industry's consolidation accelerate and Stagecoach's development has seen it move into the larger metropolitan markets of which it has previously only had limited experience. The year opened with the launch of Stagecoach Manchester at the end of January. Although a division within Ribble, it trades separately under its own brand name on the long established 192 route from central Manchester to Hazel Grove south of Stockport. Originally set up as a unit with sixteen B6s, rapid passenger growth called for more and larger vehicles, and the year finished with 23 B10Ms allocated to the route.

The first full scale acquisition was of Western Scottish, a former SBG company, which was sixty-eight per cent owned by its employees. Western is based at Kilmarnock with depots at Ayr, Cumnock, Dumfries and Stranraer, and a number of sub-depots both on the mainland and on the Isles of Arran and Bute. The operating area runs from the southern outskirts of Glasgow right down to Annan where the services meet those of Stagecoach North West's Cumberland division while the fleet comprised 340 vehicles, including a large number of different chassis and bodies.

In July 1994 Busways Travel Services Ltd became a subsidiary company of Stagecoach. The acquisition represented an important development for the group because Busways mainly provides services in the densely populated metropolitan area of Tyne and Wear. Stagecoach had not previously had a significant presence in a metropolitan area and this development should further strengthen the group because of the high usage of public transport in the Tyne and Wear area. A further important feature is that Busways was an Employee Share Ownership Plan (ESOP) company and before the acquisition could proceed, some 1700 employee shareholders had to approve the merger. In the event 99.65% of votes were cast in favour. Busways Travel Services Ltd was a private limited company established by the Transport Act 1985 to acquire the bus undertaking of Tyne and Wear Passenger Transport Executive.

Busways commenced trading in October 1986 under the ownership of the PTA, though its origins can be found in the municipal transport undertakings in Newcastle upon Tyne, South Shields and Sunderland, and also the private companies acquired in 1973 (Armstrong and Galley) and 1975 (Economic). In May 1989 the management/employee buyout was successfully completed. Fifty-one per cent of the shares were purchased by the management of ten while 49% were purchased for employees through the ESOP. The Tyne and Wear Omnibus Company

The breakthrough into London bus operation was achieved at the beginning of September 1994 when the purchase of London Buses' subsidiaries East London and Selkent were announced as part of the privatisation of the capital's red bus fleets. Photographed at the handover ceremony at Hyde Park Corner is Barry Hinkley, Chairman of Stagecoach Selkent and Clive Hodson CBE, Managing Director of London Buses.

Ltd was acquired in November 1989 and in August 1993 Busways acquired a majority shareholding in Welcome Passenger Transport Ltd.

With a fleet of 590 buses and coaches, of which two hundred are less than six years old, the Company provides mainly urban local bus services in the Newcastle upon Tyne, South Shields and Sunderland areas whose combined population is approximately half a million.

Because of the strength of the brand names in the local market the group readily agreed that Busways should retain its distinctive liveries once Busways joined the group and the presentation of trading names was revised to include reference to group membership.

Also in the summer, Stagecoach announced its intention to buy a 20% share in Mainline, the former South Yorkshire PTE bus operation based on Sheffield and Rotherham. In October, however, the Office of Fair Trading decided to investigate this purchase and the result was awaited at the time of press.

The breakthrough into London bus operation was achieved at the beginning of September when the purchase of London Buses' subsidiaries East London and Selkent were announced as part of the privatisation of the capital's red bus fleets. In the case of East London this returned Stagecoach operations to that area of the city following the disposal of East Midland's Frontrunner South East in 1989 to Ensign Bus of Purfleet. Both companies run local suburban services in their respective areas of London as well as trunk routes into the central area. East London's fleet comprises 600 buses operating out of depots at Leyton, Barking, East Ham and Stratford, while Selkent's has 450 buses operating from depots at Bromley, Catford, Plumstead and Orpington.

November brought further expansion in the urban areas of the north east of England, with the acquisition of Cleveland Transit early in the month, and along with it 51% of the share capital of formerly troubled Kingston upon Hull City Transport. Days later, Darlington City Transport ceased trading after Busways established a competing network of services in the town, and with it the birth of Stagecoach Darlington. In the middle of the month Hartlepool Transport joined Stagecoach in an agreed sale. Hartlepool, also based in the county of Cleveland, employed some 145 staff and operated 68 vehicles.

November 1994 was planned to see the return of Stagecoach into Glasgow with the introduction of Stagecoach Glasgow, a 69 vehicle quality operation, in similar fashion to the Manchester unit. However, two days before Stagecoach Glasgow was due to commence operations, Strathclyde Buses announced they would sell 20% of their shares to Stagecoach in a similar style deal to the Mainline share exchange, and the Stagecoach Glasgow operation, staff and 18 Volvo B10Ms passed to SBL.

As 1995 commenced the corporate livery of white with orange, red and blue stripes is now a familiar sight throughout the United Kingdom and is also highly visible in a number of countries overseas.

The investment in new vehicles continues with all the 1994 vehicle order scheduled for delivery by the end of December. For 1995 a further 500 new vehicles are due for delivery within the year. This represents a total expenditure in excess of £40 million and deliveries are scheduled to start in January, with the first Volvo B10Ms and minis, and will continue throughout the year.

The delivery programme consists of 100 Mercedes-Benz 709Ds with Alexander Sprint bodywork, 240 Volvo B10M single-deck buses and 160 Volvo Olympians comprising both the 9.6m and 10.3m versions. Body orders placed so far include 100 Olympians and 200 B10Ms which will carry Alexander products. Bodywork for the remainder has yet to be announced. As regards 1996, firm orders have been placed, and options taken, for delivery of a broadly similar number of vehicles to the 1995 order, and it is intended that the 1996 programme will include a number of DPs (Interurbans or similar) and midibuses, since these types do not feature in the 1995 order.

BLUEBIRD

Bluebird Buses Ltd, Guild Street, Aberdeen, Grampian, AB9 2DR

Depots : King Street, Aberdeen; Montgarrie Road, Alford; Golf Road, Ballater; Castleton Place, Braemar; March Road, Buckie; Stirling Road, Crieff; Pinefield, Elgin; North Road, Forres; Hanover Street, Fraserburgh; Schoolhill, Fyvie; Burnett Road, Inverness; Union Road, Macduff; Longside Road, Mintlaw; Ruthvenfield Road, Perth; St Peter Street, Peterhead; Spittalfield; Spurryhillock Industrial Estate, Stonehaven; Bellabeg, Strathdon and Scotsburn Road, Tain. **Outstations** : Ellon and Inverurie.

002-007

| | | | | | | | | | Leyland Olympian ONLXB/1R | Alexander RL | | H45/32F | 1981 |

002	SSA2X	004	SSA4X	005	SSA5X	006	SSA6X	007	SSA7X
003	SSA3X								

008	K508ESS	Leyland Olympian ON2R50G13Z4	Alexander RL	DPH43/27F	1992	
009	K509ESS	Leyland Olympian ON2R50G13Z4	Alexander RL	DPH43/27F	1992	
010	K510ESS	Leyland Olympian ON2R50G13Z4	Alexander RL	DPH43/27F	1992	
011	K511ESS	Leyland Olympian ON2R50G13Z4	Alexander RL	DPH43/27F	1992	
012	TSO12X	Leyland Olympian ONLXB/1R	Eastern Coach Works	H45/32F	1982	Ex Stagecoach, 1994
013	TSO13X	Leyland Olympian ONLXB/1R	Eastern Coach Works	H45/32F	1982	Ex Stagecoach, 1994
014	TSO14X	Leyland Olympian ONLXB/1R	Eastern Coach Works	H45/32F	1982	Ex Stagecoach, 1994
015	K515ESS	Leyland Olympian ON2R50G13Z4	Alexander RL	DPH43/27F	1992	
016	TSO16X	Leyland Olympian ONLXB/1R	Eastern Coach Works	H45/32F	1982	Ex Stagecoach, 1994
017	TSO17X	Leyland Olympian ONLXB/1R	Eastern Coach Works	H45/32F	1982	Ex Stagecoach, 1994
018	K518ESS	Leyland Olympian ON2R50G13Z4	Alexander RL	DPH43/27F	1992	
019	OMS910W	Leyland Olympian B45-6LXB	Eastern Coach Works	H45/32F	1981	Ex Stagecoach, 1994

020-025

| | | | | | | | | | Leyland Olympian ONLXB/1R | Eastern Coach Works | | H45/32F | 1982 | Ex Stagecoach, 1994 |

020	TSO20X	022	9492SC	023	TSO23X	024	TSO24X	025	TSO15X
021	TSO21X								

026	L26JSA	Volvo Olympian YN2RV18Z4	Northern Counties Palatine I	DPH43/25F	1993
027	L27JSA	Volvo Olympian YN2RV18Z4	Northern Counties Palatine I	DPH43/25F	1993
028	L28JSA	Volvo Olympian YN2RV18Z4	Northern Counties Palatine I	DPH43/25F	1993

Opposite, top: **Photographed returning to its base on the Aberfeldy, Dunkeld and Pitlochry service is 031, TSO31X, a Leyland Olympian with Eastern Coach Works body.** *Bottom*: **Bluebird now operate eighteen of the Stagecoach standard single-deck, the Volvo B10M with Alexander PS bodywork. One of the latest examples is 591, M591OSO.** *R A Smith/ Bluebird Buses*

Despite the inclement weather, Bluebird Buses 015, K515ESS, is resplendent in full livery as it heads for Montrose. It is one of six Olympians supplied in 1992 with high-back seating for increased comfort on the longer services in the area. *Stewart J Brown*

029	TSO29X	Leyland Olympian ONLXB/1R	Eastern Coach Works	H45/32F	1982	Ex Stagecoach, 1994
030	TSO30X	Leyland Olympian ONLXB/1R	Eastern Coach Works	H45/32F	1982	Ex Stagecoach, 1994
031	TSO31X	Leyland Olympian ONLXB/1R	Eastern Coach Works	H45/32F	1982	Ex Stagecoach, 1994
032	TSO32X	Leyland Olympian ONLXB/1R	Eastern Coach Works	H45/32F	1982	Ex Stagecoach, 1994

033-060

Leyland Olympian ONLXB/1R* Alexander RL H45/32F* 1983-85 *044 is DPH43/27F
*049 has a 5LXCT engine

033	YSO33Y	039	YSO39Y	045	A45FRS	051	B351LSO	056	B356LSO
034	YSO34Y	040	YSO40Y	046	A46FRS	052	B352LSO	057	B357LSO
035	YSO35Y	041	YSO41Y	047	A47FRS	053	B353LSO	058	B358LSO
036	YSO36Y	042	YSO42Y	048	B348LSO	054	B354LSO	059	B359LSO
037	YSO37Y	043	YSO43Y	049	B349LSO	055	B355LSO	060	B360LSO
038	YSO38Y	044	A44FRS	050	B350LSO				

061-066

Leyland Olympian ONLXB/1RV Alexander RL DPH43/27F 1986

061	C461SSO	063	C463SSO	064	MHS4P	065	MHS5P	066	C466SSO
062	C462SSO								

067-071

Leyland Olympian ONLXB/1RV Alexander RL H47/30F 1986

067	C467SSO	068	C468SSO	069	C469SSO	070	C470SSO	071	GSO1V

076	MAU146P	Bristol VRT/SL3/6LX	Eastern Coach Works	H39/31F	1976	Ex Stagecoach, 1992
082	OCY910R	Bristol VRT/SL3/501	Eastern Coach Works	H43/31F	1977	Ex East Midland, 1992

085-089

Leyland Olympian ONLXB/1RV Alexander RL DPH43/27F 1987

085	D385XRS	086	D386XRS	087	D387XRS	088	D388XRS	089	D389XRS

090-099

Leyland Olympian ON2R56G13Z4 Alexander RL DPH47/27F 1991-92

090	J120XHH	092	J122XHH	097	J197YSS	098	J198YSS	099	J199YSS
091	J121XHH	096	J196YSS						

100	L110JSA	Volvo Olympian YN2RV18Z4	Northern Counties Palatine I	DPH43/25F	1993	
101	L101JSA	Volvo Olympian YN2RV18Z4	Northern Counties Palatine I	DPH43/25F	1993	
102	L102JSA	Volvo Olympian YN2RV18Z4	Northern Counties Palatine I	DPH43/25F	1993	
103	FDV810V	Bristol VRT/SL3/6LXB	Eastern Coach Works	H43/31F	1980	Ex Stagecoach, 1994
105	FDV816V	Bristol VRT/SL3/6LXB	Eastern Coach Works	H43/31F	1980	Ex Stagecoach, 1994
106u	UWV608S	Bristol VRT/SL3/6LXB	Eastern Coach Works	CO43/31F	1977	Ex Stagecoach, 1991
107	FDV819V	Bristol VRT/SL3/6LXB	Eastern Coach Works	H43/31F	1980	Ex Stagecoach, 1994
108u	UWV609S	Bristol VRT/SL3/6LXB	Eastern Coach Works	CO43/31F	1977	Ex Stagecoach, 1991
109	FDV840V	Bristol VRT/SL3/6LXB	Eastern Coach Works	H43/31F	1980	Ex Stagecoach, 1994
110	JAK210W	Bristol VRT/SL3/6LXB	Eastern Coach Works	H43/31F	1980	Ex Stagecoach, 1994
112	JAK212W	Bristol VRT/SL3/6LXB	Eastern Coach Works	H43/31F	1980	Ex Stagecoach, 1994
120	SAO410R	Bristol VRT/SL3/501	Eastern Coach Works	H43/31F	1977	Ex Cumberland, 1991
122	SAO412R	Bristol VRT/SL3/501	Eastern Coach Works	H43/31F	1977	Ex Cumberland, 1991
128	RJT155R	Bristol VRT/SL3/6LXB	Eastern Coach Works	H43/31F	1977	Ex Stagecoach, 1992

131-138

Leyland Leopard PSU3E/4R Duple Dominant I C49F 1977

131	RRS46R	132	RRS47R	133	RRS48R	135	RRS50R	138	RRS53R

139-144

Leyland Leopard PSU3E/4R Alexander AT DP49F 1979

139	CRS60T	141	CRS62T	142	CRS63T	143	CRS68T	144	CRS69T
140	CRS61T								

145	CRS70T	Leyland Leopard PSU3E/4R	Duple Dominant I	C49F	1979
146	CRS71T	Leyland Leopard PSU3E/4R	Duple Dominant I	C49F	1979
147	CRS73T	Leyland Leopard PSU3E/4R	Duple Dominant I	C49F	1979
148	CRS74T	Leyland Leopard PSU3E/4R	Duple Dominant I	C49F	1979

152-158

Leyland Leopard PSU3E/4R Alexander AYS DP49F* 1980 Ex Stagecoach, 1994
*155/7 are B53F

152	GSO89V	154	GSO91V	156	GSO93V	157	GSO94V	158	GSO95V
153	GSO90V	155	GSO92V						

In October 1994 the Stagecoach Scotland and Bluebird companies were merged under the Bluebird Buses name, though the operating names of Stagecoach, Perth Panther, Inverness Traction and Bluebird continue. Leyland Leopards are regularly found on the more rural services throughout Perthshire. 168, 145CLT, is seen while working a private hire. *R A Smith*

159	KRS529V	Leyland Leopard PSU3E/4R	Duple Dominant II Express	C49F	1980	
160	KRS531V	Leyland Leopard PSU3E/4R	Duple Dominant II Express	C49F	1980	
161	KRS532V	Leyland Leopard PSU3E/4R	Duple Dominant II Express	C49F	1980	
163	JSA101V	Leyland Leopard PSU3F/4R	Alexander AT	DP49F	1980	
164	JSA102V	Leyland Leopard PSU3F/4R	Alexander AT	DP49F	1980	
165	JSA103V	Leyland Leopard PSU3F/4R	Alexander AT	DP49F	1980	
166	JSA104V	Leyland Leopard PSU3F/4R	Alexander AT	DP49F	1980	

167-171

		Leyland Leopard PSU3G/4R	Duple Dominant II Express	C49F	1981	Ex Stagecoach, 1994

167	4585SC	168	145CLT	169	OVL473	170	LSK528	171	866NHT

188	DWF188V	Bristol VRT/SL3/6LXB	Eastern Coach Works	H43/31F	1979	Ex Stagecoach, 1994
190	DWF190V	Bristol VRT/SL3/6LXB	Eastern Coach Works	H43/31F	1979	Ex Stagecoach, 1994
191	DWF191V	Bristol VRT/SL3/6LXB	Eastern Coach Works	H43/31F	1979	Ex Stagecoach, 1994
193	DWF193V	Bristol VRT/SL3/6LXB	Eastern Coach Works	H43/31F	1979	Ex Stagecoach, 1994
213	HNE252V	Leyland Leopard PSU5C/4R	Duple Dominant II Express	C53F	1980	Ex Stagecoach, 1994
214	HNE254V	Leyland Leopard PSU5C/4R	Duple Dominant II Express	C53F	1980	Ex Stagecoach, 1994
215	JND260V	Leyland Leopard PSU5C/4R	Duple Dominant II Express	C53F	1980	Ex Stagecoach, 1994
216	XRM772Y	Leyland Leopard PSU5C/4R	Duple Dominant III	C57F	1983	Ex Hardie's Coaches, Aberchirder, 1994
217u	D523KSE	Bedford YNV Venturer	Duple 320	C57F	1986	Ex Hardie's Coaches, Aberchirder, 1994
218	NPA229W	Leyland Leopard PSU3E/4R	Plaxton Supreme IV Express	C53F	1981	Ex Stagecoach, 1994
219	YSF98S	Leyland Leopard PSU3D/4R	Alexander AYS	B53F	1977	Ex Stagecoach, 1994
220	YSF100S	Leyland Leopard PSU3E/4R	Alexander AYS	B53F	1977	Ex Stagecoach, 1994
221	WFS135W	Leyland Leopard PSU3F/4R	Alexander AYS	B53F	1980	Ex Stagecoach, 1994
222	WFS136W	Leyland Leopard PSU3F/4R	Alexander AYS	B53F	1980	Ex Stagecoach, 1994
223	WFS137W	Leyland Leopard PSU3F/4R	Alexander AYS	B53F	1980	Ex Stagecoach, 1994
227w	D27PVS	Freight Rover Sherpa	Dormobile	B16F	1987	Ex Norrie, New Deer, 1994
229w	E992MSE	Toyota Coaster HB31R	Caetano Optimo	C19F	1987	Ex Hardie's Coaches, Aberchirder, 1994
230	D435RYS	Mercedes-Benz 609D	Scott	C24F	1987	Ex Airpark, Linwood, 1990
231	D436RYS	Mercedes-Benz 609D	Scott	C24F	1987	Ex Airpark, Linwood, 1990
233	E364YGB	Mercedes-Benz 609D	Scott	C24F	1988	Ex Airpark, Linwood, 1990
234	E842KAS	Mercedes-Benz 609D	Reeve Burgess	C23F	1988	Ex Glenlivet & District, 1990
235	E947BHS	Mercedes-Benz 609D	Scott	C24F	1988	Ex Whitelaw, Stonehouse, 1990
236	F77HAU	Mercedes-Benz 609D	Scott	C24F	1988	Ex Skills, Sheffield, 1990

237	F164XCS	Mercedes-Benz 609D	Scott	C24F	1989	Ex Clyde Coast, Ardrossan, 1990		
238	F862FWB	Mercedes-Benz 609D	Whittaker	C24F	1989	Ex Metcalfe, Ferryhill, 1990		
239	D322MNC	Mercedes-Benz 609D	Made-to-Measure	DP25F	1986	Ex Fife Scottish, 1994		
240	B875GSG	Mercedes-Benz L608D	Northern Scottish	C24F	1984	Ex Fife Scottish, 1994		
241	C901HWF	Mercedes-Benz L608D	Reeve Burgess	DP19F	1985	Ex Fife Scottish, 1994		
248	A353ASF	Mercedes-Benz L608D	Devon Conversions	C19F	1983	Ex Norrie, New Deer, 1994		
249	C701RSS	Mercedes-Benz L608D	Scott	C25F	1986	Ex Norrie, New Deer, 1994		
250u	A121XWB	Mercedes-Benz L608D	Whittaker	C23F	1983	Ex Stagecoach, 1991		

251-292

		Mercedes-Benz 709D	Alexander Sprint	B25F*	1990	Ex Stagecoach, 1991-94		
						*279-292 are B23F		

251	G251TSL	258	G258TSL	272	G272TSL	279	G279TSL	287	G287TSL
252	G252TSL	259	G259TSL	273	G273TSL	282	G282TSL	288	G288TSL
253	G253TSL	260	G260TSL	274	G274TSL	283	G283TSL	289	G289TSL
254	G254TSL	261	G261TSL	275	G275TSL	284	G284TSL	290	G290TSL
255	G255TSL	262	G262TSL	276	G276TSL	285	G285TSL	291	G291TSL
256	G256TSL	270	G270TSL	277	G277TSL	286	G286TSL	292	G292TSL
257	G257TSL	271	G271TSL	278	G278TSL				

301	L301JSA	Mercedes-Benz 709D	Alexander Sprint	DP25F	1993
302	L302JSA	Mercedes-Benz 709D	Alexander Sprint	DP25F	1993
303	L303JSA	Mercedes-Benz 709D	Alexander Sprint	DP25F	1993

304-314

		Mercedes-Benz 709D	Alexander Sprint	DP25F	1990	Ex Stagecoach, 1991-94

304	G193PAO	307	G196PAO	309	G198PAO	311	G200PAO	313	G202PAO
305	G194PAO	308	G197PAO	310	G199PAO	312	G201PAO	314	G203PAO
306	G195PAO							

315-321

		Mercedes-Benz 709D	Alexander Sprint	DP25F	1993-94

315	L315JSA	317	M317RSO	319	M319RSO	320	M320RSO	321	M321RSO
316	L316JSA	318	M318RSO						

421	A116ESA	Leyland Tiger TRBTL11/2R	Alexander P	B52F	1983	
422	A117ESA	Leyland Tiger TRBTL11/2R	Alexander P	B52F	1983	
423	A118ESA	Leyland Tiger TRBTL11/2R	Alexander P	B52F	1983	

424-430

		Leyland Tiger TRBLXB/2RH	Alexander P	B52F	1984	

424	A121GSA	426	A123GSA	428	A125GSA	429	A126GSA	430	A127GSA
425	A122GSA	427	A124GSA						

432	PSO177W	Leyland Tiger TRCTL11/3R	Duple Dominant IV	C53F	1981	Ex Kelvin Scottish, 1989
434w	PSO178W	Leyland Tiger TRCTL11/3R	Duple Dominant IV	C51F	1981	Ex Kelvin Scottish, 1989
436w	RRS225X	Leyland Tiger TRCTL11/3R	Duple Goldliner IV	C53F	1982	Ex Eastern Scottish, 1987
440w	CSO386Y	Leyland Tiger TRCTL11/2R	Duple Dominant II Express	C49F	1983	

442-446

		Leyland Tiger TRCTL11/2RP	Alexander TC	C51F*	1985	*443 is C49F; 446 is C47F

442	TSV718	443	TSV719	444	TSV720	445	TSV721	446	TSV722

447	126ASV	Leyland Tiger TRBTL11/2R	Alexander TE	C51F	1983	Ex Kelvin Scottish, 1986
448	127ASV	Leyland Tiger TRBTL11/2R	Alexander TE	C51F	1983	Ex Kelvin Scottish, 1986
449	128ASV	Leyland Tiger TRBTL11/2R	Alexander TE	C51F	1983	Ex Kelvin Scottish, 1986

450-454

		Leyland Tiger TRCTL11/3RH	Alexander TC	C57F	1987	

450	BSK744	451	LSK547	452	LSK548	453	147YFM	454	BSK756

455	HSK760	Leyland Tiger TRCLXC/2RH	Duple 320	C53F	1986	Ex Central Scottish, 1989
456	C111JCS	Leyland Tiger TRCLXC/2RH	Duple 320	C53F	1986	Ex Central Scottish, 1989
458	WAO643Y	Leyland Tiger TRCTL11/2R	Alexander TE	C47F	1983	Ex Ribble, 1994
459	A40XHE	Leyland Tiger TRCTL11/2R	Alexander TE	DP49F	1983	Ex East Midland, 1991

460-465

		Leyland Tiger TRCTL11/3R	Duple Laser	C53F	1984	Ex National Welsh, 1992

460	AAX600A	462	AKG232A	463	AAX589A	464	AAX601A	465	AKG162A
461	AAX631A							

Photographed in Perth, complete with Stagecoach name and Perth Panther logo is 252, G252TSL, a Mercedes-Benz 709D with Alexander's Sprint design of body. A comparison with later deliveries show the newer vehicles have larger destination displays repeated on the side and rear. *Iain MacGregor*

The majority of Alexander's P-type buses are now in the Stagecoach group. Photographed in Aberdeen is Leyland Tiger 423, A118ESA, complete with attractive Bluebird names in traditional style which are to be retained in preference to the new-look fleetnames now being applied to the English and Welsh fleets. *Murdoch Currie*

Ten new Dennis Darts joined the Bluebird fleet in 1993 for Inverness Traction duties. The Inverness Traction business was purchased from receivers in 1989, the original operation being a minibus-based drivers co-operative which competed with Highland Scottish on town services.
Roy Marshall

466	NIB4138	Leyland Tiger TRCTL11/3R	Duple Laser	C51F	1984	Ex Stagecoach, 1994	
467	NIB5455	Leyland Tiger TRCTL11/3R	Duple Laser	C51F	1984	Ex Stagecoach, 1994	
468	A663WSU	Leyland Tiger TRBTL11/2RP	Alexander TE	DP53F	1983	Ex Kelvin Central, 1993	
469	NIB5232	Leyland Tiger TRCTL11/3RH	Plaxton Paramount 3200 II	C51F	1985	Ex Stagecoach, 1994	
470	NIB5233	Leyland Tiger TRCTL11/3RH	Plaxton Paramount 3200 II	C51F	1985	Ex Stagecoach, 1994	
471	E648KCX	DAF MB230LB615	Van Hool Alizée	C53FT	1987	Ex Selkent, 1994	
472	F637OHD	DAF MB230LB615	Plaxton Paramount 3500 III	C53FT	1988	Ex Selkent, 1994	
473	J35GCX	DAF SB2305DHS585	Duple 340	C57F	1992	Ex Selkent, 1994	
474	J36GCX	DAF SB2305DHS585	Duple 340	C57F	1992	Ex Selkent, 1994	
475	K536RJX	DAF MB230LB615	Van Hool Alizée	C51F	1993	Ex Selkent, 1994	
476	K537RJX	DAF MB230LB615	Van Hool Alizée	C51F	1993	Ex Selkent, 1994	
477	K538RJX	DAF MB230LB615	Van Hool Alizée	C51F	1993	Ex Selkent, 1994	
478	K539RJX	DAF MB230LB615	Van Hool Alizée	C51F	1993	Ex Selkent, 1994	

501-512   Dennis Dart 9.8SDL3017   Alexander Dash   B41F   1992

501	J501FPS	504	J504FPS	507	J507FPS	509	J509FPS	511	J511FPS
502	J502FPS	505	J505FPS	508	J508FPS	510	J510FPS	512	J512FPS
503	J503FPS	506	J506FPS						

513-522   Dennis Dart 9.8SDL3017   Alexander Dash   B40F   1993

513	K101XHG	515	K103XHG	517	K105XHG	519	K107XHG	521	K109XHG
514	K102XHG	516	K104XHG	518	K106XHG	520	K108XHG	522	K110XHG

530-536   Volvo B10M-62   Plaxton Premiére Interurban DP51F   1994

530	M530RSO	532	M532RSO	534	M534RSO	533	M533RSO	536	M536RSO
531	M531RSO	533	M533RSO						

545	1412NE	Volvo B10M-61	Van Hool Alizée	C53F	1986	Ex Hardie's Coaches, Aberchirder, 1994	
546	TSV778	Volvo B10M-61	Van Hool Alizée	C53F	1986	Ex Hardie's Coaches, Aberchirder, 1994	
547	TSV779	Volvo B10M-61	Van Hool Alizée	C53F	1987	Ex Rainworth Travel, 1992	
548	TSV780	Volvo B10M-61	Van Hool Alizée	C53F	1987	Ex Shearings, 1991	
549	TSV781	Volvo B10M-61	Van Hool Alizée	C53F	1987	Ex Shearings, 1991	
550	CSU920	Volvo B10M-61	Van Hool Alizée	C53F	1987	Ex Rainworth Travel, 1992	

551	CSU921	Volvo B10M-61	Van Hool Alizée	C53F	1987	Ex Shearings, 1991
552	CSU922	Volvo B10M-61	Van Hool Alizée	C53F	1987	Ex Shearings, 1991
553	CSU923	Volvo B10M-61	Van Hool Alizée	C53F	1987	Ex Shearings, 1991

561-570
Volvo B10M-60 — Plaxton Premiére Interurban — DP51F — 1993 — 561/70 ex Stagecoach, 1994

| 561 | K561GSA | 563 | K563GSA | 565 | K565GSA | 567 | K567GSA | 569 | K569GSA |
| 562 | K562GSA | 564 | K564GSA | 566 | K566GSA | 568 | K568GSA | 570 | K570GSA |

571-578
Volvo B10M-55 — Alexander PS — B49F — 1993 — Ex Stagecoach, 1994

| 571 | K571LTS | 573 | K573LTS | 575 | K575LTS | 577 | K577LTS | 578 | K578LTS |
| 572 | K572LTS | 574 | K574LTS | 576 | K576LTS | | | | |

579-588
Volvo B10M-60 — Plaxton Premiére Interurban — DP51F — 1993

| 579 | L579JSA | 581 | L581JSA | 583 | L583JSA | 585 | L585JSA | 587 | L587JSA |
| 580 | L580JSA | 582 | L582JSA | 584 | L584JSA | 586 | L586JSA | 588 | L588JSA |

589-598
Volvo B10M-55 — Alexander PS — DP49F — 1994

| 589 | M589OSO | 591 | M591OSO | 593 | M593OSO | 595 | M595OSO | 597 | M597OSO |
| 590 | M590OSO | 592 | M592OSO | 594 | M594OSO | 596 | M596OSO | 598 | M598OSO |

601	UYJ654	AEC Routemaster R2RH	Park Royal	H36/28R	1962	Ex Stagecoach, 1994
602	EDS50A	AEC Routemaster R2RH	Park Royal	H36/28R	1960	Ex Stagecoach, 1994
603	NSG636A	AEC Routemaster R2RH	Park Royal	H36/28R	1962	Ex Stagecoach, 1994
604	YTS820A	AEC Routemaster 2R2RH	Park Royal	H36/28R	1963	Ex Stagecoach, 1994
605	USK625	AEC Routemaster R2RH	Park Royal	H36/28R	1961	Ex Stagecoach, 1994
607	LDS201A	AEC Routemaster 2R2RH	Park Royal	H36/28R	1963	Ex Stagecoach, 1994
608	490CLT	AEC Routemaster R2RH	Park Royal	H36/28R	1962	Ex Selkent, 1994
609	XSL596A	AEC Routemaster 2R2RH	Park Royal	H36/28R	1962	Ex Stagecoach, 1994
614	LDS210A	AEC Routemaster R2RH	Park Royal	H36/28R	1962	Ex Stagecoach, 1994
616	ALD968B	AEC Routemaster 2R2RH	Park Royal	H36/28R	1964	Ex Stagecoach, 1994
621	J917LEM	Volvo B10M-61	Plaxton Paramount 3500 III	C46FT	1991	Ex Express Travel, 1994
622	J919LEM	Volvo B10M-61	Plaxton Paramount 3500 III	C46FT	1991	Ex Express Travel, 1994
623	J455FSR	Volvo B10M-61	Plaxton Paramount 3500 III	C46FT	1991	Ex Express Travel, 1994
624	J456FSR	Volvo B10M-61	Plaxton Paramount 3500 III	C46FT	1992	Ex Speedlink, 1994
625	G386PNV	Volvo B10M-61	Plaxton Paramount 3500 III	C46FT	1990	Ex Express Travel, 1994
626	G387PNV	Volvo B10M-61	Plaxton Paramount 3500 III	C46FT	1990	Ex Speedlink, 1994
650	FES831W	Volvo B58-61	Duple Dominant IV	DP59F	1981	Ex Stagecoach, 1994
651u	NMY640E	AEC Routemaster R2RH2	Park Royal	H32/24F	1967	Ex Kelvin Scottish, 1993
652w	GRS343E	Albion Viking VK43AL	Alexander Y	DP40F	1967	Ex Stagecoach, 1994
653u	HGM335E	Bristol FLF6G	Eastern Coach Works	H44/34F	1967	Ex Stagecoach, 1994
657u	DGS625	Leyland Tiger PS1/2	McLennan	C37F	1951	Ex Stagecoach, 1994
696	UWV605S	Bristol VRT/SL3/6LXB	Eastern Coach Works	CO43/31F	1977	Ex East Midland, 1992

Previous Registrations:

126ASV	BMS511Y	CSU920	D550MVR	NIB5233	B48DWE
127ASV	BMS513Y	CSV921	D551MVR	NIB5455	A46YAK
128ASV	BMS515Y	CSU922	D552MVR	NSG636A	164CLT
1412NE	C325DND	CSU923	D553MVR	OVL473	ORS108W, TSV720, PSO29W
145CLT	ORS107W, TSV719, PSO28W	DGS625	From new	PSO177W	BSG549W, 630DYE, WGB175W, CSU920
147YFM	D439XRS	GSO1V	C471SSO	PSO178W	BSG547W, WLT742, WGB176W, CSU921
4585SC	ORS106W, TSV718, PSO27W			RRS225X	MSC556X, CSU923
866NHT	ORS110W, TSV722, PSO32W	HSK760	C110JCS	TSV718	B328LSA
9492SC	TSO19X	KRS529V	EDS50A, WLT560	TSV719	B329LSA
A663WSU	A120GLS, WLT976	KRS531V	HSA97V, CSU921	TSV720	B330LSA
AAX589A	A216VWO	KRS532V	HSA98V, CSU922	TSV721	B331LSA
AAX600A	A219VWO	LDS201A	607DYE	TSV722	B332LSA
AAX601A	A218VWO	LDS210A	245CLT	TSV778	C330DND
AAX631A	A222VWO	LSK528	ORS109W, TSV721, PSO31W	TSV779	D547MVR
AKG162A	A223VWO	LSK547	D437XRS	TSV780	D548MVR
AKG232A	A229VWO	LSK548	D438XRS	TSV781	D549MVR
BSK744	D436XRS	MHS4P	C464SSO	USK625	WLT980
BSK756	E640BRS	MHS5P	C465SSO	UYJ654	224CLT
CSO386Y	ASA9Y, TSV779	NIB4138	A45YAK	XSL596A	289CLT
CSO389Y	ASA8Y, TSV778	NIB5232	B47DWE	YTS820A	599CLT

BUSWAYS

Busways Travel Services Ltd, Manors,
Newcastle-upon-Tyne, NE1 2EL

Depots : Shields Road, Byker (Armstrong Galley, Blue Bus, Newcastle Busways); Stamfordham Road, Slatyford (Newcastle Busways); Wheatsheaf, Sunderland (Sunderland Busways, Tyne & Wear Omnibus and Favourite); Dean Road, Chichester, South Shields (Economic, South Shields).

3	ONL645X	Leyland Leopard PSU5D/4R	Plaxton Supreme V	C53F	1982	Ex Jumbulance project, 1986
4	KSU454	Leyland Tiger TRCTL11/3R	Van Hool Alizée	C50FT	1985	
5	KSU455	Leyland Tiger TRCTL11/3R	Van Hool Alizée	C50FT	1985	
6	KSU456	Leyland Tiger TRCTL11/3R	Van Hool Alizée	C53F	1985	
7	KSU457	Leyland Tiger TRCTL11/3RZ	Plaxton Paramount 3500 III	C53F	1988	
8	KSU458	Leyland Royal Tiger RT	Van Hool Alizée	C49FT	1986	
9	KSU459	Leyland Tiger TRCTL11/3RH	Van Hool Alizée	C48FT	1986	
14	644HKX	Leyland Tiger TRCTL11/3R	Plaxton Paramount 3500 II	C53F	1985	Ex Fowler, Holbeach, 1989
15	1JVK	Leyland Tiger TRCTL11/3RH	Plaxton Paramount 3500 III	C53F	1987	
16	2JVK	Leyland Tiger TRCL10/3ARZM	Plaxton Paramount 3200 III	C53F	1988	Ex Shearings, 1993
17	491JVX	Leyland Tiger TRCL10/3ARZM	Plaxton Paramount 3200 III	C53F	1988	Ex Shearings, 1993
18	552UTE	Leyland Tiger TRCL10/3ARZM	Plaxton Paramount 3200 III	C53F	1988	Ex Shearings, 1993
19	813VPU	Volvo B10M-60	Plaxton Excalibur	C46FT	1993	Ex Park's, Hamilton, 1993
51	KSU461	MCW Metroliner DR130/5	MCW	CH53/16DT	1984	
55	KSU465	MCW Metroliner DR130/28	MCW	CH53/16DT	1986	
56	KSU466	MCW Metroliner DR130/29	MCW	CH53/17DT	1986	Ex London Buses, 1987
60	KSV460	Volvo B10M-60	Van Hool Alizée	C49FT	1991	Ex Park's, Hamilton, 1994
61	HTY139W	Leyland Leopard PSU3E/4R	Duple Dominant II Express	C49F	1980	Ex Grey-Green, 1988
62	HTY137W	Leyland Leopard PSU3E/4R	Duple Dominant II Express	C49F	1980	Ex Grey-Green, 1988
63	HTY138W	Leyland Leopard PSU3E/4R	Duple Dominant II Express	C49F	1980	Ex Grey-Green, 1988
65	TBC1X	Leyland Leopard PSU3F/4R	Plaxton Supreme IV Express	C53F	1981	Ex Nottingham, 1988
66	TBC2X	Leyland Leopard PSU3F/4R	Plaxton Supreme IV Express	C53F	1981	Ex Nottingham, 1988
71	CMJ447T	Leyland Leopard PSU3E/4R	Plaxton Supreme III Express	C53F	1979	Ex Southend, 1988
81	L81YBB	Volvo B10M-62	Plaxton Expressliner 2	C44FT	1993	
82	L82YBB	Volvo B10M-62	Plaxton Expressliner 2	C46FT	1994	
83	L83YBB	Volvo B10M-62	Plaxton Expressliner 2	C46FT	1994	
84	L84YBB	Volvo B10M-62	Plaxton Expressliner 2	C46FT	1994	
85	KSU462	Volvo B10M-60	Plaxton Excalibur	C46FT	1992	Ex Park's, Hamilton, 1993
86	KSU463	Volvo B10M-60	Plaxton Excalibur	C46FT	1992	Ex Park's, Hamilton, 1993
87	KSU464	Volvo B10M-60	Plaxton Excalibur	C46FT	1992	Ex Park's, Hamilton, 1993

Busways operate three of Plaxton's top-of-the-range model, the Excalibur, the only examples with Stagecoach. Photographed at Heathrow while working National Express service 230 to Newcastle is 86, KSU463. *Colin Lloyd*

In July 1994 Busways Travel Services Ltd became a subsidiary company of Stagecoach Holdings plc. Because of the strength of the brand names in the local market Stagecoach agreed that Busways should retain its distinctive liveries. The Blue Bus services livery is dark blue and white. Seen in New Bridge Street is 268, SCN268S. *Tony Wilson*

101-125

Leyland Lynx LX112L10ZR1S — Leyland — B49F — 1988-89

101	F101HVK	106	F106HVK	111	F111HVK	116	F116HVK	121	F121HVK
102	F102HVK	107	F107HVK	112	F112HVK	117	F117HVK	122	F122HVK
103	F103HVK	108	F108HVK	113	F113HVK	118	F118HVK	123	F123HVK
104	F104HVK	109	F109HVK	114	F114HVK	119	F119HVK	124	F124HVK
105	F105HVK	110	F110HVK	115	F115HVK	120	F120HVK	125	F125HVK

126	H126ACU	Leyland Lynx LX2R11C15Z4S	Leyland	DP47F	1990
127	H127ACU	Leyland Lynx LX2R11C15Z4S	Leyland	DP47F	1990
140	LCU112	Daimler CCG6	Roe	H35/28R	1964

204-223

Leyland Atlantean AN68A/2R — Alexander AL — H49/37F — 1980

204	EJR104W	208	EJR108W	212	EJR112W	217	EJR117W	221	EJR121W
205	EJR105W	209	EJR109W	213	EJR113W	218	EJR118W	222	EJR122W
206	EJR106W	210	EJR110W	214	EJR114W	219	EJR119W	223	EJR123W
207	EJR107W	211	EJR111W	215	EJR115W				

244-312

Leyland Atlantean AN68A/2R — Alexander AL — H49/37F — 1978

244	SCN244S	258	SCN258S	270	SCN270S	283	SCN283S	297	UVK297T
247	SCN247S	259	SCN259S	271	SCN271S	284	SCN284S	298	UVK298T
248	SCN248S	260	SCN260S	273	SCN273S	285	SCN285S	299	UVK299T
249	SCN249S	261	SCN261S	274	SCN274S	286	SCN286S	300	UVK300T
250	SCN250S	262	SCN262S	275	SCN275S	287	UVK287T	301	VCU301T
251	SCN251S	263	SCN263S	276	SCN276S	288	UVK288T	302	VCU302T
252	SCN252S	264	SCN264S	277	SCN277S	289	UVK289T	303	VCU303T
253	SCN253S	265	SCN265S	278	SCN278S	290	UVK290T	304	VCU304T
254	SCN254S	266	SCN266S	279	SCN279S	291	UVK291T	309	VCU309T
255	SCN255S	267	SCN267S	280	SCN280S	292	UVK292T	310	VCU310T
256	SCN256S	268	SCN268S	281	SCN281S	294	UVK294T	312	VCU312T
257	SCN257S	269	SCN269S	282	SCN282S	295	UVK295T		

Typical of the Busways' Newcastle operation is the Leyland Atlantean with Alexander AL-type bodywork which were purchased in large quantities by Tyne and Wear PTE. Photographed in Pilgrim Street is 334, AVK154V. *Tony Wilson*

314-363

									Leyland Atlantean AN68A/2R	Alexander AL	H49/37F	1980

314	AVK134V	324	AVK144V	334	AVK154V	344	AVK164V	354	AVK174V
315	AVK135V	325	AVK145V	335	AVK155V	345	AVK165V	355	AVK175V
316	AVK136V	326	AVK146V	336	AVK156V	346	AVK166V	356	AVK176V
317	AVK137V	327	AVK147V	337	AVK157V	347	AVK167V	357	AVK177V
318	AVK138V	328	AVK148V	338	AVK158V	348	AVK168V	358	AVK178V
319	AVK139V	329	AVK149V	339	AVK159V	349	AVK169V	359	AVK179V
320	AVK140V	330	AVK150V	340	AVK160V	350	AVK170V	360	AVK180V
321	AVK141V	331	AVK151V	341	AVK161V	351	AVK171V	361	AVK181V
322	AVK142V	332	AVK152V	342	AVK162V	352	AVK172V	362	AVK182V
323	AVK143V	333	AVK153V	343	AVK163V	353	AVK173V	363	AVK183V

413	JFT413X	Scania BR112DH	Alexander RH	H47/31F	1982
414	JFT414X	Scania BR112DH	Alexander RH	H47/31F	1982

421-430

									Scania N113DRB	Alexander RH	H47/29F	1990

421	H421BNL	423	H423BNL	425	H425BNL	427	H427BNL	429	H429BNL
422	H422BNL	424	H424BNL	426	H426BNL	428	H428BNL	430	H430BNL

500-565

									Leyland Atlantean AN68A/2R	Alexander AL	H48/33F*	1976	*500/40-4 are H48/34F

500	MVK500R	521	MVK521R	542	MVK542R	554	MVK554R	561	MVK561R
507	MVK507R	532	MVK532R	543	MVK543R	555w	MVK555R	563	MVK563R
509	MVK509R	540	MVK540R	544	MVK544R	556	MVK556R	564	MVK564R
519	MVK519R	541	MVK541R	551	MVK551R	558	MVK558R	565	MVK565R

Busways' Alexander-bodied Leyland Olympians feature a large bumper as seen on this picture of 626, C626LFT, taken in Newcastle while bound for Killingworth. *Tony Wilson*

601-665

Leyland Olympian ONLXB/1R   Alexander RH   H45/31F   1985-86

601	C601LFT	615	C615LFT	628	C628LFT	641	C641LFT	654	C654LFT
602	C602LFT	616	C616LFT	629	C629LFT	642	C642LFT	655	C655LFT
603	C603LFT	617	C617LFT	630	C630LFT	643	C643LFT	656	C656LFT
604	C604LFT	618	C618LFT	631	C631LFT	644	C644LFT	657	C657LFT
605	C605LFT	619	C619LFT	632	C632LFT	645	C645LFT	658	C658LFT
606	C606LFT	620	C620LFT	633	C633LFT	646	C646LFT	659	C659LFT
608	C608LFT	621	C621LFT	634	C634LFT	647	C647LFT	660	C660LFT
609	C609LFT	622	C622LFT	635	C635LFT	648	C648LFT	661	C661LFT
610	C610LFT	623	C623LFT	636	C636LFT	649	C649LFT	662	C662LFT
611	C611LFT	624	C624LFT	637	C637LFT	650	C650LFT	663	C663LFT
612	C612LFT	625	C625LFT	638	C638LFT	651	C651LFT	664	C664LFT
613	C613LFT	626	C626LFT	639	C639LFT	652	C652LFT	665	C665LFT
614	C614LFT	627	C627LFT	640	C640LFT	653	C653LFT		

667-676

Leyland Olympian ON2R50C13Z4 Northern Counties Palatine H47/30F   1990-91

667	H667BNL	669	H669BNL	671	H671BNL	673	H673BNL	675	H675BNL
668	H668BNL	670	H670BNL	672	H672BNL	674	H674BNL	676	H676BNL

677-697

Leyland Olympian ONLXB/1RH   Northern Counties   H43/30F   1988   Ex London Buses, 1991

677	E901KYR	682	E909KYR	686	E914KYR	690	E919KYR	694	E923KYR
678	E905KYR	683	E910KYR	687	E915KYR	691	E920KYR	695	E924KYR
679	E906KYR	684	E911KYR	688	E917KYR	692	E921KYR	696	E925KYR
680	E907KYR	685	E912KYR	689	E918KYR	693	E922KYR	697	E927KYR
681	E908KYR								

800-839

Leyland Fleetline FE30AGR Alexander AL H44/30F 1977

800	OCU800R	808	OCU808R	819	OCU819R	826	RCU826S	833	RCU833S
801	OCU801R	811	OCU811R	820	OCU820R	827	RCU827S	834	RCU834S
802	OCU802R	813	OCU813R	821	OCU821R	828	RCU828S	835	RCU835S
803	OCU803R	814	OCU814R	822	OCU822R	829	RCU829S	836	RCU836S
804	OCU804R	815	OCU815R	823	OCU823R	830	RCU830S	837	RCU837S
805	OCU805R	816	OCU816R	824	OCU824R	831	RCU831S	838	RCU838S
806	OCU806R	817	OCU817R	825	OCU825R	832	RCU832S	839	RCU839S
807	OCU807R	818	OCU818R						

901-920

Scania N113CRB Alexander PS B49F 1988-89

901	F901JRG	905	F905JRG	909	F909JRG	913	F913JRG	917	F917JRG
902	F902JRG	906	F906JRG	910	F910JRG	914	F914JRG	918	F918JRG
903	F903JRG	907	F907JRG	911	F911JRG	915	F915JRG	919	F919JRG
904	F904JRG	908	F908JRG	912	F912JRG	916	F916JRG	920	F920JRG

921-926

Scania N113CRB Alexander PS B51F* 1989-90 *926 is B49F

921	G921TCU	923	G923TCU	924	G924TCU	925	G925TCU	926	G926TCU
922	G922TCU								

927	G113SKX	Scania N113CRB	Alexander PS	B51F	1989	Ex Scania demonstrator, 1991

928-937

Scania N113CRB Alexander PS B51F 1991

928	H428EFT	930	H430EFT	932	H432EFT	934	H434EFT	936	H436EFT
929	H429EFT	931	H431EFT	933	H433EFT	935	H435EFT	937	H437EFT

938	G108CEH	Scania N113CRB	Alexander PS	B49F	1990	Ex Stevensons, 1993
951	M951DRG	Scania L113CRL	Northern Counties Paladin	B49F	1994	
952	M952DRG	Scania L113CRL	Northern Counties Paladin	DP49F	1994	
953	M953DRG	Scania L113CRL	Alexander Strider	B51F	1994	
954	M954DRG	Scania L113CRL	Alexander Strider	B51F	1994	
1201	M201DRG	Dennis Lance 11SDA3113	Plaxton Verde	B49F	1994	
1202	M202DRG	Dennis Lance 11SDA3113	Plaxton Verde	B49F	1994	
1203	M203DRG	Dennis Lance 11SDA3113	Plaxton Verde	B49F	1994	
1204	M204DRG	Dennis Lance 11SDA3113	Optare Sigma	B47F	1994	
1218	KBB118D	Leyland Atlantean PDR1/1R	MCW	O44/34F	1966	
1227	SVK627G	Leyland Atlantean PDR1A/1R	Alexander J	O44/30F	1969	

During 1994 several evaluation vehicles have been added to the Busways operation. These are alloated to various units. Working in Newcastle is 1201, M201DRG, a Dennis Lance with Plaxton Verde bodywork incorporating a split-level entrance. *Busways*

Stagecoach Darlington commenced in November 1994 with vehicles transferred from several Stagecoach fleets. The double-deck need was met by Leyland Atlanteans from Busways, repainted into corporate colours. Seen during the first week of service is 831, RCU831S, complete with nearside staircase - a typical Tyne and Wear PTE specified feature. *Andrew Jarosz*

The evaluation fleet contains four Scania L113s, two bodied with Alexander's Strider design and two with Northern Counties Paladin style. One of the latter is, 951, M951DRG which is allocated to South Shields. *C J Clark*

1301-1310

Volvo B6-9.9M · Alexander Dash · B40F · 1994

1301	M741PRS	1303	M743PRS	1305	M745PRS	1307	M847PRS	1309	M749PRS
1302	M742PRS	1304	M744PRS	1306	M746PRS	1308	M748PRS	1310	M750PRS

1401-1460

Mercedes-Benz 709D · Reeve Burgess Beaver · B20F* · 1987-88 · *1431/49/51/3 are B23F
*1444 is DP22F

1401	D401TFT	1413	D413TFT	1425	E425AFT	1437	E437AFT	1449	E449AFT
1402	D402TFT	1414	D414TFT	1426	E426AFT	1438	E438AFT	1450	E450AFT
1403	D403TFT	1415	D415TFT	1427	E427AFT	1439	E439AFT	1451	E451AFT
1404	D404TFT	1416	D416TFT	1428	E428AFT	1440	E440AFT	1452	E452AFT
1405	D405TFT	1417	D417TFT	1429	E429AFT	1441	E441AFT	1453	E453AFT
1406	D406TFT	1418	D418TFT	1430	E430AFT	1442	E442AFT	1454	E454AFT
1407	D407TFT	1419	D419TFT	1431	E431AFT	1443	E443AFT	1455	E455AFT
1408	D408TFT	1420	D420TFT	1432	E432AFT	1444	E444AFT	1456	E456AFT
1409	D409TFT	1421	E421AFT	1433	E433AFT	1445	E445AFT	1457	E457AFT
1410	D410TFT	1422	E422AFT	1434	E434AFT	1446	E446AFT	1458	E458AFT
1411	D411TFT	1423	E423AFT	1435	E435AFT	1447	E447AFT	1459	E459AFT
1412	D412TFT	1424	E424AFT	1436	E436AFT	1448	E448AFT	1460	E460AFT

1604	TPJ55S	Bristol LHS6L	Eastern Coach Works	B35F	1977	Ex South Yorkshire, 1986
1605	TPJ60S	Bristol LHS6L	Eastern Coach Works	B35F	1977	Ex South Yorkshire, 1986
1606	TPJ62S	Bristol LHS6L	Eastern Coach Works	B35F	1977	Ex South Yorkshire, 1986
1607	TPJ64S	Bristol LHS6L	Eastern Coach Works	B35F	1977	Ex South Yorkshire, 1986
1610	WEX927S	Bristol LH6L	Eastern Coach Works	B43F	1977	Ex Tyne & Wear Omnibus, 1989
1615	TTC787T	Bristol LH6L	Eastern Coach Works	B43F	1979	Ex Tyne & Wear Omnibus, 1989
1616	WEX928S	Bristol LH6L	Eastern Coach Works	B43F	1978	Ex Tyne & Wear Omnibus, 1989
1619	DTL548T	Bristol LH6L	Eastern Coach Works	B43F	1979	Ex Tyne & Wear Omnibus, 1989

1621-1640

Renault-Dodge S56 · Alexander AM · B25F · 1987

1621	E621BVK	1625	E625BVK	1629	E629BVK	1633	E633BVK	1637	E637BVK
1622	E622BVK	1626	E626BVK	1630	E630BVK	1634	E634BVK	1638	E638BVK
1623	E623BVK	1627	E627BVK	1631	E631BVK	1635	E635BVK	1639	E639BVK
1624	E624BVK	1628	E628BVK	1632	E632BVK	1636	E636BVK	1640	E640BVK

1642	G22CSG	Renault-Dodge S56	Reeve Burgess Beaver	B25F	1989	Ex Fife Scottish, 1994
1643	G23CSG	Renault-Dodge S56	Reeve Burgess Beaver	B25F	1989	Ex Fife Scottish, 1994

1651-1662

Iveco Daily 49-10 · Carlyle Dailybus 2 · B23F · 1988-89

1651	F651KNL	1654	F654KNL	1658	F658KNL	1659	F659KNL	1661	F661KNL
1653	F653KNL								

1663	H401DMJ	Renault S75	Reeve Burgess Beaver	B29F	1990	Ex Welcome, 1993

1664-1678

Renault S75 · Plaxton Beaver · B28F · 1991 · Ex Welcome, 1993

1664	J553NGS	1667	J227JJR	1670	J230JJR	1673	J233JJR	1676	K343PJR
1665	J225JJR	1668	J228JJR	1671	J231JJR	1674	K341PJR	1677	K344PJR
1666	J226JJR	1669	J229JJR	1672	J232JJR	1675	K342PJR	1678	K345PJR

1679-1693

Optare MetroRider · Optare · B29F · 1991-92 Ex Welcome, 1993

1679	J371BNW	1682	J374BNW	1685	J377BNW	1688	J380BNW	1691	K164FYG
1680	J372BNW	1683	J375BNW	1686	J378BNW	1689	K162FYG	1692	K165FYG
1681	J373BNW	1684	J376BNW	1687	J379BNW	1690	K163FYG	1693	K166FYG

1694-1700

Iveco 59.12 · Dormobile Routemaker · B27F · 1992 · Ex Welcome, 1993

1694	K330RCN	1696	K332RCN	1698	K335RCN	1699	K336RCN	1700	K337RCN
1695	K331RCN	1697	K334RCN						

1701	J701KCU	Dennis Dart 9.8SDL3017	Plaxton Pointer	B40F	1992
1702	J702KCU	Dennis Dart 9.8SDL3017	Plaxton Pointer	B40F	1992

Opposite: **Busways became a member of Stagecoach Holdings in July 1994, continuing for the present with its established liveries based on yellow.** *Above*: **Photographed in Newcastle on the MetroCentre service is 903, F903JRG, an Alexander-bodied Scania, complete with new fleetname and stripe for the latest marketing initiative - Blue Ribband.** *Below*: **Also in Blue Ribband livery is Dennis Dart 1740, L740VNL, one of the Alexander-bodied examples supplied in 1993.** *J Clarke/David Cole*

1703-1743 — Dennis Dart 9.8SDL3017 — Alexander Dash — B40F* — 1992-93

*1723-28 are 9.8SDL3025; 1729-43 are 9.8SDL3035

1703	K703PCN	1712	K712PCN	1720	K720PCN	1728	K728PNL	1736	L736VNL
1704	K704PCN	1713	K713PCN	1721	K721PCN	1729	L729VNL	1737	L737VNL
1705	K705PCN	1714	K714PCN	1722	K722PCN	1730	L730VNL	1738	L738VNL
1706	K706PCN	1715	K715PCN	1723	K723PNL	1731	L731VNL	1739	L739VNL
1707	K707PCN	1716	K716PCN	1724	K724PNL	1732	L732VNL	1740	L740VNL
1708	K708PCN	1717	K717PCN	1725	K725PNL	1733	L733VNL	1741	L741VNL
1709	K709PCN	1718	K718PCN	1726	K726PNL	1734	L734VNL	1742	L742VNL
1710	K710PCN	1719	K719PCN	1727	K727PNL	1735	L735VNL	1743	L743VNL
1711	K711PCN								

1744-1759 — Dennis Dart 9.8SDL3035 — Plaxton Pointer — B40F — 1993

1744	L744VNL	1748	L748VNL	1751	L751VNL	1754	L754VNL	1757	L757VNL
1745	L745VNL	1749	L749VNL	1752	L752VNL	1755	L755VNL	1758	L758VNL
1746	L746VNL	1750	L750VNL	1753	L753VNL	1756	L756VNL	1759	L759VNL

1760-1765 — Dennis Dart 9.8SDL3040 — Alexander Dash — B40F — 1994

1760	L760ARG	1762	L762ARG	1763	L763ARG	1764	L764ARG	1765	L765ARG
1761	L761ARG								

1766-1771 — Dennis Dart 9.8SDL3040 — Plaxton Pointer — B40F — 1994

1766	M766DRG	1768	M768DRG	1769	M769DRG	1770	M770DRG	1771	M771DRG
1767	M767DRG								

1800	RAH681F	Bristol RESL6G	Eastern Coach Works	B53F	1968	
1801	ECU201E	Bristol RESL6L	Eastern Coach Works	B45D	1967	Ex Bickers, Coddenham, 1988
1802	TRY118H	Bristol RELL6L	Eastern Coach Works	B48F	1969	Ex Ipswich, 1988
1803	LPU452J	Bristol RELL6L	Eastern Coach Works	B53F	1971	Ex Buckinghamshire RC, 1994
1804	EHU383K	Bristol RELL6L	Eastern Coach Works	B50F	1972	Ex Buckinghamshire RC, 1994
1805	EPW516K	Bristol RELL6G	Eastern Coach Works	B53F	1972	Ex Buckinghamshire RC, 1994
1806	PVT221L	Bristol RELL6L	Eastern Coach Works	B53F	1972	Ex Buckinghamshire RC, 1994
1808	HPW522L	Bristol RELL6L	Eastern Coach Works	B53F	1972	Ex Buckinghamshire RC, 1994

1810-1816 — Bristol RELL6L — Eastern Coach Works — B49F* — 1972 — Ex Colchester, 1988

*1810/2 are B53F

1810	YWC16L	1812	OWC720M	1814	OWC723M	1815 SWC25K
1811	YWC18L	1813	OWC722M			1816 SWC26K

1817-1821 — Bristol RESL6G — Eastern Coach Works — B43F — 1975 — Ex Thamesdown, 1987-88

1817	JMW166P	1818	JMW167P	1819	JMW168P	1820	JMW169P	1821	JMW170P

1822	TDL567K	Bristol RELL6G	Eastern Coach Works	B53F	1971	Ex Catch-a-Bus, 1993
1823	NKG246M	Bristol RESL6G	Eastern Coach Works	B44F	1973	Ex Buckinghamshire RC, 1994
1824u	OCK363K	Bristol RESL6G	Eastern Coach Works	B47F	1972	Ex Buckinghamshire RC, 1994
1825u	OCK369K	Bristol RESL6G	Eastern Coach Works	B47F	1972	Ex Buckinghamshire RC, 1994
1826u	KTX242L	Bristol RESL6G	Eastern Coach Works	B47F	1973	Ex Buckinghamshire RC, 1994
1832	LBN201P	Leyland Leopard PSU3C/4R	Plaxton Elite III Express	C51F	1976	Ex Southend, 1987
1833	LBN202P	Leyland Leopard PSU3C/4R	Plaxton Elite III Express	C51F	1976	Ex Southend, 1988
1847	MTE16R	Leyland Leopard PSU3D/2R	Plaxton Derwent	B48F	1976	Ex GM Buses, 1987
1863	ESU263	Leyland Tiger TRCTL11/3R	Plaxton Paramount 3500	C49FT	1984	Ex Armchair, Brentford, 1992
1864	FYX824W	Leyland Leopard PSU3E/4R	Duple Dominant II Express	C49F	1980	Ex Grey-Green, 1988
1868	AHN388T	Leyland Leopard PSU3E/4R	Plaxton Supreme IV Express	DP55F	1978	Ex Cleveland Transit, 1990
1869	AHN389T	Leyland Leopard PSU3E/4R	Plaxton Supreme IV Express	DP55F	1978	Ex Cleveland Transit, 1990
1870	AHN390T	Leyland Leopard PSU3E/4R	Plaxton Supreme IV Express	DP55F	1978	Ex Cleveland Transit, 1990
1872	CMJ450T	Leyland Leopard PSU3E/4R	Plaxton Supreme III Express	C51F	1978	Ex Southend, 1988
1876	CBB476V	Leyland Leopard PSU3F/4R	Duple Dominant I	C53F	1980	
1877	CBB477V	Leyland Leopard PSU3F/4R	Duple Dominant I	C47F	1980	
1895	OTD824R	Leyland Leopard PSU3E/4R	Plaxton Supreme III Express	C51F	1977	Ex GM Buses, 1987
1896	OTD825R	Leyland Leopard PSU3E/4R	Plaxton Supreme III Express	C51F	1977	Ex GM Buses, 1987
1901	M901DRG	Volvo B10B	Alexander Strider	B51F	1994	
1902	M902DRG	Volvo B10B	Alexander Strider	B51F	1994	
2006	F496NTR	Iveco Daily 49.10	Robin Hood City Nippy	B25F	1988	Ex United Counties, 1994
2007	F494NTR	Iveco Daily 49.10	Robin Hood City Nippy	B25F	1988	Ex United Counties, 1994
2008	F495NTR	Iveco Daily 49.10	Robin Hood City Nippy	B25F	1988	Ex United Counties, 1994
2009	D606MKH	Iveco Daily 49-10	Robin Hood City Nippy	B25F	1987	Ex Stagecoach Hull, 1994
2010	D604MKH	Iveco Daily 49-10	Robin Hood City Nippy	B25F	1987	Ex Stagecoach Hull, 1994

Inherited from the high quality Welcome operation are sixteen Renault S75s, all bar one having Plaxton Beaver bodies. Several of these are now part of the Darlington operation. Seen in the town is 1673, J233JJR.
Andrew Jarosz

While Alexander bodied two of the Scania L113s for evaluation, they also bodied the pair of Volvo B10Bs. Wearing Sunderland livery is 1901, M901DRG. The B10B has been developed by Volvo as the replacement for the Lynx for the city and intercity market. *C J Clark*

Twelve Leyland Tiger coaches were transferred from Bluebird Buses and Fife Scottish to Busways for the Stagecoach Darlington operation. Several of these changed index marks immediately prior to transfer. Photographed in Darlington is 2108, CSO388Y, previously with Bluebird Buses.
Andrew Jarosz

2011	D607MKH	Iveco Daily 49-10	Robin Hood City Nippy	B25F	1987	Ex Stagecoach Hull, 1994
2101	PES188Y	Leyland Tiger TRCTL11/3R	Duple Goldliner IV	C51F	1983	Ex Fife Scottish, 1994
2102	PES189Y	Leyland Tiger TRCTL11/3R	Duple Goldliner IV	C51F	1983	Ex Fife Scottish, 1994
2103	PES190Y	Leyland Tiger TRCTL11/3R	Duple Laser	C55F	1983	Ex Fife Scottish, 1994
2104	A940XGG	Leyland Tiger TRCTL11/3R	Duple Laser	C51F	1984	Ex Fife Scottish, 1994
2105	A941XGG	Leyland Tiger TRCTL11/3R	Duple Laser	C51F	1984	Ex Fife Scottish, 1994
2106	A942XGG	Leyland Tiger TRCTL11/3R	Duple Laser	C51F	1984	Ex Fife Scottish, 1994
2107	PSO179W	Leyland Tiger TRCTL11/3R	Duple Dominant IV	C51F	1981	Ex Bluebird Buses, 1994
2108	CSO388Y	Leyland Tiger TRCTL11/2R	Duple Dominant II Express	C49F	1983	Ex Bluebird Buses, 1994
2109	CSO389Y	Leyland Tiger TRCTL11/2R	Duple Dominant II Express	C49F	1983	Ex Bluebird Buses, 1994
2110	VSS3X	Leyland Tiger TRCTL11/3R	Duple Goldliner IV	C51F	1982	Ex Bluebird Buses, 1994
2111	CSO387Y	Leyland Tiger TRCTL11/2R	Duple Dominant II Express	C49F	1983	Ex Bluebird Buses, 1994
2112	RRS226X	Leyland Tiger TRCTL11/3R	Duple Goldliner IV	C47FT	1982	Ex Bluebird Buses, 1994
2121	TRN805V	Leyland National 10351B/1R		B44F	1977	Ex Ribble, 1994
2122	NEO833R	Leyland National 11351A/1R		B49F	1978	Ex Ribble, 1994
2123	SNS822W	Leyland National 2 NL116AL11/1R		B52F	1980	Ex Ribble, 1994
2124	AHH201T	Leyland National 10351B/1R		B44F	1978	Ex Ribble, 1994
2125	MAO368P	Leyland National 11351/1R		B52F	1976	Ex Ribble, 1994
2126	WAO397Y	Leyland National 2 NL116HLXB/1R		B52F	1983	Ex Ribble, 1994
2127	OLS806T	Leyland National 10351B/1R		B44F	1978	Ex Ribble, 1994
2128	SNS828W	Leyland National 2 NL116AL11/1R		B52F	1980	Ex Ribble, 1994
2129	UHG739R	Leyland National 11351A/1R		B49F	1976	Ex Ribble, 1994

2141-2146

		Mercedes-Benz L608D	Reeve Burgess	B20F	1986	Ex Ribble, 1994

2141	D33UAO	**2143**	D538RCK	**2144**	D526RCK	**2145**	D535RCK	**2146**	D543RCK
2142	D523RCK								

Liveries and allocations:

Armstrong Galley (Blue, yellow, orange and red): 3-9/14-19, 51/5/6, 81-7

Blue Bus Services (Dark blue and cream): 61/3/5/6, 244/61/8/73/7, 302/3/12, 500/7/21/32/41-4/51/8/63/5, 1614/7, 1701/2/44-6, 1800/2/5/8/10/11-21/32/3/47/68/95

Economic (Deep maroon and cream): 115/7/8/25/7, 271/4/9, 641-9/76, 1227, 1749/50.

Favourite (Orange, white and brown): 62, 71, 262/86/8/97, 540/61/4, 1437/44, 1634-40, 1748/70/1, 1863/9/70/6/7/96

Newcastle -Byker (Yellow, white and maroon): 260/3/81/98, 301/33/4/6-44/6-54/6-63, 421-30, 601-6/8-20/5, 690-7, 906/28/9/33-7/52/3, 1201, 1412/6/21/3/6-30/2-6/8-43/55, 1703-14/9/20, 1902

Newcastle -Slatyford (Yellow, white and maroon): 247-59/94, 304/9/10/4-30, 621/6-40/84-89, 901-5/7-27/30/1/2/8, 1204, 1404/8/13/4/7/8, 1679-93, 1715-21/39-43.

South Shields (Yellow, white and blue): B140, 116/9-24/6, 264-7/70/5/6/8/80/2/3/5/7/9-92/5/300, 951, 1202, 1405/7/31/45/6/8-51/3/4/6-60, 1664/5/7/9, 1751-9/66-9, 1801/72.

Stagecoach Darlington (Stagecoach corporate): 801-4/7/8/14-7/31, 1653/8/9/61/68/70/1/3/6-8, 2006-11, 2101-12/21-29, 2141-6

Sunderland (Yellow, white and green): 101-114, 204-15/7-9/22/3, 650-65/7-74/7-83, 816/8-22/4-30/2-5/7/8, 954, 1203, 1621-33/94-1700, 1722-38/60-5, 1864, 1901.

Reserve 221/69/84/99, 332/3/45/55, 413/4 509/19/54-6, 800/5/6/11/3/23/36/9, 1218, 1604-7/10/5/6/9/51/4, 1803/4/6/22-26,

Previous registrations:

1JVK	F900JRG	KSU457	From New
2JVK	F715ENE	KSU458	C110PCU
491JVX	F716ENE	KSU459	C109PCU
552UTE	F717ENE	KSU460	J691LGE
644HKX	E664JAV	KSU461	A751CRG
813VPU	J423HDS	KSU462	J420HDS
A940XGG	A507PST, GSU344	KSU463	J422HDS
A941XGG	A505PST, GSU342	KSU464	J424HDS
A942XGG	A506PST, GSU343	KSU465	C155LJR
CSO387Y	ASA11Y, TSV781	KSU466	C103DYE
CSO388Y	ASA7Y, TSV777	LCU112	From new
CSO389Y	ASA9Y, TSV779	LVK123	From new
ESU263	A829PPP	ONL645X	MCN827X, 813VPU, ONL450X, 813VPU
HTY137W	FYX820W, KSU464	PES188Y	SFS583Y, MSU445, PSP722Y, MSU463
HTY138W	FYX821W, KSU463	PES189Y	SFS582Y, MSU445
HTY139W	FYX819W, KSU460	PES190Y	VTY130Y, GSU341
KSU454	B104DVK	PSO179W	BSG545W, CSU922
KSU455	B105DVK	RRS226X	KSL41X,1412NE
KSU456	B103DVK	WBR248	From new

CHELTENHAM & GLOUCESTER

Cheltenham & Gloucester Omnibus Company Ltd
Cheltenham District Traction Company Ltd,
Swindon & District Bus Company Ltd,
3/4 Bath Street, Cheltenham, GL50 1YE

Depots : St Marks, Cheltenham; London Road, Gloucester; London Road, Stroud and Eastcott Road, Swindon;

101-105
Leyland Olympian ONLXB/2RZ   Alexander RL   H51/36F   1990

101	G101AAD	102	G102AAD	103	G103AAD	104	G104AAD	105	G105AAD

106-111
Leyland Titan TNLXB/1RF   Park Royal   H47/26F   1979-80   Ex Thames Transit, 1990

106	GNF6V	108	GNF8V	109	GNF9V	110	GNF10V	111	GNF11V

112-124
Leyland Olympian ONLXB/1R   Roe   H47/29F   1982-83   Ex Bristol, 1983
113 ex Yorkshire Rider, 1987

112	JHU899X	115	LWS33Y	118	LWS36Y	121	LWS39Y	123	LWS41Y
113	UWW7X	116	LWS34Y	119	LWS37Y	122	LWS40Y	124	NTC132Y
114	JHU912X	117	LWS35Y	120	LWS38Y				

| 201 | JOU160P | Bristol VRT/SL3/501(6LXB) | Eastern Coach Works | H43/28F | 1975 | Ex Bristol, 1983 |
| 202 | MUA872P | Bristol VRT/SL3/6LX | Eastern Coach Works | H43/31F | 1975 | Ex Bristol, 1983 |

204-213
Bristol VRT/SL3/6LXB   Eastern Coach Works   H43/28F*   1976-77   Ex Bristol, 1983; *210 is H43/31F

| 204 | MOU739R | 208 | NWS288R | 210u | PEU515R | 212 | REU310S | 213 | REU311S |
| 205 | NHU670R | 209 | NWS289R | 211 | REU309S | | | | |

| 214 | RFB617S | Bristol VRT/SL3/6LXB | Eastern Coach Works | H43/31F | 1978 | Ex Bristol, 1983 |

215-220
Bristol VRT/SL3/6LXB   Eastern Coach Works   H43/31F*   1978   Ex Devon General, 1987
*215 is H43/29F

| 215 | XDV602S | 217 | VOD593S | 218 | VOD596S | 219 | VOD597S | 220 | VOD598S |
| 216 | XDV606S | | | | | | | | |

221	TWS903T	Bristol VRT/SL3/6LXB	Eastern Coach Works	H43/28F	1979	Ex Bristol, 1983
222	TWS906T	Bristol VRT/SL3/6LXB	Eastern Coach Works	H43/28F	1979	Ex Bristol, 1983
223	TWS913T	Bristol VRT/SL3/6LXB	Eastern Coach Works	H43/28F	1979	Ex Bristol, 1983
224	TWS914T	Bristol VRT/SL3/6LXB	Eastern Coach Works	H43/28F	1979	Ex Bristol, 1983

The Leyland Titan was bought new by few operators, the high initial cost and engineering complexity being a significant deterrent. Five of the type delivered to the Greater Manchester PTE moved to Cheltenham and Gloucester in 1990 and have been based at Swindon ever since. One of the early repaints into Stagecoach corporate livery is 109, GNF9V, photographed before the Swindon & District fleetnames had been applied. *Mike Harris*

225-231		Bristol VRT/SL3/680*		Eastern Coach Works		H43/31F	1981	Ex Bristol, 1983
								*225-9 fitted with 6LXB engines

225	DHW350W	227	EWS740W	229	EWS746W	230	EWS748W	231	EWS751W
226	DHW352W	228	EWS743W						

301-313		Leyland National 11351A/1R(DAF)				B52F*	1977-79	Ex Bristol, 1983
								*301 is B25DL/B52F

301	467WYA	304	PHW985S	307	SAE752S	310	VEU231T	312	TAE644S
302	YFB973V	305	PHW989S	308	TAE642S	311	SAE756S	313	TAE639S
303	TAE641S	306	PHW988S	309	SAE754S				

322w	GOL406N	Leyland National 11351/1R	B49F	1975	Ex Midland Red South, 1992
323w	HEU120N	Leyland National 11351/1R	B52F	1975	Ex Badgerline, 1991
331u	JHW103P	Leyland National 11351/1R	B52F	1975	Ex Bristol, 1983
332	NFB602R	Leyland National 11351A/1R	B52F	1976	Ex Bristol, 1983
333	NFB603R	Leyland National 11351A/1R	B52F	1976	Ex Bristol, 1983
334	NOE584R	Leyland National 11351A/1R	B49F	1977	Ex Midland Red South, 1991
335	NOE585R	Leyland National 11351A/1R	B49F	1977	Ex Midland Red South, 1991
336	NOE587R	Leyland National 11351A/1R	B49F	1977	Ex Midland Red South, 1991
337	NOE555R	Leyland National 11351A/1R	B49F	1976	Ex Midland Red South, 1992

339-351		Leyland National 11351A/1R				B52F	1977-79	Ex Bristol, 1983

339	PHW986S	342	SAE755S	345	TAE643S	348	VEU229T	350	VEU232T
340	PHW987S	343	TAE638S	346	TTC532R	349	VEU230T	351	YFB972V
341	SAE751S	344	UHW101T	347	VEU228T				

361-375		Leyland National 2 NL116L11/1R				B52F	1980	Ex Bristol, 1983
								*368 is B25DL/B52F

361	AAE644V	364	AAE648V	367	AAE651V	370	AAE660V	373	BHY997V
362	HIL6075	365	AAE649V	368	YJV806	371	AAE665V	374	BHY998V
363	511OHU	366	AAE650V	369	AAE659V	372	BHY996V	375	BOU6V

376	ARN892Y	Leyland National 2 NL116HLXB/1R		B52F	1983	Ex Ribble, 1994
377	RHG880X	Leyland National 2 NL116AL11/1R		B52F	1982	Ex Ribble, 1994
378	NHH382W	Leyland National 2 NL116AL11/1R		DP52F	1981	Ex Ribble, 1994
379	CHH389X	Leyland National 2 NL116AL11/1R		B52F	1981	Ex Ribble, 1994
500	VAE499T	Leyland National 10351B/1R		B44F	1978	Ex Bristol, 1983
501	VAE501T	Leyland National 10351B/1R		B44F	1978	Ex Bristol, 1983
503	VAE507T	Leyland National 10351B/1R		B44F	1978	Ex Bristol, 1983
533	G533LWU	Volvo B10M-60	Plaxton Paramount 3500 III	C48FT	1990	Ex Wallace Arnold, 1993
534	G534LWU	Volvo B10M-60	Plaxton Paramount 3500 III	C48FT	1990	Ex Wallace Arnold, 1993
546	G546LWU	Volvo B10M-60	Plaxton Paramount 3500 III	C48FT	1990	Ex Wallace Arnold, 1993
547	G547LWU	Volvo B10M-60	Plaxton Paramount 3500 III	C48FT	1990	Ex Wallace Arnold, 1993
548	G548LWU	Volvo B10M-60	Plaxton Paramount 3500 III	C48FT	1990	Ex Wallace Arnold, 1993
600u	A871KDF	Mercedes-Benz L608D	PMT Hanbridge	DP18F	1984	

617-645		Ford Transit 190		Alexander AM		B16F	1985

617u	C617SFH	631	C631SFH	636	C636SFH	640	C640SFH	643	C643SFH
621	C621SFH	632	C632SFH	637	C637SFH	641	C641SFH	644	C644SFH
626	C626SFH	633	C633SFH	639u	C639SFH	642	C642SFH	645	C645SFH

647	C591SHC	Mercedes-Benz L608D	Alexander AM	B20F	1986	Ex Stagecoach South, 1993
648	C594SHC	Mercedes-Benz L608D	Alexander AM	B20F	1986	Ex Stagecoach South, 1993

649-662		Mercedes-Benz L608D		Alexander AM		B20F	1986

649	C649XDF	652	C652XDF	655	C655XDF	658	C658XDF	661	C661XDF
650	C650XDF	653	C653XDF	656	C656XDF	659	C659XDF	662	C662XDF
651	C651XDF	654	C654XDF	657	C657XDF	660	C660XDF		

Opposite, top: **Cheltenham & Gloucester Omnibus Company use five operating names. The one employed on minibuses is Metro as shown by 688, L688CDD, a Mercedes-Benz 709D seen on Gloucester services.** *Robert Edworthy*

Opposite, bottom: **Gloucester Citybus operate several Leyland Olympians, most with bodies fitted by Roe. Photographed in the city is 121, LWS39Y.** *David Cole*

663-676   MCW MetroRider MF150   MCW B25F*   1987-88   *670/1/5/6 are DP25F

663	E663JAD	666	E666JAD	669	E669JAD	672w	E672KDG	675	E675KDG
664	E664JAD	667	E667JAD	670	E670JDG	673	E673KDG	676	E676KDG
665	E665JAD	668	E668JAD	671	E671JDG	674	E674KDG		

677	F677PDF	Mercedes-Benz 709D	PMT	B25F	1988	
678	F311DET	Mercedes-Benz 709D	Reeve Burgess Beaver	B25F	1988	Ex Reeve Burgess demonstrator, 1989

679-684   Mercedes-Benz 709D   PMT   B25F   1989

679	G679AAD	681	G681AAD	682	G682AAD	683	G683AAD	684	G684AAD
680	G680AAD								

686-703   Mercedes-Benz 709D   Alexander Sprint   B25F   1994

686	L686CDD	690	L690CDD	694	L694CDD	697	M697EDD	701	M701EDD
687	L687CDD	691	L691CDD	695	L695CDD	698	M698EDD	702	M702EDD
688	L688CDD	692	L692CDD	696	L696CDD	699	M699EDD	703	M703EDD
689	L689CDD	693	L693CDD						

801	K801OMW	Mercedes-Benz 811D	Wright	B33F	1993	
802	K802OMW	Mercedes-Benz 811D	Wright	B33F	1993	
803	L803XDG	Mercedes-Benz 811D	Marshall C16	B33F	1993	
804	L804XDG	Mercedes-Benz 811D	Marshall C16	B33F	1993	
805	L805XDG	Mercedes-Benz 811D	Marshall C16	B33F	1993	
806	L806XDG	Mercedes-Benz 811D	Marshall C16	B33F	1993	
807	L330CHB	Mercedes-Benz 811D	Marshall C16	B33F	1993	Ex Red & White, 1994

831-842   Volvo B6-9.9M   Alexander Dash   B40F   1994

831	L831CDG	834	L834CDG	837	L837CDG	839	L839CDG	841	L841CDG
832	L832CDG	835	L835CDG	838	L838CDG	840	L840CDG	842	L842CDG
833	L833CDG	836	L836CDG						

Operating Units:
Cheltenham District: 117/9, 201/2/4/5/12, 301/4/6/12, 335/6/43-6/51, 361/4-7/70/4/5, 501, 533/4/46-8, 633/6/7/40-3/9/50/2-4/63/5-71/89-98.
Gloucester Citybus: 112/4/21-3, 213/7/23/4, 302/3/5/7-11/3/32, 500/3, 656-62/80-2/4/7/8/99, 701-3, 831-42.
Stroud Valleys: 103/15/8/20, 211/5/25-8/30/1, 334/7-42/7-50, 362/3/8/76-9, 621/31/2/44/5/51/5/77-9/83/6, 803-6.
Swindon & District: 101/2/4-6/8-11/3/6/24, 208/9/14/6/8-22, 333, 369/71-3, 626/64/73-6, 801/2.

Previous Registrations:
467WYA	TAE645S		HIL6075	AAE646V
511OUH	AAE647V		YJV806	AAE658V

Cheltenham & Gloucester Omnibus Company use five operating names. The one which covers the minibuses is Metro as shown by 703, M703EDD, a recently delivered Mercedes-Benz 709D seen on Gloucester services.
Robert Edworthy

CLEVELAND

Cleveland Transit Ltd, Church Road, Stockton-on-Tees, Cleveland, TS18 2HW
Cleveland Coaches Ltd, Church Road, Stockton-on-Tees, Cleveland, TS18 2HW

1-10				Leyland Lynx LX112L10ZR1R		Leyland Lynx		B49F		1989			
1	F601UVN	3	F603UVN	5	F605UVN		7	F607UVN		9	F609UVN
2	F602UVN	4	F604UVN	6	F606UVN		8	F608UVN		10	F610UVN

11-20				Leyland Lynx LX2R11C15Z4R		Leyland Lynx 2		B51F		1989			
11	G611GEF	13	G613GEF	15	G615GEF		17	G617GEF		19	G619GEF
12	G612GEF	14	G614GEF	16	G616GEF		18	G618GEF		20	G620GEF

21	J901UKV		Leyland Lynx LX2R11V18Z4S		Leyland Lynx 2		B49F	1991	Ex Volvo demonstrator, 1992

22-30				Leyland Lynx LX2R11V18Z4R		Leyland Lynx 2		B49F		1992			
22	K622YVN	24	K624YVN	26	K626YVN		28	K628YVN		30	K630YVN
23	K623YVN	25	K625YVN	27	K627YVN		29	K629YVN			

31-42				Volvo B10B		Plaxton Verde		B52F		1994			
31	L31HHN	34	L34HHN	37	L37HHN		39	M39PVN		41	M41PVN
32	L32HHN	35	L35HHN	38	M38PVN		40	M40PVN		42	M42PVN
33	L33HHN	36	L36HHN								

101-108				Volvo B6-9.9M		Plaxton Pointer		B41F		1993-94			
101	L101GHN	103	L103GHN	105	M105PVN		107	M107PVN		108	M108PVN
102	L102GHN	104	M104PVN	106	M106PVN						

Cleveland Transit joined the Stagecoach group in November 1994 and, like Busways, is to retain its present livery for some time. Newly delivered were five Volvo B6s. These feature Plaxton Pointer bodies as seen in this picture of 104, M104PVN, taken shortly after delivery. *Andew Jarosz*

Although Cleveland Transit adminstered Kingston upon Hull City Transport, there was little movement between the two fleets. One example which did move is now Cleveland 901, H201XKH. This is a Leyland Swift with Reeve Burgess Harrier coach body. A similar vehicle is still in the Hull fleet and with two on loan to Stagecoach South these total all of the type in the group. *Andrew Jarosz*

121-157 — Leyland Fleetline FE30AGR — Northern Counties — H43/31F — 1979-83

121	YVN521T	131	GAJ131V	138	JAJ138W	145	JAJ145W	152	VEF152Y
125	GAJ125V	132	GAJ132V	139	JAJ139W	146	JAJ146W	153	VEF153Y
126	GAJ126V	133	GAJ133V	140	JAJ140W	147	PEF147X	154	YAJ154Y
127	GAJ127V	134	GAJ134V	141	JAJ141W	148	PEF148X	155	YAJ155Y
128	GAJ128V	135	GAJ135V	142	JAJ142W	149	PEF149X	156	YAJ156Y
129	GAJ129V	136	GAJ136V	143	JAJ143W	150	VEF150Y	157	YAJ157Y
130	GAJ130V	137	JAJ137W	144	JAJ144W	151	VEF151Y		

209	A209FHN	Dennis Dominator DDA167	Northern Counties	H43/31F	1983	
211	A211FHN	Dennis Dominator DDA167	Northern Counties	H43/31F	1983	
212	A212FHN	Dennis Dominator DDA167	Northern Counties	H43/31F	1984	
213	A213FHN	Dennis Dominator DDA172	Northern Counties	H43/31F	1984	

214-222 — Dennis Dominator DD906* — Northern Counties — H43/31F — 1985-86 *219-22 are DDA1009

214	B214OAJ	216	B216OAJ	218	B218OAJ	220	C220WAJ	222	C222WAJ
215	B215OAJ	217	B217OAJ	219	C219WAJ	221	C221WAJ		

336-345 — Renault-Dodge S56 — Northern Counties — B23F — 1989

336	F336VEF	338	F338VEF	340	F340VEF	342	F342VEF	344	F344VEF
337	F337VEF	339	F339VEF	341	F341VEF	343	F343VEF	345	F345VEF

500	PRX189B	Leyland Titan PD3/4	Northern Counties	FCO39/30F	1964	Ex Southdown, 1988
900	CVN400T	Bedford YLQ/S	Duple Dominant II	C35F	1979	
901	H201XKH	Leyland Swift ST2R44C97	Reeve Burgess Harrier	C37F	1990	Ex Kingston upon Hull, 1994
902	BPY402T	Leyland Leopard PSU3E/4R	Plaxton Supreme IV Express	DP53F	1979	
903	BPY403T	Leyland Leopard PSU3E/4R	Plaxton Supreme IV Express	DP53F	1979	
905	CPY705T	Leyland Leopard PSU3E/4R	Plaxton Supreme IV Express	C53F	1979	
912	HPY422V	Leyland Leopard PSU3F/4R	Plaxton Supreme IV Express	C53F	1980	
914	HPY424V	Leyland Leopard PSU3F/4R	Plaxton Supreme IV Express	C53F	1980	
916	HDC416V	Leyland Leopard PSU3E/4R	Plaxton Supreme IV Express	C53F	1979	

While Cleveland took the Volvo B6 for its mid-sized saloon the Volvo B10B was chosen to meet the full length requirement. Twelve of the type arrived during 1994, all fitted with Plaxton Verde bodywork. Preparing for a journey to Thornaby is 42, M42PVN. *Andrew Jarosz*

920	YVN520T	Leyland Fleetline FE30AGR	Northern Counties	H43/31F	1979	
922	YVN522T	Leyland Fleetline FE30AGR	Northern Counties	H43/31F	1979	
923	HPY423V	Leyland Leopard PSU3F/4R	Plaxton Supreme IV Express	DP53F	1980	
924	E324JVN	Renault-Dodge S56	Northern Counties	B20F	1987	
925	HPY425V	Leyland Leopard PSU3F/4R	Plaxton Supreme IV Express	DP53F	1980	
926	HPY426V	Leyland Leopard PSU3F/4R	Plaxton Supreme IV Express	DP53F	1980	
927	OHN427X	Leyland Leopard PSU3F/4R	Plaxton Supreme IV Express	C53F	1981	
928	OHN428X	Leyland Leopard PSU3F/4R	Plaxton Supreme IV Express	C53F	1981	
929	OHN429X	Leyland Leopard PSU3F/4R	Plaxton Supreme IV Express	C53F	1981	
933	E333LHN	Renault-Dodge S56	Northern Counties	DP21F	1988	
935	F335SPY	Renault-Dodge S56	Northern Counties	DP21F	1988	
951	OIB3516	Leyland Tiger TRCTL11/2R	Plaxton Paramount 3200	C49F	1983	
952	OIB3515	Leyland Tiger TRCTL11/2R	Plaxton Paramount 3200	C49F	1983	
953	OIB3514	Leyland Tiger TRCTL11/2RP	Plaxton Paramount 3200	C49F	1984	
954	OIB3513	Leyland Tiger TRCTL11/2RP	Plaxton Paramount 3200	C49F	1984	
955	OIB3512	Leyland Royal Tiger RTC	Roe Doyen	C53F	1987	
983	PJI4983	Leyland Olympian ONTL11/2RSp	Eastern Coach Works	CH45/28F	1985	Ex Clyde Coast, Ardrossan, 1992
986	PJI4986	Volvo B10M-61	Van Hool Alizée	C49F	1988	Ex Excelsior, 1993
997	AHN397T	Leyland Leopard PSU3E/4R	Plaxton Supreme IV Express	DP55F	1979	

Livery: Green, yellow and white (Cleveland Transit); orange, yellow and white (Cleveland Coaches); maroon, yellow and white (Tees Valley).

Previous Registrations:

OIB3512	D455GHN	OIB3515	YHN452Y	PJI4986	E304OPR
OIB3513	A454HPY	OIB3516	YHN451Y	PRX189B	417DCD
OIB3514	A453HPY	PJI4983	B577LPE		

CUMBERLAND

Cumberland Motor Services, PO Box 17, Tangier Street, Whitehaven,
Cumbria, CA28 7XF

Depots : Hindpool Road, Barrow; Willowholme Industrial Estate, Carlisle; Station Road, Kendal; and Lillyhall. **Outstations**
Ambleside, Appleby, Askam, Grange, Haverthwaite, Millom, Orton, Penrith, Sedbergh and Ulverston.

31	D514RCK	Mercedes-Benz L608D	Reeve Burgess	DP19F	1986	Ex Ribble, 1994	
32	D539RCK	Mercedes-Benz L608D	Reeve Burgess	B20F	1986	Ex Ribble, 1994	
33	D547RCK	Mercedes-Benz L608D	Reeve Burgess	B20F	1986	Ex Ribble, 1994	

34-46

Mercedes-Benz L608D   Reeve Burgess   B20F   1986-87

34	D34UAO	37	D37UAO	40	D40UAO	43	D43UAO	45	D45UAO
35	D35UAO	38	D38UAO	41	D41UAO	44	D44UAO	46	D46UAO
36	D36UAO	39	D39UAO	42	D42UAO				

47-53

Mercedes-Benz 709D   Alexander Sprint   B25F   1988   51-53 ex Hampshire Bus, 1989

47	E47CHH	49	E49CHH	51	E510PVV	52	E511PVV	53	E512PVV
48	E48CHH	50	E50CHH						

54-70

Mercedes-Benz 709D   Alexander Sprint   B25F*   1990   55-70 ex Magicbus, 1990-91
    *54-6/68/70 are B23F

54	G178PAO	58	G268TSL	61	G263TSL	64	G266TSL	67	G295TSL
55	G299TSL	59	G269TSL	62	G264TSL	65	G297TSL	68	G294TSL
56	G300TSL	60	G296TSL	63	G265TSL	66	G298TSL	70	G293TSL
57	G267TSL								

71-78

Mercedes-Benz 709D   Alexander Sprint   B25F   1993

71	K871GHH	73	K873GHH	75	K875GHH	77	K877GHH	78	K878GHH
72	K872GHH	74	K874GHH	76	K876GHH				

79-86

Mercedes-Benz 709D   Alexander Sprint   B25F   1993   Ex Ribble, 1994

79	K626UFR	81	K622UFR	83	K121XHG	85	L123DRN	86	K113XHG
80	K623UFR	82	K114XHG	84	L126DRN				

90	E317BRM	MCW MetroRider MF150	MCW	C25F	1988	Ex Cook & Marshall, 1988
101	109DRM	Leyland Tiger TRCTL11/3R	Duple Laser	C50F	1984	
102	A102DAO	Leyland Tiger TRCTL11/3R	Duple Laser	C50F	1984	
103	B103HAO	Leyland Tiger TRCTL11/3RH	Duple Laser 2	C50F	1984	
105	B105HAO	Leyland Tiger TRCTL11/3RH	Duple Laser 2	C53F	1984	
106	B106HAO	Leyland Tiger TRCTL11/3RH	Duple Laser 2	C49FT	1984	
107	TCK841	Leyland Tiger TRCTL11/3RH	Duple Laser 2	C44FT	1985	
109	WLT706	Leyland Tiger TRCTL11/3RH	Plaxton Paramount 3500 II	C48FT	1987	
110	WLT824	Leyland Tiger TRCTL11/3RH	Plaxton Paramount 3500 II	C46FT	1987	
111	VRR447	Leyland Tiger TRCTL11/3RH	Plaxton Paramount 3500 II	C48FT	1985	Ex Hampshire Bus, 1988

120-124

Volvo B10M-60   Plaxton Expressliner   C46FT   1992

120	J120AHH	121	J121AHH	122	J122AHH	123	J123AHH	124	J124AHH

125	L125NAO	Volvo B10M-60	Plaxton Expressliner 2	C46FT	1994	
126	L126NAO	Volvo B10M-60	Plaxton Expressliner 2	C46FT	1994	
127	L127NAO	Volvo B10M-60	Plaxton Expressliner 2	C46FT	1994	
149	IIL3503	Volvo B10M-61	Van Hool Alizée	C49FT	1988	Ex East Midland, 1993
150	IIL3505	Volvo B10M-61	Van Hool Alizée	C49FT	1988	Ex East Midland, 1993
151	VLF578	Volvo B10M-61	Van Hool Alizée	C48F	1981	Ex Magicbus, 1988
152	RUT842	Volvo B10M-61	Van Hool Alizée	C48F	1981	Ex Magicbus, 1988
153	LJC800	Volvo B10M-61	Van Hool Alizée	C48F	1982	Ex Magicbus, 1988
155	ORY640	Volvo B10M-61	Van Hool Alizée	C48F	1982	Ex Magicbus, 1988
156	PCK335	Leyland Tiger TRCTL11/3RH	Duple Laser 2	C53F	1985	Ex Ribble, 1989

Cumberland painted their coaches in a yellow and orange livery with Coachline titles, though a red scheme is being introduced as we go to press. Photographed in Blackpool is 111, VRR447, a Leyland Tiger with Plaxton Paramount 3500 bodywork transferred to the fleet from Hampshire Bus. *Colin Lloyd*

Five Leyland Lynx operate for Cumberland and are most likely to be found running from the Penrith outstation. Photographed in Keswick is 255, C544RAO a pre-production Lynx model which first went to NBC for evaluatuion at Ribble. *Roy Marshall*

157	WVT618	Volvo B10M-61		Plaxton Paramount 3500 III	C50F	1987	Ex Wallace Arnold, 1990		
158	DSV943	Volvo B10M-61		Plaxton Paramount 3500 III	C50F	1987	Ex Wallace Arnold, 1990		
161	JPU817	Volvo B10M-61		Plaxton Paramount 3500 III	C50F	1987	Ex Wallace Arnold, 1990		
162	B162WRN	Leyland Tiger TRCTL11/3RH		Duple Laser 2	C53F	1985	Ex Ribble, 1991		
251	F251JRM	Leyland Lynx LX112L10ZR1		Leyland	B51F	1989			
252	F252JRM	Leyland Lynx LX112L10ZR1		Leyland	B51F	1989			
253	F253KAO	Leyland Lynx LX112L10ZR1		Leyland	B51F	1989			
254	E709MFR	Leyland Lynx LX112L10ZR1		Leyland	B51F	1988	Ex Leyland Bus, 1989		
255	C544RAO	Leyland Lynx LX1126LXCTFR1 (Cummins) Leyland			B51F	1986	Ex Ribble, 1991		

270-282		Volvo B6-9.9M			Alexander Dash		B40F	1993-94	
270	L270LHH	272	L272LHH	274	L274LHH	276	L276JAO	282	L282JAO
271	L271LHH	273	L273LHH	275	L275JAO				

420-437		Bristol VRT/SL3/6LXB			Eastern Coach Works		H43/31F	1980	
420	FAO420V	424	FAO424V	428	FAO428V	432	KRM432W	435	KRM435W
421	FAO421V	425	FAO425V	429	FAO429V	433	KRM433W	436	KRM436W
422	FAO422V	426	FAO426V	430	KRM430W	434	KRM434W	437	KRM437W
423	FAO423V	427	FAO427V	431	KRM431W				

The first large delivery of Volvo B10Ms to Stagecoach were allocated to Cumberland where they almost eliminated Leyland Nationals. With the type the Carlisle city services were transformed with increased patronage and much kudos. Photographed while working service 67 is 711, K711DAO. *Brian Pritchard*

Amid Cumberland's operational area is the popular English Lake District, with much seasonal tourist traffic. A popular service which runs from Keswick south through the Lakes and Kendal down to Lancaster is the 555, recently branded as the Lakeslink. Cumberland have allocated the 1991 Olympian delivery to this service, the type being the extended version. Also featured is high-back seating. *Roy Marshall*

505	LUA273V	Leyland Leopard PSU3F/4R	Plaxton Supreme IV	C51F	1980	Ex Yeowart, Whitehaven, 1988
509	E986AHH	DAF SB2305DHTD585	Plaxton Paramount 3200 III	C53F	1988	Ex Yeowart, Whitehaven, 1988
511	D511RCK	Mercedes-Benz L608D	Reeve Burgess	DP19F	1986	Ex Ribble, 1994
518	D518RCK	Mercedes-Benz L608D	Reeve Burgess	DP19F	1986	Ex Ribble, 1989
519	D519RCK	Mercedes-Benz L608D	Reeve Burgess	DP19F	1986	Ex Ribble, 1989
520	D520RCK	Mercedes-Benz L608D	Reeve Burgess	DP19F	1986	Ex Ribble, 1989

522-561

Mercedes-Benz L608D   Reeve Burgess   B20F   1986   Ex Ribble, 1989

522	D522RCK	529	D529RCK	533	D533RCK	558	D558RCK	560	D560RCK
525	D525RCK	530	D530RCK	534	D534RCK	559	D559RCK	561	D561RCK
528	D528RCK	531	D531RCK	557	D557RCK				

| 569 | LUA275V | Leyland Leopard PSU3E/4R | Plaxton Supreme IV | C51F | 1980 | Ex Kirkpatrick, Brigham, 1988 |
| 625 | GRM625V | Leyland Leopard PSU3F/4R | Duple Dominant II | C49F | 1980 | |

699-788

Volvo Citybus B10M-60   Alexander PS   B49F*   1992-93   *772-788 are DP48F

699	K699ERM	717	K717DAO	735	K735DAO	754	K754DAO	772	K772DAO
700	K700DAO	718	K718DAO	736	K736DAO	755	K755DAO	773	K773DAO
701	K701DAO	719	K719DAO	737	K737DAO	756	K756DAO	774	K774DAO
702	K702DAO	720	K720DAO	738	K738DAO	757	K757DAO	775	K775DAO
703	K703DAO	721	K721DAO	739	K739DAO	758	K758DAO	776	K776DAO
704	K704ERM	722	K722DAO	740	K740DAO	759	K759DAO	777	K777DAO
705	K705DAO	723	K723DAO	741	K741DAO	760	K760DAO	778	K778DAO
706	K706DAO	724	K724DAO	742	K742DAO	761	K761DAO	779	K779DAO
707	K707DAO	725	K725DAO	743	K743DAO	762	K762DAO	780	K780DAO
708	K708DAO	726	K726DAO	744	K744DAO	763	K763DAO	781	K781DAO
709	K709DAO	727	K727DAO	745	K745DAO	764	K764DAO	782	K782DAO
710	K710DAO	728	K728DAO	746	K746DAO	765	K765DAO	783	K783DAO
711	K711DAO	729	K729DAO	748	K748DAO	766	K766DAO	784	K784DAO
712	K712DAO	730	K730DAO	749	K749DAO	767	K767DAO	785	K785DAO
713	K713DAO	731	K731DAO	750	K750DAO	768	K768DAO	786	K786DAO
714	K714DAO	732	K732DAO	751	K751DAO	769	K769DAO	787	K787DAO
715	K715DAO	733	K733DAO	752	K752DAO	770	K770DAO	788	K788DAO
716	K716DAO	734	K734DAO	753	K753DAO	771	K771DAO		

810	TRN810V	Leyland National 10351B/1R		B44F	1979	Ex Ribble, 1989
1001	URM801Y	Leyland Olympian ONLXB/1R	Eastern Coach Works	DPH45/30F	1982	
1002	URM802Y	Leyland Olympian ONLXB/1R	Eastern Coach Works	DPH45/30F	1982	

1003-1011

Leyland Olympian ONLXB/2RZ   Alexander RL   H51/36F   1988

| 1003 | F803FAO | 1005 | F805FAO | 1007 | F807FAO | 1009 | F809FAO | 1011 | F811FAO |
| 1004 | F804FAO | 1006 | F806FAO | 1008 | F808FAO | 1010 | F810FAO | | |

1012-1019

Leyland Olympian ON2R56G13Z4 Alexander RL   H51/34F   1990

| 1012 | H112SAO | 1014 | H114SAO | 1016 | H116SAO | 1018 | H118SAO | 1019 | H119SAO |
| 1013 | H113SAO | 1015 | H115SAO | 1017 | H117SAO | | | | |

1020-1027

Leyland Olympian ON2R56G13Z4 Alexander RL   DPH47/27F 1991

| 1020 | J120AAO | 1022 | J122AAO | 1024 | J124XHH | 1026 | J126XHH | 1027 | J127XHH |
| 1021 | J121AAO | 1023 | J123XHH | 1025 | J125XHH | | | | |

1028-1035

Leyland Olympian ON2R50G13Z4 Alexander RL   DPH43/27F 1992

| 1028 | K128DAO | 1030 | K130DAO | 1032 | K132DAO | 1034 | K134DAO | 1035 | K135DAO |
| 1029 | K129DAO | 1031 | K131DAO | 1033 | K133DAO | | | | |

1090	C382SAO	Leyland Olympian ONLXB/1RV	Alexander RL	H47/30F	1986	Ex Bluebird, 1991
1091	C383SAO	Leyland Olympian ONLXB/1RV	Alexander RL	H47/30F	1986	Ex Bluebird, 1991
1092	D384XAO	Leyland Olympian ONLXB/1RV	Alexander RL	H47/30F	1987	Ex Bluebird, 1991
1093	D380XRS	Leyland Olympian ONLXB/1RV	Alexander RL	H47/30F	1987	Ex Bluebird, 1992
1094	D381XRS	Leyland Olympian ONLXB/1RV	Alexander RL	H47/30F	1987	Ex Bluebird, 1992
1103	KRN103T	Leyland Leopard PSU3E/4R	Duple Dominant II	C47F	1978	Ex Ribble, 1986
1105	KRN105T	Leyland Leopard PSU3E/4R	Duple Dominant II	C47F	1978	Ex Ribble, 1986
1113	KRN113T	Leyland Leopard PSU3E/4R	Duple Dominant II	C47F	1979	Ex Ribble, 1986
1119	KRN119T	Leyland Leopard PSU3E/4R	Duple Dominant II	C47F	1979	Ex Ribble, 1986
1140	WCK140V	Leyland Leopard PSU3E/4R	Duple Dominant II	C51F	1980	Ex Ribble, 1986

1151	B151WRN	Leyland Tiger TRCTL11/3RH	Duple Laser 2	C49F	1985	Ex Ribble, 1991
1153	B153WRN	Leyland Tiger TRCTL11/3RH	Duple Laser 2	C49F	1985	Ex Ribble, 1991
1154	B154WRN	Leyland Tiger TRCTL11/3RH	Duple Laser 2	C49F	1985	Ex Ribble, 1991
1155	B43MAO	Leyland Tiger TRCTL11/3RH	Duple Laser 2	C53F	1985	Ex Ribble, 1991
1162	WLT980	Volvo B10M-61	Plaxton Paramount 3500 II	C48F	1986	Ex Ribble, 1994
1175	MRJ275W	Leyland Leopard PSU5D/4R	Plaxton Supreme IV	C50F	1981	Ex Ribble, 1989
1199	FDV799V	Leyland Leopard PSU3E/4RT	Plaxton Supreme IV Express	C49F	1980	Ex Ribble, 1989
1201	F201FHH	Leyland Olympian ON6LXCT/3RZ	Alexander RL	DPH55/41F	1989	
1202	F202FHH	Leyland Olympian ON6LXCT/3RZ	Alexander RL	DPH55/41F	1989	
1253	HNE253V	Leyland Leopard PSU5C/4R	Duple Dominant II	C53F	1980	Ex Ribble, 1989
1928	ERV251D	Leyland Atlantean PDR1/1 MkII	Metro Cammell	O43/31F	1966	Ex Southdown, 1991
2002	CBV2S	Bristol VRT/SL3/501 (6LXB)	Eastern Coach Works	O43/31F	1977	Ex Ribble, 1986
2024	DBV24W	Bristol VRT/SL3/6LXB	Eastern Coach Works	H43/31F	1980	Ex Ribble, 1986
2032	DBV32W	Bristol VRT/SL3/6LXB	Eastern Coach Works	H43/31F	1980	Ex Ribble, 1986
2035	UWV610S	Bristol VRT/SL3/6LXB	Eastern Coach Works	O43/31F	1978	Ex Southdown, 1990
2036	UWV612S	Bristol VRT/SL3/6LXB	Eastern Coach Works	O43/31F	1978	Ex Southdown, 1990
2037	UWV618S	Bristol VRT/SL3/6LXB	Eastern Coach Works	O43/31F	1978	Ex Southdown, 1990
2038	UWV620S	Bristol VRT/SL3/6LXB	Eastern Coach Works	O43/31F	1978	Ex Southdown, 1990
2134	DBV134Y	Leyland Olympian ONLXB/1R	Eastern Coach Works	H45/32F	1983	Ex Ribble, 1989
2175	C175ECK	Leyland Olympian ONLXB/1R	Eastern Coach Works	DPH42/30F	1985	Ex Ribble, 1989
2176	C176ECK	Leyland Olympian ONLXB/1R	Eastern Coach Works	DPH42/30F	1985	Ex Ribble, 1989
2177	C177ECK	Leyland Olympian ONLXB/1R	Eastern Coach Works	DPH42/30F	1986	Ex Ribble, 1989
5031	D503RCK	Mercedes-Benz L608D	Reeve Burgess	DP19F	1986	Ex Ribble, 1989
5041	D504RCK	Mercedes-Benz L608D	Reeve Burgess	DP19F	1986	Ex Ribble, 1989

Previous Registrations:

109DRM	A101DAO	LJC800	From new
B43MAO	B155WRN, PCK335	ORY640	From new
C382SAO	C473SSO, GSO3V	PCK335	B156WRN
C383SAO	C474SSO, GSO4V	RUT842	From new
D384XAO	D375XRS, GSO5V	TCK841	B107HAO
D560RCK	D561RCK	VLF578	TGD766W
D561RCK	D560RCK	VRR447	B180RLJ
DSV943	D203LWX	WLT706	C109OHH
IIL3503	E625UNE, TXI2426, E936XSB	WLT824	C110OHH
IIL3505	E623UNE, XIA257, E942XSB	WLT980	C105DWR
JPU817	D207LWX	WVT618	D202LWX

Livery variations:

Coachline:	109/11, 153/5/7/8/61, 509, 1151/3-5/62.
Lakeland Experience:	520/58/60, 810, 1928, 2002/35-8.
National Express:	110, 120-7/49/50

Named vehicles: 520 *William Wordsworth*, 558 *John Ruskin*, 560 *Beatrix Potter*.

To avoid a clash of fleet numbers, two minibuses transferred from the Ribble fleet were given numbers with 1 suffix, these numbers remain despite the subsequent withdrawal of the other vehicles. Photographed in Kendal is 5041, D504RCK, one of many Mercedes-Benz L608Ds transferred from Ribble with the Carlisle area work in 1990 prior to the National Bus Company sale.
Brian Pritchard

EAST LONDON

East London Bus & Coach Company Ltd, 16-20 Clements Road, Ilford, Essex, IG1 1BA

Depots : Longbridge Road, Barking; Fairfield Road, Bow; High Road, Leyton; North Street, Romford; Waterden Road, Stratford and Priory Road, Upton Park.

DA10	G684KNW	DAF SB220LC550	Optare Delta	B36D	1989	Ex London Buses, 1994

DA11-DA35 DAF SB220LC550   Optare Delta   B40D   1992-93 Ex London Buses, 1994

11	J711CYG	16	J716CYG	21	J721CYG	26	J726CYG	31	K631HWX
12	J712CYG	17	J717CYG	22	J722CYG	27	J727CYG	32	K632HWX
13	J713CYG	18	J718CYG	23	J723CYG	28	J728CYG	33	K633HWX
14	J714CYG	19	J719CYG	24	J724CYG	29	J729CYG	34	K634HWX
15	J715CYG	20	J720CYG	25	J725CYG	30	K630HWX	35	K635HWX

DRL109-138 Dennis Dart 9SDL3024   Plaxton Pointer   B34F   1993   Ex London Buses, 1994

109	K109SRH	115	K115SRH	121	K121SRH	127	K127SRH	133	K133SRH
110	K110SRH	116	K116SRH	122	K122SRH	128	K128SRH	134	K134SRH
111	K211SRH	117	K117SRH	123	K123SRH	129	K129SRH	135	K135SRH
112	K112SRH	118	K118SRH	124	K124SRH	130	K130SRH	136	L136VRH
113	K113SRH	119	K119SRH	125	K125SRH	131	K131SRH	137	L137VRH
114	K114SRH	120	K120SRH	126	K126SRH	132	K132SRH	138	L138VRH

DRL139-146 Dennis Dart 9SDL3034   Plaxton Pointer   B34F   1993   Ex London Buses, 1994

139	L139VRH	141	L141VRH	143	L143VRH	145	L145VRH	146	L146VRH
140	L140VRH	142	L142VRH	144	L144VRH				

London bus operation was achieved at the beginning of September 1994 when the purchase of London Buses' subsidiaries East London and Selkent were announced as part of the privatisation of the capital's red bus fleets. The East London fleet contains 26 of the Optare Delta product. Passing through Barking is DA16, J716CYG, photographed in London Buses livery. *Malc McDonald*

The Dennis Dart was chosen by London Buses for much of its midi-bus needs, many replacing double deck buses when introduced. Those operating with East London have bodywork by Plaxton and Wrights. One of the latter examples is DW158, NDZ3158, seen in Ilford while heading for Redbridge Station. *Tony Wilson*

DWL15-26

						B35F	1993	Ex London Buses, 1994	

Dennis Dart 9SDL3016 — Wright Handy-bus — B35F — 1993 — Ex London Buses, 1994

15	NDZ3015	18	NDZ3018	21	NDZ3021	23	NDZ3023	25	NDZ3025
16	NDZ3016	19	NDZ3019	22	NDZ3022	24	NDZ3024	26	NDZ3026
17	NDZ3017	20	NDZ3020						

DW133-159

Dennis Dart 8.5SDL3015 — Wright Handy-bus — B29F — 1993 — Ex London Buses, 1994

133	NDZ3133	139	NDZ3139	145	NDZ3145	150	NDZ3150	155	NDZ3155
134	NDZ3134	140	NDZ3140	146	NDZ3146	151	NDZ3151	156	NDZ3156
135	NDZ3135	141	NDZ3141	147	NDZ3147	152	NDZ3152	157	NDZ3157
136	NDZ3136	142	NDZ3142	148	NDZ3148	153	NDZ3153	158	NDZ3158
137	NDZ3137	143	NDZ3143	149	NDZ3149	154	NDZ3154	159	NDZ3159
138	NDZ3138	144	NDZ3144						

MR16	D476PON	MCW MetroRider MF150/14	MCW		B23F	1987	Ex London Buses, 1994

MRL65-73

MCW MetroRider MF158/1 — MCW — B30F — 1988 — Ex London Buses, 1994

65	E641KYW	67	E643KYW	69	E645KYW	71	E647KYW	73	E649KYW
66	E642KYW	68	E644KYW	70	E646KYW	72	E648KYW		

MRL74	E650KYW	MCW MetroRider MF158/2	MCW	DP33F	1988	Ex London Buses, 1994
MRL75	E705LYU	MCW MetroRider MF158/2	MCW	DP33F	1988	Ex London Buses, 1994
MRL76	E706LYU	MCW MetroRider MF158/2	MCW	DP33F	1988	Ex London Buses, 1994
MRL77	F197YDA	MCW MetroRider MF158/18	MCW	B28F	1988	Ex London Buses, 1994

Opposite, top: **New arrivals for service 101 are sixteen Scania N113s with Wright Endurance low floor bodywork and fitted with power-operated destination blinds. Seen prior to its entry into service is SLW15, RDZ6115, the first to be delivered.** *Nick Coleman*

Opposite, bottom: **One of the early repaints into all-red with Stagecoach transfers was Leyland Titan T751, OHV751Y, seen at Goswell Road while working service 56.** *Mike Harris*

The 1995 Stagecoach Bus Handbook

MRL106-131 — MCW MetroRider MF158/16 — MCW B28F — 1988 — Ex London Buses, 1994

106	F106YVP	112	F112YVP	118	F118YVP	121	F121YVP	128	F128YVP
109	F109YVP	113	F113YVP	119	F119YVP	125	F125YVP	130	F130YVP
110	F110YVP	114	F114YVP	120	F120YVP	126	F126YVP	131	F131YVP
111	F111YVP								

MRL132	F132YVP	MCW MetroRider MF158/17	MCW	DP31F	1988	Ex London Buses, 1994
RMA5	NMY635E	AEC Routemaster R2RH2	Park Royal	H32/24F	1967	Ex London Buses, 1994
RMA8	NMY640E	AEC Routemaster R2RH2	Park Royal	H32/24F	1967	Ex London Buses, 1994
RM613	WLT613	AEC Routemaster R2RH	Park Royal	H36/28R	1961	Ex London Buses, 1994
RML886	WLT886	AEC Routemaster R2RH1	Park Royal	H36/28R	1961	Ex London Buses, 1994
RML890	WLT890	AEC Routemaster R2RH1	Park Royal	H36/28R	1961	Ex London Buses, 1994
RML898	WLT898	AEC Routemaster R2RH1	Park Royal	H36/28R	1961	Ex London Buses, 1994
RMC1456	LFF875	AEC Routemaster R2RH	Park Royal	H32/25RD	1962	Ex London Buses, 1994
RMC1461	461CLT	AEC Routemaster R2RH	Park Royal	H32/25RD	1962	Ex London Buses, 1994
RMC1485	485CLT	AEC Routemaster R2RH	Park Royal	H32/25RD	1962	Ex London Buses, 1994
RM1527	527CLT	AEC Routemaster 2R2RH	Park Royal	H36/28R	1963	Ex London Buses, 1994

RML2272-2592 — AEC Routemaster R2RH1 — Park Royal — H40/32R — 1965-66 — Ex London Buses, 1994

2272	CUV272C	2399	JJD399D	2444	JJD444D	2470	JJD470D	2497	JJD497D
2286	CUV286C	2402	JJD402D	2445	JJD445D	2481	JJD481D	2541	JJD541D
2300	CUV300C	2415	JJD415D	2450	JJD450D	2488	JJD488D	2550	JJD550D
2303	CUV303C	2429	JJD429D	2451	JJD451D	2493	JJD493D	2565	JJD565D
2311	CUV311C	2435	JJD435D	2456	JJD456D	2495	JJD495D	2581	JJD581D
2392	JJD392D	2437	JJD437D	2462	JJD462D	2496	JJD496D	2592	JJD592D

RML2607-2760 — AEC Routemaster R2RH1 — Park Royal — H40/32R — 1967-68 — Ex London Buses, 1994

2607	NML607E	2641	NML641E	2665	SMK665F	2705	SMK705F	2743	SMK743F
2610	NML610E	2642	NML642E	2670	SMK670F	2709	SMK709F	2748	SMK748F
2616	NML616E	2657	NML657E	2671	SMK671F	2723	SMK723F	2749	SMK749F
2624	NML624E	2661	SMK661F	2696	SMK696F	2738	SMK738F	2760	SMK760F
2639	NML639E								

S22-29 — Scania N113DRB — Alexander RH — H47/31F — 1991 — Ex London Buses, 1994

22	J822HMC	24	J824HMC	26	J826HMC	28	J828HMC	29	J829HMC
23	J823HMC	25	J825HMC	27	J827HMC				

S30	J230XKY	Scania N113DRB	Northern Counties	H47/30F	1991	Ex London Buses, 1994
S31	J231XKY	Scania N113DRB	Northern Counties	H47/30F	1991	Ex London Buses, 1994

S32-71 — Scania N113DRB — Northern Counties — H41/25D — 1991-92 — Ex London Buses, 1994

32	J132HMT	40	J140HMT	48	K848LMK	56	K856LMK	64	K864LMK
33	J133HMT	41	J141HMT	49	K849LMK	57	K857LMK	65	K865LMK
34	J134HMT	42	J142HMT	50	K850LMK	58	K858LMK	66	K866LMK
35	J135HMT	43	J143HMT	51	K851LMK	59	K859LMK	67	K867LMK
36	J136HMT	44	J144HMT	52	K852LMK	60	K860LMK	68	K868LMK
37	J137HMT	45	J145HMT	53	K853LMK	61	K861LMK	69	K869LMK
38	J138HMT	46	K846LMK	54	K854LMK	62	K862LMK	70	K870LMK
39	J139HMT	47	K847LMK	55	K855LMK	63	K863LMK	71	K871LMK

SP2	K302FYG	DAF DB250HS505	Optare Spectra	H44/23D	1992	Ex London Buses, 1994
SR1	E155CGJ	Mercedes-Benz 811D	Optare StarRider	B26F	1988	Ex London Buses, 1994
SR2	E712LYU	Mercedes-Benz 811D	Optare StarRider	B26F	1988	Ex London Buses, 1994
SR3	E713LYU	Mercedes-Benz 811D	Optare StarRider	B26F	1988	Ex London Buses, 1994
SR4	E714LYU	Mercedes-Benz 811D	Optare StarRider	B26F	1988	Ex London Buses, 1994

SR12-119 — Mercedes-Benz 811D — Optare StarRider — B26F — 1988-89 — Ex London Buses, 1994

12	F912YWY	65	F165FWY	72	F172FWY	77	F177FWY	91	G91KUB
13	F913YWY	66	F166FWY	73	F173FWY	78	F178FWY	105	G105KUB
32	F32CWY	69	F169FWY	74	F174FWY	79	F179FWY	106	G106KUB
50	F50CWY	70	F170FWY	75	F175FWY	80	F180FWY	107	G107KUB
56	F156FWY	71	F171FWY	76	F176FWY	86	G86KUB	119	G119KUB
60	F160FWY								

Routemaster operation will continue for some time from East London, most of the stock having been refurbished and fitted with Iveco engines. One example RML2760, the last Routemaster to be built remains in 'as new' condition and retains an original unit, however. Typical of the type is RML2541, JJD541D, seen passing on service 8. *Tony Wilson*

Scania N113s with both Alexander and Northern Counties bodywork operate for East London. Seen passing St Paul's Cathedral is S59, K859LMK, a Northern Counties example. This Scania chassis can also be found in the Busways, Hull and East Kent operations. *David Donati collection*

SLW15-30 — Scania N113CRL — Wright Pathfinder — B37D — 1994

15	RDZ6115	19	RDZ6119	22	RDZ6122	25	RDZ6125	28	RDZ6128
16	RDZ6116	20	RDZ6120	23	RDZ6123	26	RDZ6126	29	RDZ6129
17	RDZ6117	21	RDZ6121	24	RDZ6124	27	RDZ6127	30	RDZ6130
18	RDZ6118								

T1-248 — Leyland Titan TNLXB2RRSp — Park Royal — H44/26D — 1978-80 Ex London Buses, 1994
*63/80 are DPH44/26F

1	THX401S	12	WYV12T	23	WYV23T	34	WYV34T	140	CUL140V
2	THX402S	13	WYV13T	24	WYV24T	35	WYV35T	175	CUL175V
3	WYV3T	14	WYV14T	25	WYV25T	36	WYV36T	193	CUL193V
4	WYV4T	15	WYV15T	26	WYV26T	37	WYV37T	197	CUL197V
5	WYV5T	16	WYV16T	27	WYV27T	38	WYV38T	214	CUL214V
6	WYV6T	17	WYV17T	28	WYV28T	39	WYV39T	222	CUL222V
7	WYV7T	18	WYV18T	29	WYV29T	40	WYV40T	223	CUL223V
8	WYV8T	19	WYV19T	30	WYV30T	63	WYV63T	230	EYE230V
9	WYV9T	20	WYV20T	31	WYV31T	66	WYV66T	246	EYE246V
10	WYV10T	21	WYV21T	32	WYV32T	80	CUL80V	248	EYE248V
11	WYV11T	22	WYV22T	33	WYV33T				

T252-263 — Leyland Titan TNLXB2RR — Park Royal/Leyland — H44/24D — 1981 Ex London Buses, 1994
*T261 is TNTL112RR

252	GYE252W	260	GYE252W	261	GYE261W	262	GYE262W	263	GYE263W
254	GYE254W								

T264-549 — Leyland Titan TNLXB2RR — Leyland — H44/24D — 1981-82 Ex London Buses, 1994

264	GYE264W	378	KYV378X	454	KYV454X	496	KYV496X	526	KYV526X
266	GYE266W	379	KYV379X	456	KYV456X	497	KYV497X	527	KYV527X
268	GYE268W	380	KYV380X	458	KYV458X	498	KYV498X	529	KYV529X
270	GYE270W	386	KYV386X	460	KYV460X	500	KYV500X	531	KYV531X
272	GYE272W	387	KYV387X	461	KYV461X	501	KYV501X	532	KYV532X
273	GYE273W	394	KYV394X	462	KYV462X	502	KYV502X	533	KYV533X
281	KYN281X	395	KYV395X	465	KYV465X	503	KYV503X	535	KYV535X
285	KYN285X	403	KYV403X	466	KYV466X	504	KYV504X	536	KYV536X
286	KYN286X	404	KYV404X	467	KYV467X	505	KYV505X	537	KYV537X
298	KYN298X	406	KYV406X	469	KYV469X	506	KYV506X	539	KYV539X
306	KYN306X	428	KYV428X	470	KYV470X	508	KYV508X	540	KYV540X
311	KYV311X	434	KYV434X	471	KYV471X	512	KYV512X	541	KYV541X
318	KYV318X	437	KYV437X	473	KYV473X	513	KYV513X	542	KYV542X
320	KYV320X	439	KYV439X	476	KYV476X	514	KYV514X	543	KYV543X
326	KYV326X	441	KYV441X	480	KYV480X	515	KYV515X	544	KYV544X
331	KYV331X	444	KYV444X	486	KYV486X	517	KYV517X	545	KYV545X
334	KYV334X	445	KYV445X	488	KYV488X	521	KYV521X	546	KYV546X
340	KYV340X	446	KYV446X	490	KYV490X	522	KYV522X	548	KYV548X
360	KYV360X	448	KYV448X	492	KYV492X	525	KYV525X	549	KYV549X
366	KYV366X	453	KYV453X	495	KYV495X				

A suprise transfer from London Buses was Optare Spectra SP2, K302FYG. The only dual-door example with London Buses it is now operating for East London Coaches where it performs on many of the regular contracts linked to school duties. It was photographed while crossing Putney Bridge on one such duty.
Colin Lloyd

T550-675

Leyland Titan TNLXB2RR — Leyland — H44/24D — 1982-83 Ex London Buses, 1994

550	NUW550Y	575	NUW575Y	598	NUW598Y	626	NUW626Y	650	NUW650Y
551	NUW551Y	576	NUW576Y	600	NUW600Y	627	NUW627Y	651	NUW651Y
552	NUW552Y	577	NUW577Y	601	NUW601Y	629	NUW629Y	652	NUW652Y
553	NUW553Y	578	NUW578Y	602	NUW602Y	630	NUW630Y	653	NUW653Y
554	NUW554Y	579	NUW579Y	603	NUW603Y	631	NUW631Y	654	NUW654Y
555	NUW555Y	580	NUW580Y	604	NUW604Y	632	NUW692Y	657	NUW657Y
556	NUW556Y	581	NUW581Y	605	NUW605Y	633	NUW633Y	658	NUW658Y
557	NUW557Y	582	NUW582Y	606	NUW606Y	634	NUW634Y	659	NUW659Y
558	NUW558Y	583	NUW583Y	608	NUW608Y	636	NUW636Y	660	NUW660Y
559	NUW559Y	584	NUW584Y	609	NUW609Y	637	NUW637Y	662	NUW662Y
560	NUW560Y	585	NUW585Y	610	NUW610Y	639	NUW639Y	663	NUW663Y
562	NUW562Y	586	NUW586Y	613	NUW613Y	640	NUW640Y	664	NUW664Y
563	NUW563Y	587	NUW587Y	614	NUW614Y	641	NUW641Y	665	NUW665Y
564	NUW564Y	588	NUW588Y	615	NUW615Y	642	NUW642Y	666	NUW666Y
565	NUW565Y	589	NUW589Y	617	NUW617Y	643	NUW643Y	668	NUW668Y
566	NUW566Y	590	NUW590Y	619	NUW619Y	644	NUW644Y	669	NUW669Y
568	NUW568Y	591	NUW591Y	621	NUW621Y	645	NUW645Y	670	NUW670Y
569	NUW569Y	592	NUW592Y	622	NUW622Y	646	NUW646Y	671	NUW671Y
571	NUW571Y	593	NUW593Y	623	NUW623Y	647	NUW647Y	672	NUW672Y
572	NUW572Y	595	NUW595Y	624	NUW624Y	648	NUW648Y	673	NUW673Y
573	NUW573Y	597	NUW597Y	625	NUW625Y	649	NUW649Y	675	NUW675Y
574	NUW574Y								

T684-971

Leyland Titan TNLXB2RR — Leyland H44/24D — 1983-84 — Ex London Buses, 1994
*T876 is TNTL112RR (6LXB)

684	OHV684Y	729	OHV729Y	769	A769SUL	840	A840SUL	922	A922SYE
686	OHV686Y	731	OHV731Y	784	A784SUL	846	A846SUL	935	A935SYE
688	OHV688Y	738	OHV738Y	789	A789SUL	849	A849SUL	944	A944SYE
691	OHV691Y	743	OHV743Y	802	A802SUL	867	A867SUL	945	A945SYE
697	OHV697Y	744	OHV744Y	819	A819SUL	873	A873SUL	949	A949SYE
699	OHV699Y	749	OHV749Y	826	A826SUL	876	A876SUL	953	A953SYE
702	OHV702Y	751	OHV751Y	827	A827SUL	902	A902SUL	960	A960SYE
719	OHV719Y	759	OHV759Y	832	A832SUL	905	A905SUL	965	A965SYE
724	OHV724Y	761	OHV761Y	833	A833SUL	921	A921SUL	971	A970SYE

T1022	A622THV	Leyland Titan TNLXB2RR	Leyland	H44/24D	1984	Ex London Buses, 1994
T1026	A626THV	Leyland Titan TNLXB2RR	Leyland	H44/24D	1984	Ex London Buses, 1994
T1050	A650THV	Leyland Titan TNLXB2RR	Leyland	H44/24D	1984	Ex London Buses, 1994
T1128	468CLT	Leyland Titan TNLXB2RR	Leyland	DPH43/29F	1979	Ex London Buses, 1994
TPL7	H642GRO	Leyland Tiger TRCL10/3ARZA	Plaxton Paramount 3200 III	C53F	1991	Ex London Buses, 1994
VP2	F24HGG	Volvo B10M-60	Plaxton Paramount 3500 III	C53F	1991	Ex London Buses, 1994

Vehicles operated on behalf of London Transport Buses on Mobility routes:

LS121	THX121S	Leyland National 10351/2R	B21DL	1977
LS308	AYR308T	Leyland National 10351/2R	B21DL	1979
LS403	BYW403V	Leyland National 10351/2R	B21DL	1979

Previous Registrations:

461CLT	From new	E155CGJ	E711LYU, WLT461	WLT886	From new
468CLT	WDA3T	LFF875	456CLT	WLT890	From new
485CLT	From new	WLT613	From new	WLT898	From new
527CLT	From new				

Livery: Red; Green(1962 Green Line) RMC1461.

EAST MIDLAND

East Midland Motor Services Ltd, New Street, Chesterfield, Derbyshire, S40 2LQ
Grimsby Cleethorpes Transport Ltd, Victoria Street, Grimsby,
South Humberside, DN31 1NS

Depots : New Street, Chesterfield; Victoria Street, Grimsby; Sutton Road, Mansfield and Hardy Street, Worksop.

1-9		Dennis Lance 11SDA3106*	East Lancashire EL2000	B45F	1993	Ex Grimsby Cleethorpes, 1993
						*5-9 are type 11SDA3111
1	K701NDO	3	K703NDO	5	L705HFU	7	L707HFU	9	L709HFU
2	K702NDO	4	K704NDO	6	L706HFU	8	L708HFU		

27	E927PBE	Leyland Tiger TRBLXCT/2RH	Alexander P	DP51F	1987	Ex Grimsby Cleethorpes, 1993
28	E928PBE	Leyland Tiger TRBLXCT/2RH	Alexander P	DP51F	1987	Ex Grimsby Cleethorpes, 1993
29	E929PBE	Leyland Tiger TRBLXCT/2RH	Alexander P	DP51F	1987	Ex Grimsby Cleethorpes, 1993
30	E930PBE	Leyland Tiger TRBLXCT/2RH	Alexander P	DP51F	1987	Ex Grimsby Cleethorpes, 1993
31	EJV31Y	Dennis Falcon H SDA411	Wadham Stringer Vanguard	B42F	1983	Ex Grimsby Cleethorpes, 1993
31	SKY31Y	Leyland Tiger TRCTL11/3R	Eastern Coach Works B51	C51F	1983	
32	SKY32Y	Leyland Tiger TRCTL11/3R	Eastern Coach Works B51	C51F	1983	
32	EJV32Y	Dennis Falcon H SDA411	Wadham Stringer Vanguard	B42F	1983	Ex Grimsby Cleethorpes, 1993
33	EJV33Y	Dennis Falcon H SDA411	Wadham Stringer Vanguard	B42F	1983	Ex Grimsby Cleethorpes, 1993
34	EJV34Y	Dennis Falcon H SDA411	Wadham Stringer Vanguard	B42F	1983	Ex Grimsby Cleethorpes, 1993
37	PJI4316	Leyland Tiger TRCTL11/2R	Duple Dominant IV	C47F	1983	
38	PJI4317	Leyland Tiger TRCTL11/2R	Duple Dominant IV	C47F	1983	

Many of the former Grimsby fleet have now been repainted into corporate livery increasing the number of designs supporting the colours. Seen in Grimsby is Dennis Falcon 33, EJV33Y, which carries a Wadham Stringer body to its Vanguard design. The Grimsby business has been incorporated into the East Midlands company for administrative purposes and only four fleet numbers are duplicated at present. *Tony Wilson*

Dennis Dominator 75, F75TFU, is one of four delivered in 1989 and carries Alexander RH-type bodywork. With the addition of buses from Hull the number of this type in the group has increased with a potential for rationalisation of types. Currently, the former Grimsby-Cleethorpes buses still operate in those towns. *Tony Wilson*

39-44		Leyland Tiger TRCTL11/2R		Alexander TE		DP45F*	1983-84	*42/3 are DP49F	
39	A39XHE	**41**	A41XHE	**42**	A42XHE	**43**	A43XHE	**44**	A44XHE

45-49		MCW MetroRider MF150/94		MCW		B23F	1988	Ex Grimsby Cleethorpes, 1993	
45	E45HFE	**46**	E46HFE	**47**	E47HFE	**48**	E48HFE	**49**	E49HFE

49	B49DWE	Leyland Tiger TRCTL11/2RH	Alexander TE	DP49F	1984
50	E50HFE	MCW MetroRider MF150/94	MCW	B23F	1988	Ex Grimsby Cleethorpes, 1993
51	E51HFE	MCW MetroRider MF150/94	MCW	B23F	1988	Ex Grimsby Cleethorpes, 1993
52	B52DWE	Leyland Tiger TRCTL11/2RH	Alexander TE	DP49F	1984
53	B53DWJ	Leyland Tiger TRCTL11/2RH	Alexander TE	DP49F	1985
54	B54DWJ	Leyland Tiger TRCTL11/2RH	Alexander TE	DP49F	1985
56	E56HFE	MCW MetroRider MF150/94	MCW	DP23F	1988	Ex Grimsby Cleethorpes, 1993
57	E57HFE	MCW MetroRider MF150/94	MCW	DP23F	1988	Ex Grimsby Cleethorpes, 1993
58	E58HFE	MCW MetroRider MF150/94	MCW	DP23F	1988	Ex Grimsby Cleethorpes, 1993

59-70		Leyland Fleetline FE30AGR		Roe		H45/29D	1979-80	Ex Grimsby Cleethorpes, 1993	
59	TFU59T	**62**	TFU62T	**65**	WFU465V	**67**	WFU467V	**69**	WFU469V
60	TFU60T	**63**	TFU63T	**66**	WFU466V	**68**	WFU468V	**70**	WFU470V
61	TFU61T	**64**	TFU64T						

71	A71GEE	Leyland Olympian ONTL11/1R	Eastern Coach Works	H45/31F	1983	Ex Grimsby Cleethorpes, 1993
72	A72GEE	Leyland Olympian ONTL11/1R	Eastern Coach Works	H45/31F	1983	Ex Grimsby Cleethorpes, 1993
73	A73GEE	Leyland Olympian ONTL11/1R	Eastern Coach Works	H47/28D	1983	Ex Grimsby Cleethorpes, 1993
74	A74GEE	Leyland Olympian ONTL11/1R	Eastern Coach Works	H47/28D	1983	Ex Grimsby Cleethorpes, 1993
75	F75TFU	Dennis Dominator DDA1021	Alexander RH	H45/33F	1989	Ex Grimsby Cleethorpes, 1993
76	F76TFU	Dennis Dominator DDA1021	Alexander RH	H45/33F	1989	Ex Grimsby Cleethorpes, 1993
77	F77TFU	Dennis Dominator DDA1021	Alexander RH	H45/33F	1989	Ex Grimsby Cleethorpes, 1993
78	F78TFU	Dennis Dominator DDA1022	Alexander RH	H45/33F	1989	Ex Grimsby Cleethorpes, 1993
79	G79VFW	Dennis Dominator DDA1028	Alexander RH	H45/33F	1990	Ex Grimsby Cleethorpes, 1993
80	G80VFW	Dennis Dominator DDA1028	Alexander RH	H45/33F	1990	Ex Grimsby Cleethorpes, 1993
81	G81VFW	Dennis Dominator DDA1029	Alexander RH	H45/33F	1990	Ex Grimsby Cleethorpes, 1993

82-94

Dennis Dominator DDA1034* — East Lancashire — H45/33F — 1991-92 — 91-4 are DDA1036
Ex Grimsby Cleethorpes, 1993

| 82 | H482BEE | 84 | H484BEE | 91 | J91DJV | 93 | J93DJV | 94 | J94DJV |
| 83 | H483BEE | 85 | H485BEE | 92 | J92DJV |

101-109

Volvo Olympian YN2RV18Z4 — Northern Counties Palatine — H47/29F — 1993

| 101 | K101JWJ | 103 | K103JWJ | 105 | K105JWJ | 107 | K107JWJ | 109 | L109LHL |
| 102 | K102JWJ | 104 | K104JWJ | 106 | K106JWJ | 108 | L108LHL |

| 103 | BJV103L | Daimler Fleetline CRG6LX | Roe | | O45/29D | 1973 | Ex Grimsby Cleethorpes, 1993 |
| 113 | MBE613R | Leyland Fleetline FE30AGR | Roe | | O45/29D | 1976 | Ex Grimsby Cleethorpes, 1993 |

120-130

Leyland Fleetline FE30AGR — Roe — H45/29D — 1977-80 — Ex Grimsby Cleethorpes, 1993

120	OJV120S	123	OJV123S	125	XFU125V	127	XFU127V	129	XFU129V
121	OJV121S	124	OJV124S	126	XFU126V	128	XFU128V	130	XFU130V
122	OJV122S

No.	Reg	Chassis	Body	Seating	Year	Notes
159	BFW136W	Ford R1114	Plaxton Supreme IV	C53F	1981	Ex Grimsby Cleethorpes, 1993
172	XGS736S	Leyland Leopard PSU3E/4R	Plaxton Supreme III	C53F	1978	Ex Grimsby Cleethorpes, 1993
173	BHO441V	Leyland Leopard PSU5C/4R	Duple Dominant II	C55F	1980	Ex Grimsby Cleethorpes, 1993
174	MRJ270W	Leyland Leopard PSU5C/4R	Plaxton Supreme IV	C41DL	1980	Ex Grimsby Cleethorpes, 1993
175	EFU935Y	Leyland Leopard PSU5C/4R	Duple Dominant I	C53F	1983	Ex Grimsby Cleethorpes, 1993
176	OJL823Y	Leyland Leopard PSU5C/4R	Duple Dominant III	C53F	1983	Ex Grimsby Cleethorpes, 1993
177	OJL822Y	Leyland Leopard PSU5C/4R	Duple Dominant III	C49F	1983	Ex Grimsby Cleethorpes, 1993
178	PSU787	Leyland Tiger TRCTL11/3RZ	Duple Caribbean 2	C49FT	1986	Ex Grimsby Cleethorpes, 1993
183	PJI4314	Leyland Tiger TRCTL11/2R	Plaxton Paramount 3200 E	C47F	1983	
184	PSU788	Leyland Tiger TRCTL11/3RZ	Duple Caribbean 2	C48FT	1985	Ex Grimsby Cleethorpes, 1993
185	PSU775	Leyland Tiger TRCTL11/3RZ	Duple Caribbean 2	C48FT	1985	Ex Grimsby Cleethorpes, 1993
187	PYE841Y	Leyland Tiger TRCTL11/3R	Duple Laser	C53F	1983	Ex Grimsby Cleethorpes, 1993
188	PYE842Y	Leyland Tiger TRCTL11/3R	Duple Laser	C53F	1983	Ex Grimsby Cleethorpes, 1993
189	PSU764	Leyland Tiger TRCTL11/3R	Duple Laser	C53F	1983	Ex Grimsby Cleethorpes, 1993
190	PSU443	Leyland Tiger TRCTL11/3R	Duple Laser	C53F	1983	Ex Grimsby Cleethorpes, 1993
191	A243YGF	Leyland Tiger TRCTL11/3RH	Duple Laser	C57F	1984	Ex Grimsby Cleethorpes, 1993
192	PS2743	Leyland Tiger TRCTL11/3RH	Duple Laser	C57F	1984	Ex Grimsby Cleethorpes, 1993
193	PS3696	Leyland Tiger TRCTL11/3RH	Duple Laser	C57F	1984	Ex Grimsby Cleethorpes, 1993

A new blue Stagecoach fleetname was introduced during 1994 for the English and Welsh fleets. These include the local company or trading name in white on the red bar. Photographed in Meadowhall bus station, Sheffield, with the new transfers is 363, K363DWJ, an Alexander-bodied Leyland Olympian. *Lee Whitehead*

202-224

Bristol VRT/SL3/6LXB* · Eastern Coach Works · H43/31F · 1980-81 · *215-9 are type 6LXC

202	EWE202V	207	HWG207W	214	KWA214W	218	KWA218W	222	KWA222W
203	EWE203V	209	JAK209W	215	KWA215W	219	KWA219W	223	KWA223W
205	EWE205V	211	JAK211W	216	KWA216W	221	KWA221W	224	KWA224W
206	EWE206V	213	KWA213W						

301-325

Leyland Olympian ONLXB/1R · Eastern Coach Works · H45/32F · 1981-84

301	NHL301X	306	SHE306Y	311	SHE311Y	316	A316XWG	321	A321YWJ
302	NHL302X	307	SHE307Y	312	UDT312Y	317	A317XWG	322	A322AKU
303	NHL303X	308	SHE308Y	313	UDT313Y	318	A318XWG	323	A323AKU
304	NHL304X	309	SHE309Y	314	A314XWG	319	A319YWJ	324	A324AKU
305	NHL305X	310	SHE310Y	315	A315XWG	320	A320YWJ	325	A325AKU

326-330

Leyland Olympian ONLXB/1R · Eastern Coach Works · CH40/32F · 1985

326	C326HWJ	327	C327HWJ	328	C328HWJ	329	C329HWJ	330.	C330HWJ

331-336

Leyland Olympian ONLXB/1R · Eastern Coach Works · H45/32F · 1986

331	C331HWJ	333	C333HWJ	334	C334HWJ	335	C335HWJ	336	C336HWJ
332	C332HWJ								

337	GSO8V	Leyland Olympian ONLXB/1RV	Alexander RL	H45/32F	1987	Ex United Counties, 1992

339-343

Leyland Olympian ON6LXB/2RZ · Alexander RL · DPH51/31F · 1989

339	G339KKW	340	G340KKW	341	G341KKW	342	G342KKW	343	G343KKW

344-353

Leyland Olympian ON25R6G13Z4 · Alexander RL · DPH51/31F* · 1990-91 · *349-353 are DPH47/27F

344	H344SWA	346	H346SWA	348	H348SWA	350	J350XET	352	J352XET
345	H345SWA	347	H347SWA	349	J349XET	351	J351XET	353	J353XET

354-358

Leyland Olympian ON2R50G13Z4 · Northern Counties Palatine · H47/29F · 1992

354	K354DWJ	355	K355DWJ	356	K356DWJ	357	K357DWJ	358	K358DWJ

359-363

Leyland Olympian ON2R54G13Z4 · Alexander RL · DPH43/27F · 1992

359	K359DWJ	360	K360DWJ	361	K361DWJ	362	K362DWJ	363	K363DWJ

412	DWF22V	Leyland Leopard PSU3E/4R	Duple Dominant(1985)	B55F	1979
413	DWF23V	Leyland Leopard PSU3E/4R	Duple Dominant(1985)	B51F	1979
414	DWF24V	Leyland Leopard PSU3E/4R	Alexander P(1985)	B52F	1979
415	DWF25V	Leyland Leopard PSU3E/4R	Duple Dominant(1985)	B51F	1980
416	DWF26V	Leyland Leopard PSU3E/4R	Duple Dominant(1985)	B55F	1980

Looking smart and ready for service is East Midland 425, B625DWF seen preparing to leave Meadowhall bus station for its home town of Chesterfield.
David Cole

425-433 Leyland Tiger TRCTL11/2RH Alexander P B52F 1985

425	B625DWF	427	B627DWF	429	B629DWF	431	B631DWF	433	B633DWF
426	B626DWF	428	B628DWF	430	B630DWF	432	B632DWF		

435-453 Volvo B6-9.9M Alexander Dash B40F 1993

435	L435LWA	439	L438LWA	443	L443LWA	448	L448LWA	451	L451LWA
436	L436LWA	440	L440LWA	445	L445LWA	449	L449LWA	452	L452LWA
437	L437LWA	441	L441LWA	446	L446LWA	450	L450LWA	453	L453LHL
438	L438LWA	442	L442LWA	447	L447LWA				

614	EKW614V	Leyland National 2 NL106L11/1R		B44F	1980
615	EKW615V	Leyland National 2 NL106L11/1R		B44F	1980
616	EKW616V	Leyland National 2 NL106L11/1R		B44F	1980

617-621 Leyland National 2 NL116L11/1R B49F 1980

617	GWE617V	618	GWE618V	619	GWE619V	620	HWJ620W	621	HWJ621W

622	MWG622X	Leyland National 2 NL116AL11/1R		B49F	1981
623	MWG623X	Leyland National 2 NL116AL11/1R		B49F	1981
624	MWG624X	Leyland National 2 NL116AL11/1R		B49F	1981

625	LAG188V	Leyland National 2 NL116L11/1R	B49F	1980	Ex East Yorkshire, 1988
626	LAG189V	Leyland National 2 NL116L11/1R	B49F	1980	Ex East Yorkshire, 1988
627	NRP580V	Leyland National 2 NL116L11/1R	B49F	1980	Ex United Counties, 1992
628	SVV586W	Leyland National 2 NL116L11/1R	B49F	1981	Ex United Counties, 1992
634	VWA34Y	Leyland National 2 NL116HLXB/1R	DP47F	1983	
635	VWA35Y	Leyland National 2 NL116HLXB/1R	DP47F	1983	
636	VWA36Y	Leyland National 2 NL116HLXB/1R	DP47F	1983	

637-643 Volvo B10M-62 Plaxton Premiére Interurban DP51F 1993

637	L637LDT	639	L639LDT	641	L641LDT	642	L642LDT	643	L643LDT
638	L638LDT	640	L640LDT						

720-727 Mercedes-Benz 811D Reeve Burgess Beaver B31F 1989-90

720	G820KWF	722	G822KWF	724	G824KWF	726	G826KWF	727	G827KWF
721	G821KWF	723	G823KWF	725	G825KWF				

728	E721BVO	Mercedes-Benz 811D	Optare StarRider	B33F	1988	Ex Maun, Mansfield, 1990
729	E880DRA	Mercedes-Benz 811D	Optare StarRider	B33F	1988	Ex Maun, Mansfield, 1990
730	E481DAU	Mercedes-Benz 811D	Optare StarRider	B33F	1988	Ex Maun, Mansfield, 1990

731-751 Mercedes-Benz 709D Alexander Sprint B25F 1993

731	L731LWA	735	L735LWA	739	L739LWA	743	L743LWA	748	L748LWA
732	L732LWA	736	L736LWA	740	L740LWA	744	L744LWA	749	L749LWA
733	L733LWA	737	L737LWA	741	L741LWA	745	L745LWA	750	L750LWA
734	L734LWA	738	L738LWA	742	L742LWA	746	L746LWA	751	L751LHL

915	G915KWF	Iveco Daily 49.10	Reeve Burgess Beaver	B25F	1989
916	G916KWF	Iveco Daily 49.10	Reeve Burgess Beaver	B25F	1989

Previous Registrations:

A243YGF	A601HVT, PS2045	PJI4314	UWJ33Y	PSU443	A844SYR
BFW136W	LCX566W, PS3696	PJI4316	UHE37Y	PSU764	PYE843Y
GSO8V	D378XRS	PJI4317	UHE38Y	PSU775	B148ACK
OJL822Y	SSG321Y, PS2945	PS2743	A602HVT	PSU787	C495LJV
OJL823Y	EJV419Y, PS2743	PS3696	A603HVT	PSU788	B146ACK

Deliveries to East Midland during 1993 saw the demise of many of the older buses including the remaining mark 1 Leyland Nationals. The intake included Mercedes-Benz 709Ds and Volvo B6s both with Alexander bodywork to the standard Stagecoach specification. All the B6s are allocated to Mansfield where 451, L451LWA was heading when photographed at Wellow. The Mercedes-Benz, however, are allocated throughout the East Midlands area with 748, L748LWA, based in Chesterfield, seen here at Heath Village. *Tony Wilson*

FIFE SCOTTISH

Fife Scottish Omnibuses Ltd, Esplanade, Kirkcaldy, Fife, KY1 1SP

Depots : Methilhaven Road, Methil (Aberhill); Broad Street, Cowdenbeath; St Leonard's Street, Dunfermline; Flemington Road, Glenrothes; Esplanade, Kirkcaldy and City Road, St Andrews.

1w	D891DSF	Renault-Dodge S56	Alexander AM	B25F	1987	
9w	E809JSX	Renault-Dodge S56	Alexander AM	B25F	1988	

50-69

		MCW MetroRider MF150/98	MCW	B25F*	1988	*50/67-9 are MF150/102 and DP25F
						62/4 are MF150/99; 63 is MF150/100; 65/6 are MF150/101.

50	MSU463	54	F54RFS	58	F58RFS	62	F62RFS	66	F66RFS
51	F51RFS	55	F55RFS	59	F59RFS	63	F63RFS	67	F67RFS
52	F52RFS	56	F56RFS	60	F60RFS	64	F64RFS	68	F68RFS
53	F53RFS	57	F57RFS	61	F61RFS	65	F65RFS	69	F69RFS

70-76

		Mercedes-Benz 709D	Alexander Sprint	B25F	1994	

70	M770TFS	72	M772TFS	74	M774TFS	75	M775TFS	76	M776TFS
71	M771TFS	73	M773TFS						

77	VLT77	Mercedes-Benz 811D	Reeve Burgess Beaver	DP33F	1991	Ex Selkent, 1994
78	M778TFS	Mercedes-Benz 709D	Alexander Sprint	B25F	1994	
79	M779TFS	Mercedes-Benz 709D	Alexander Sprint	B25F	1994	
80	G280TSL	Mercedes-Benz 709D	Alexander Sprint	B23F	1990	Ex Bluebird, 1992
81	G281TSL	Mercedes-Benz 709D	Alexander Sprint	B23F	1990	Ex Bluebird, 1992
82	M780TFS	Mercedes-Benz 709D	Alexander Sprint	B25F	1994	

85-94

		Mercedes-Benz 709D	Alexander Sprint	B25F	1993	

85	K485FFS	87	K487FFS	89	K489FFS	91	K491FFS	93	K493FFS
86	K486FFS	88	K488FFS	90	K490FFS	92	K492FFS	94	K494FFS

104	TMS404X	Leyland Leopard PSU3G/4R	Alexander AYS	B53F	1982	Ex Ribble, 1992
122	XMS422Y	Leyland Leopard PSU3G/4R	Alexander AYS	B53F	1982	Ex Ribble, 1992
123	XMS423Y	Leyland Leopard PSU3G/4R	Alexander AYS	B53F	1982	Ex Ribble, 1992

138-160

		Leyland Leopard PSU3F/4R*	Alexander AYS	B53F	1980-81	*159/60 are PSU3G/4R

138	WFS138W	141	WFS141W	148	WFS148W	150	WFS150W	159	CSF159W
139	WFS139W	142	WFS142W	149	WFS149W	158	CSF158W	160	CSF160W
140	WFS140W	147	WFS147W						

180-189

		Leyland Leopard PSU3G/4R	Alexander AYS	B53F	1982	

180	PSX180Y	182	PSX182Y	184	PSX184Y	186	PSX186Y	188	PSX188Y
181	PSX181Y	183	PSX183Y	185	PSX185Y	187	PSX187Y	189	PSX189Y

200	XMS420Y	Leyland Leopard PSU3G/4R	Alexander AYS	DP49F	1982	Ex Ribble, 1992
205	TMS405X	Leyland Leopard PSU3G/4R	Alexander AYS	DP49F	1982	Ex Ribble, 1992
206	TMS406X	Leyland Leopard PSU3G/4R	Alexander AYS	DP49F	1982	Ex Ribble, 1992
207	TMS407X	Leyland Leopard PSU3G/4R	Alexander AYS	DP49F	1982	Ex Ribble, 1992
261	CSF161W	Leyland Leopard PSU3G/4R	Alexander AYS	DP49F	1981	
262	CSF162W	Leyland Leopard PSU3G/4R	Alexander AYS	DP47F	1981	

263-269

		Leyland Leopard PSU3F/4R	Alexander AYS	DP49F	1981	

263	CSF163W	265	CSF165W	267	CSF167W	268	CSF168W	269	CSF169W
264	CSF164W	266	CSF166W						

270-279

		Leyland Leopard PSU3G/4R	Alexander AT	DP49F	1982	

270	NFS170Y	272	NFS172Y	274	NFS174Y	276	NFS176Y	278	NFS178Y
271	NFS171Y	273	NFS173Y	275	NFS175Y	277	NFS177Y	279	NFS179Y

Many of Fife Scottish services in the north of the Kingdom cross the Tay Bridge to Dundee. One such service is the 93 to Tayport on the Fife coast. Photographed in Crichton Street, Dundee about to leave on this service is 85, K485FFS, a Mercedes-Benz 709D from 1993 and one of the last not to include a deeper destination box with number repeaters side and rear.
Murdoch Currie

1994 saw the first Volvo B10M buses allocated to Fife Scottish. By the time of this delivery the orange and red bands on the front of the vehicle were applied by Alexanders in a way which left a white area where the fleetname should be placed by the operating company. Shown here is 309, L309PSC.
Murdoch Currie

282	GSO82V	Leyland Leopard PSU3E/4R	Alexander AYS	DP49F	1980	Ex Stagecoach, 1994
283	GSO83V	Leyland Leopard PSU3E/4R	Alexander AYS	DP49F	1980	Ex Stagecoach, 1994
284	GSO84V	Leyland Leopard PSU3E/4R	Alexander AYS	DP49F	1980	Ex Stagecoach, 1994

290-294		Leyland Leopard PSU3G/4R	Alexander AT	DP49F	1982	
290	RSC190Y	291	RSC191Y	292	RSC192Y	293	RSC193Y	294	RSC194Y

301-310		Volvo B10M-55	Alexander PS	B49F	1994	
301	L301PSC	303	L303PSC	305	L305PSC	307	L307PSC	309	L309PSC
302	L302PSC	304	L304PSC	306	L306PSC	308	L308PSC	310	L310PSC

316	RSG816V	Leyland National 2 NL116L11/1R		B52F	1980	
320	RSG820V	Leyland National 2 NL116L11/1R		B52F	1980	
322	RSG822V	Leyland National 2 NL116L11/1R		B52F	1980	
323	RSG823V	Leyland National 2 NL116L11/1R		B52F	1980	
328	YSX928W	Leyland National 2 NL106L11/1R		B44F	1980	
329	YSX929W	Leyland National 2 NL106L11/1R		B44F	1980	
330	YSX930W	Leyland National 2 NL106L11/1R		B44F	1981	

380-388 | Leyland National 2 NL116L11/1R | B52F | 1980 | Ex Northern Scottish, 1989

380	DMS20V	**382**	DMS22V	**386**	NLS986W	**387**	NLS987W	**388**	NLS988W
381	DMS21V	**385**	MSO15W				

412-419 | Leyland Tiger TRCTL11/3RH | Alexander P | B61F | 1986-87

412	D512CSF	**414**	D614ASG	**416**	D516DSX	**418**	D518DSX	**419**	D519DSX
413	D713CSC	**415**	D615ASG	**417**	D517DSX				

420-424 | Leyland Tiger TRBTL11/2RH | Alexander P | B57F | 1987

420	D520DSX	**421**	D521DSX	**422**	D522DSX	**423**	D523DSX	**424**	D524DSX

441-445 | Leyland Tiger TRCTL11/2RH | Alexander TC | C47F | 1985

441	GSU341	**442**	GSU342	**443**	GSU343	**444**	GSU344	**445**	MSU445

466-470 | Leyland Tiger TRBTL11/2R | Alexander TE | DP49F* | 1983 | Ex Kelvin Central, 1989
*470 is DP47F

466	MNS6Y	**467**	MNS7Y	**468**	MNS8Y	**469**	MNS9Y	**470**	MNS10Y

477	D277FAS	Leyland Tiger TRCTL11/3RH	Alexander TE	DP53F	1987	Ex Highland Scottish, 1987
478	D278FAS	Leyland Tiger TRCTL11/3RH	Alexander TE	DP53F	1987	Ex Highland Scottish, 1987
479	D279FAS	Leyland Tiger TRCTL11/3RH	Alexander TE	DP53F	1987	Ex Highland Scottish, 1987
499	MSU499	Leyland Tiger TRCTL11/3RZ	Duple 340	C48FT	1987	Ex Kelvin Central, 1990
504	IIL3504	Volvo B10M-61	Van Hool Alizée	C53F	1988	Ex Rainworth Travel, 1993
506	IIL3506	Volvo B10M-61	Van Hool Alizée	C53F	1988	Ex Rainworth Travel, 1993

542-556 | Volvo B10M-62 | Plaxton Premiére 320 | C53F | 1994

542	M942TSX	**545**	M945TSX	**548**	M948TSX	**551**	M951TSX	**554**	M954TSX
543	M943TSX	**546**	M946TSX	**549**	M949TSX	**552**	M952TSX	**555**	M955TSX
544	M944TSX	**547**	M947TSX	**550**	M950TSX	**553**	M953TSX	**556**	M956TSX

571-577 | Volvo B10M-60 | Plaxton Premiére 320 | C53F | 1993

571	K571DFS	**573**	K573DFS	**575**	K575DFS	**576**	K576DFS	**577**	K577DFS
572	K572DFS	**574**	K574DFS				

578-590 | Volvo B10M-60 | Plaxton Premiére Interurban | DP51F | 1993

578	L578HSG	**581**	L581HSG	**584**	L584HSG	**587**	L587HSG	**589**	L589HSG
579	L579HSG	**582**	L582HSG	**585**	L585HSG	**588**	L588HSG	**590**	L590HSG
580	L580HSG	**583**	L583HSG	**586**	L586HSG			

601-605 | Dennis Dart 9.8SDL3017 | Alexander Dash | B40F | 1992

601	K601ESH	**602**	K602ESH	**603**	K603ESH	**604**	K604ESH	**605**	K605ESH

623-628 | Volvo B6-9.9M | Alexander Dash | B40F | 1993 | Ex Ribble, 1994

623	L423MVV	**625**	L425MVV	**626**	L426MVV	**627**	L427MVV	**628**	L428MVV
624	L424MVV						

651-659 | Volvo B6-9.9M | Alexander Dash | B40F | 1993-94

651	L651HKS	**653**	L653HKS	**655**	L655HKS	**657**	L657HKS	**659**	L659HKS
652	L652HKS	**654**	L654HKS	**656**	L656HKS	**658**	L658HKS		

667	L267CCK	Volvo B6-9.9M	Alexander Dash	B40F	1993	Ex Ribble, 1994
668	L268CCK	Volvo B6-9.9M	Alexander Dash	B40F	1993	Ex Ribble, 1994
669	L269CCK	Volvo B6-9.9M	Alexander Dash	B40F	1993	Ex Ribble, 1994
670	M670SSX	Volvo B6-9.9M	Alexander Dash	B40F	1994	
671	M671SSX	Volvo B6-9.9M	Alexander Dash	B40F	1994	
672	M672SSX	Volvo B6-9.9M	Alexander Dash	B40F	1994	
673	M673SSX	Volvo B6-9.9M	Alexander Dash	B40F	1994	

Volvo 504, IIL 3504, was one of a pair transferred to Fife from East Midland subsidiary Rainworth Travel in 1993. This B10M is fitted with a Van Hool Alizeé body built at Lier in Belgium. The principal operator of the type in the UK is Shearings, from whom this pair, and several others in the Stagecoach group have derived. *R A Smith*

1994 saw the transfer of several Volvo B6s between Scotland and Ribble resulting in bus seated ones with Fife and dual purpose seated versions with Ribble and Western Scottish. Photographed in Kirkcaldy bus station is 668, L268CCK now in service with Fife. *Max Fowler*

Fife Scottish was noted for vehicles not normally found in other Scottish Bus Group fleets. In latter years it took some 74 of the front-engined Ailsa double deck bus, more than any other member of the SBG. Many of the type remain, including 859, OSC59V.
Iain MacGregor

701-725

Leyland Olympian ON2R50G13Z4   Alexander RL   H47/32F   1992

701	J801WFS	704	J804WFS	707	J807WFS	720	K720ASC	723	K723ASC
702	J802WFS	705	J805WFS	718	K718ASC	721	K721ASC	724	K724ASC
703	J803WFS	706	J806WFS	719	K719ASC	722	K722ASC	725	K725ASC

| 737 | G337KKW | Leyland Olympian ON2R56G13Z4 Alexander RL | DPH51/31F 1989 | Ex East Midland, 1992 |
| 738 | G338KKW | Leyland Olympian ON2R56G13Z4 Alexander RL | DPH51/31F 1989 | Ex East Midland, 1992 |

801-838

Ailsa B55-10   Alexander AV   H44/35F   1975   801/6/10 ex Highland Scottish, 1990

| 801 | KSF1N | 810 | LSX10P | 817 | LSX17P | 832 | LSX32P | 838 | LSX38P |
| 806 | KSF6N | 816 | LSX16P | | | | | | |

847-866

Ailsa B55-10 MkII   Alexander AV   H44/35F   1979

847	OSC47V	851	OSC51V	855	OSC55V	859	OSC59V	863	OSC63V
848	OSC48V	852	OSC52V	856	OSC56V	860	OSC60V	864	OSC64V
849	OSC49V	853	OSC53V	857	OSC57V	861	OSC61V	865	OSC65V
850	OSC50V	854	OSC54V	858	OSC58V	862	OSC62V	866	OSC66V

867-874

Volvo B55-10 MkIII   Alexander RV   H44/37F   1984

| 867 | A967YSX | 869 | A969YSX | 871 | A971YSX | 873 | A973YSX | 874 | A974YSX |
| 868 | A968YSX | 870 | A970YSX | 872 | A972YSX | | | | |

875-879

Ailsa B55-10   Alexander AV   H44/35F   1977

| 875 | UFS875R | 876 | UFS876R | 877 | UFS877R | 878 | UFS878R | 879 | UFS879R |

901-920

Volvo Citybus B10M-50   Alexander RV   DPH47/33F* 1985-87   908 ex Volvo demonstrator, 1986   *909/10 are DPH45/35F

901	C801USG	907	C807USG	910	E910KSG	915	C795USG	919	C799USG
905	C805USG	908	B108CCS	914	C794USG	918	C798USG	920	C800USG
906	C806USG	909	E909KSG						

940	F310MYJ	Volvo Citybus B10M-50	Northern Counties	DPH43/33F 1989	Ex Southdown, 1991
941	F311MYJ	Volvo Citybus B10M-50	Northern Counties	DPH43/33F 1989	Ex Southdown, 1991
942	F312MYJ	Volvo Citybus B10M-50	Northern Counties	DPH43/33F 1989	Ex Southdown, 1991

The Volvo Citybus followed the Ailsa into the Fife Scottish fleet. This model was based on the mid-engined Volvo B10M coach chassis and featured a double-deck body to Alexander's RV design, Fife's included high-back seating. Photographed in Kirkcaldy is 905, C805USG.
Max Fowler

972-997

972-997			Volvo Citybus B10M-50		Alexander RV	H47/37F	1985-86

972	C802USG	979	B179FFS	984	B184FFS	988	C788USG	992	C792USG
973	C803USG	980	B180FFS	985	B185FFS	989	C789USG	993	C793USG
974	C804USG	981	B181FFS	986	B186FFS	990	C790USG	996	C796USG
977	B177FFS	982	B182FFS	987	C787USG	991	C791USG	997	C797USG
978	B178FFS	983	B183FFS						

1102	ABV669A	Leyland Atlantean PDR1/1	Metro Cammell	O44/31F	1961	Ex Cumberland, 1992
1107	UWV617S	Bristol VRT/SL3/6LXB	Eastern Coach Works	CO43/31F	1978	Ex Stagecoach South, 1994
1110	OVV850R	Bristol VRT/SL3/501(6LX)	Eastern Coach Works	H43/31F	1976	Ex Stagecoach, 1994
1111	VTV167S	Bristol VRT/SL3/6LXB	Eastern Coach Works	H43/31F	1978	Ex Stagecoach, 1994
1112	RJT153R	Bristol VRT/SL3/6LXB	Eastern Coach Works	H43/31F	1977	Ex Stagecoach, 1994
1113	RJT157R	Bristol VRT/SL3/6LXB	Eastern Coach Works	H43/31F	1977	Ex Stagecoach, 1994
1114	XAP643S	Bristol VRT/SL3/6LXB	Eastern Coach Works	H43/31F	1978	Ex Stagecoach, 1994
1115	EWE204V	Bristol VRT/SL3/6LXB	Eastern Coach Works	H43/31F	1980	Ex East Midlands, 1994
1116	HWG208W	Bristol VRT/SL3/6LXB	Eastern Coach Works	H43/31F	1980	Ex East Midlands, 1994
1117	RTH924S	Bristol VRT/SL3/6LXB	Eastern Coach Works	H43/31F	1977	Ex East Midlands, 1994
1118	KWA217W	Bristol VRT/SL3/6LXB	Eastern Coach Works	H43/31F	1981	Ex East Midlands, 1994
1119	KKY220W	Bristol VRT/SL3/6LXB	Eastern Coach Works	H43/31F	1981	Ex East Midlands, 1994
1120	DWF198V	Bristol VRT/SL3/501	Eastern Coach Works	H43/31F	1980	Ex East Midlands, 1994
1121	DWF199V	Bristol VRT/SL3/501	Eastern Coach Works	H43/31F	1980	Ex East Midlands, 1994
1122	DWF200V	Bristol VRT/SL3/501	Eastern Coach Works	H43/31F	1980	Ex East Midlands, 1994
1123	RVB973S	Bristol VRT/SL3/6LXB	Willowbrook	H43/31F	1978	Ex Stagecoach South, 1994
1124	RVB974S	Bristol VRT/SL3/6LXB	Willowbrook	H43/31F	1978	Ex Stagecoach South, 1994
1125	RVB978S	Bristol VRT/SL3/6LXB	Willowbrook	H43/31F	1978	Ex Stagecoach South, 1994
1126	TFN990T	Bristol VRT/SL3/6LXB	Willowbrook	H43/31F	1978	Ex Stagecoach South, 1994
1127	PRU917R	Bristol VRT/SL3/6LXB	Eastern Coach Works	H43/31F	1977	Ex Bluebird, 1994
1128	RPR716R	Bristol VRT/SL3/6LXB	Eastern Coach Works	H43/31F	1977	Ex Bluebird, 1994
1129	WHH415S	Bristol VRT/SL3/501	Eastern Coach Works	H43/31F	1978	Ex Bluebird, 1994

Previous Registrations:

ABV669A	927GTA		IIL3504	E626UNE, GIL2967, E937XSB
GSU341	B207FFS		IIL3506	E624UNE, MIB658, E931XSB
GSU342	B208FFS		MSU463	F70RFS
GSU343	B209FFS		MSU499	D319SGB
GSU344	B210FFS		VLT77	F396DHL
GSU345	B211FFS, MSU445			

HARTLEPOOL

Hartlepool Transport Ltd, 1 Church Street, Hartlepool, Cleveland, TS24 7DS

1-7			Leyland National 11351A/2R				B46D*	1977	*2 is B49F, 7 is B50F	
1	SHN401R	3	SHN403R	5	SHN405R	6	SHN406R	7		SHN407R
2	SHN402R	4	SHN404R							

14-20			Leyland National 2 NL116L11/2R		B46D*	1980	*15/16 are DP47F, 18 DP50F, 19 B50F		
14	KAJ214W	16	KAJ216W	18	KAJ218W	19	KAJ219W	20	KAJ220W
15	KAJ215W	17	KAJ217W						

21-26			Dennis Falcon HC SDA409		Wadham Stringer	B46D	1983		
21	YDC21Y	23	YDC23Y	24	YDC24Y	25	YDC25Y	26	YDC26Y
22	YDC22Y								

27-32			Dennis Falcon HC SDA409		Northern Counties	B47D	1985		
27	B27PAJ	29	B29PAJ	30	B30PAJ	31	B31PAJ	32	B32PAJ
28	B28PAJ								

38	RUF38R	Leyland National 11351A/2R		B44D	1977	Ex Brighton & Hove, 1990
40	RUF40R	Leyland National 11351A/2R		B44D	1977	Ex Brighton & Hove, 1990
49	UFG49S	Leyland National 11351A/2R		B44D	1977	Ex Brighton & Hove, 1990
52	UFG52S	Leyland National 11351A/2R		B50F	1977	Ex Brighton & Hove, 1990

Hartlepool joined the Stagecoach group during December 1994, bringing a fleet comprised entirely of single decks dominated by Bristol REs and Leyland Nationals. One of the former is 89, GEF189N seen passing through the town centre. *Bill Potter*

The latest buses in the Hartlepool fleet are Dennis Falcons and these carry bodywork by Wadham Stringer built in 1983 and Northern Counties in 1985. Of the former make is 23, YDC23Y. *Bill Potter*

59-79   Bristol RELL6L   Eastern Coach Works   B46D   1970-72

59	LEF59H	65	MEF65J	70	MEF70J	74	OEF74K	77	OEF77K
60	LEF60H	66	MEF66J	71	MEF71J	75	OEF75K	78	OEF78K
61	LEF61H	67	MEF67J	72	MEF72J	76	OEF76K	79	OEF79K
64	LEF64H	69	MEF69J	73	OEF73K				

80-96   Bristol RELL6L   Eastern Coach Works   B46D*   1973-75   *91 is DP47F

80	SEF80L	84	SEF84L	88	GEF188N	91	GEF191N	94	JAJ294N
81	SEF81L	85	GEF185N	89	GEF189N	92	JAJ292N	95	JAJ295N
82	SEF82L	86	GEF186N	90	GEF190N	93	JAJ293N	96	JAJ296N
83	SEF83L	87	GEF187N						

101	XCC94V	Leyland Leopard PSU3E/4R	Plaxton Supreme IV Express	C49F	1980	Ex Vale of Llangollen, 1986
102	BTU33W	Leyland Leopard PSU3E/4R	Plaxton Supreme IV Express	C49F	1981	Ex Vale of Llangollen, 1986
103	FSL61W	Leyland Leopard PSU3G/4R	Plaxton Supreme IV Express	C49F	1982	Ex Tayside, 1987
104	FSL62W	Leyland Leopard PSU3G/4R	Plaxton Supreme IV Express	C49F	1982	Ex Tayside, 1987
105	HDZ8683	Volvo B10M-61	Plaxton Paramount 3500	C49F	1984	Ex Allander, Milngavie, 1989
106	837XHW	Leyland Leopard PSU3/4R	Plaxton Supreme IV(1979)	C41F	1965	Ex Matthews, Cwmbran, 1990

Previous Registrations:

837XHW	CHA106C, WHT825T	FSL62W	ESL306W, 6689DP
BTU33W	WLG380W, 93FYB	HDZ8683	A845UGB, 2367AT, A491WYS
FSL61W	ESL307W, 666TPJ	XCC94V	UMA953V, UAM829

For some time Kingston upon Hull have displayed names on the Scania single deckers. These names are now to be phased out. Photographed outside the rail station is 704, F704BAT, a N112 model with East Lancashire bodywork, and one of a batch of six. *Tony Wilson*

The acquisition of Kingston upon Hull has brought the first Mark 1 Metrobuses into the fleet - Mark 2 examples operate for East Kent. These feature the isometric windscreen as seen in this photograph of 507, LAT507V. *Tony Wilson*

KINGSTON UPON HULL

Kingston-upon-Hull City Transport Ltd, Lombard Street,
Kingston-upon-Hull, North Humberside, HU2 8QN

5	KKH650	AEC Regal III	Weymann	B35F	1949	Owned by Kingston-upon-Hull City Council.
42	BUT24Y	Dennis Dorchester SDA801	Plaxton Paramount 3200	C49F	1983	Ex Leicester, 1987
43	BUT25Y	Dennis Dorchester SDA801	Plaxton Paramount 3200	C49F	1983	Ex Leicester, 1987
50	IIL1319	Volvo B10M-61	Plaxton Paramount 3200 II	C50FT	1986	
51	IIL1321	Volvo B10M-61	Plaxton Paramount 3200 III	C50FT	1986	
52	E52WAG	Volvo B10M-61	Plaxton Paramount 3200 III	C50FT	1988	
53	F53EAT	Dennis Javelin SDA1907	Plaxton Paramount 3200 III	C48FT	1989	
55	F55EAT	Dennis Javelin SDA1907	Plaxton Paramount 3200 III	C49FT	1989	
56	G56SAG	Volvo B10M-61	Plaxton Paramount 3500 III	C48FT	1990	
60	B60WKH	Leyland National 2 NL116HLXCT/1R		B24DL	1984	
61	YAY21Y	Dennis Lancet SD506	Duple Dominant	B25DL	1982	Ex Leicester, 1987
71	H71XKH	Leyland Swift ST2R44C97A4	Reeve Burgess Harrier	C34FT	1990	

106-110 — Dennis Dominator DDA904 — Alexander RL — H43/32F — 1984

106	B106UAT	**107**	B107UAT	**108**	B108UAT	**109**	B109UAT	**110**	B110UAT

111	C111CAT	Dennis Dominator DDA1007	East Lancashire	H43/28F	1985
112	C112CAT	Dennis Dominator DDA1007	East Lancashire	H43/28F	1985
113	C113CAT	Dennis Dominator DDA1007	East Lancashire	DPH43/28F	1985

122-131 — Dennis Dominator DDA1006 — East Lancashire — H45/30F — 1985

122	C122CAT	**124**	C124CAT	**126**	C126CAT	**128**	C128CAT	**131**	C131CAT
123	C123CAT	**125**	C125CAT	**127**	C127CAT	**129**	C129CAT		

132	E132SAT	Dennis Dominator DDA1014	East Lancashire (1992)	H45/21D	1987

133-141 — Dennis Dominator DDA1014 — East Lancashire — H45/32F — 1987

133	E133SAT	**135**	E135SAT	**137**	E137SAT	**139**	E139SAT	**141**	E141SAT
134	E134SAT	**136**	E136SAT	**138**	E138SAT	**140**	E140SAT		

142-151 — Dennis Dominator DDA1016 — East Lancashire — H45/31F — 1988

142	E142BKH	**144**	E144BKH	**146**	E146BKH	**148**	E148BKH	**150**	E150BKH
143	E143BKH	**145**	E145BKH	**147**	E147BKH	**149**	E149BKH	**151**	E151BKH

152-157 — Dennis Dominator DDA1027 — East Lancashire — H47/33F — 1989

152	F152HAT	**154**	F154HAT	**155**	F155HAT	**156**	F156HAT	**157**	F157HAT
153	F153HAT								

204	J204JKH	Volvo B10M-60	Plaxton Paramount 3500 III	C51FT	1991	Ex York Pullman, 1993
205	J205JKH	Volvo B10M-60	Plaxton Paramount 3500 III	C51FT	1991	Ex York Pullman, 1993

506-515 — MCW Metrobus DR102 — MCW — H43/32F — 1980

506	LAT506V	**508**	LAT508V	**510**	LAT510V	**512**	LAT512V	**514**	LAT514V
507	LAT507V	**509**	LAT509V	**511**	LAT511V	**513**	LAT513V	**515**	LAT515V

516-530 — MCW Metrobus DR102 — MCW — H43/32F — 1981

516	SAG516W	**519**	SAG519W	**522**	SAG522W	**525**	SAG525W	**528**	SAG528W
517	SAG517W	**520**	SAG520W	**523**	SAG523W	**526**	SAG526W	**529**	SAG529W
518	SAG518W	**521**	SAG521W	**524**	SAG524W	**527**	SAG527W	**530**	SAG530W

601-615 — Iveco Daily 49-10 — Robin Hood City Nipper — B25F* — 1987 — *602 is B18F

601	D601MKH	**605**	D605MKH	**609**	D609MKH	**612**	D612MKH	**614**	D614MKH
602	D602MKH	**608**	D608MKH	**611**	D611MKH	**613**	D613MKH	**615**	D615MKH
603	D603MKH								

The latest double-deck intake for Kingston upon Hull were sixteen Scania N113s with East Lancashire bodywork delivered in two batches. While East Kent, East London and Busways also operate Scania N113s, their examples are bodied by Alexander and Northern Counties.
Tony Wilson

No132 in the Hull fleet, E132SAT, was rebodied during 1992 with a dual-door body by East Lancashire. The lower-deck seating capacity is reduced to give extra luggage space for use on a service linking with the North Sea Ferry. It is seen on ordinary stage service.
Tony Wilson

701-706

						East Lancashire		DP49F	1988		

Scania N112CRB

701	F701BAT	**703**	F703BAT	**704**	F704BAT	**705**	F705BAT	**706**	F706CAG
702	F702BAT								

801-816

Scania N113DRB · East Lancashire · H51/37F · 1989-90 *809-16 are H47/37F

801	G801JRH	**805**	G805JRH	**808**	G808LAG	**811**	H811WKH	**814**	H814WKH
802	G802JRH	**806**	G806JRH	**809**	H809WKH	**812**	H812WKH	**815**	H815WKH
803	G803JRH	**807**	G807LAG	**810**	H810WKH	**813**	H813WKH	**816**	H816WKH
804	G804JRH								

Previous Registrations:

IIL1319	C50FRH		IIL1321	D51ORH		KKH650	From new

MIDLAND RED

Midland Red (South) Ltd, Railway Terrace, Rugby, Warwickshire, CV21 3HS

Depots : Canal Street, Banbury; Rowley Drive, Coventry; Station Approach, Leamington Spa; Newtown Road, Nuneaton; Railway Terrace, Rugby and Avenue Farm, Stratford-on-Avon.

1	A75NAC	Leyland Tiger TRCTL11/2R	Plaxton Paramount 3200 E	C47FT	1983	
2	A76NAC	Leyland Tiger TRCTL11/2R	Plaxton Paramount 3200 E	C47FT	1983	
3	Q275UOC	Leyland Leopard PSU3C/4R	Plaxton P'mount 3200 E(1983)	C49F	1976	
4	230HUE	Leyland Leopard PSU3E/4R	Plaxton Supreme IV Express	C46FT	1980	Ex Midland Red North, 1981
5	331HWD	Leyland Leopard PSU3E/4R	Plaxton Supreme IV Express	C49F	1980	Ex Midland Red North, 1981
6	3273AC	Leyland Leopard PSU3E/4R	Plaxton Supreme IV Express	C46FT	1980	Ex Midland Red North, 1981
9	BVP791V	Leyland Leopard PSU3E/4R	Willowbrook 003	C49F	1980	
10	BVP801V	Leyland Leopard PSU3E/4R	Willowbrook 003	C49F	1980	
15	NPA230W	Leyland Leopard PSU3E/4R	Plaxton Supreme IV Express	C53F	1981	Ex East Midland, 1994
28	NAK28X	Leyland Leopard PSU3F/4R	Duple Dominant IV	C47F	1981	Ex East Midland, 1994
30	NAK30X	Leyland Leopard PSU3F/4R	Duple Dominant IV	C47F	1981	Ex East Midland, 1994

60-65

Volvo B10M-60 — Plaxton Paramount 3500 III — C48FT — 1990 — Ex Wallace Arnold, 1993

60	G528LWU	62	G530LWU	63	G531LWU	64	G532LWU	65	G535LWU
61	G529LWU							

70	BIW4977	Leyland Tiger TRCTL11/3R	Plaxton Paramount 3200 E	C49FT	1984	
73	491GAC	Leyland Tiger TRCTL11/3RH	Plaxton Paramount 3200 II	C51F	1984	
90	552OHU	Leyland Tiger TRCTL11/3R	Plaxton Paramount 3200	C57F	1983	Ex Cheltenham & Gloucester, 1990
91	CDG213Y	Leyland Tiger TRCTL11/3R	Plaxton Paramount 3200	C46FT	1983	Ex Cheltenham & Gloucester, 1991
92	420GAC	Leyland Tiger TRCTL11/3R	Plaxton Paramount 3200	C53F	1983	Ex Cheltenham & Gloucester, 1991
300	E433YHL	Mercedes-Benz 709D	Reeve Burgess Beaver	B25F	1988	Ex Loftys, Bridge Trafford, 1993
301	G301WHP	Mercedes-Benz 709D	PMT	B25F	1989	
302	G302WHP	Mercedes-Benz 709D	PMT	B25F	1989	
303	G303WHP	Mercedes-Benz 709D	PMT	B25F	1989	
304	J304THP	Mercedes-Benz 709D	Alexander Sprint	B25F	1992	
305	J305THP	Mercedes-Benz 709D	Alexander Sprint	B25F	1992	
306	K306ARW	Mercedes-Benz 709D	Wright	B25F	1992	
307	L307SKV	Mercedes-Benz 709D	Wright	B25F	1993	

308-330

Mercedes-Benz 709D — Alexander Sprint — B23F — 1994

308	L308YDU	313	L313YDU	318	L318YDU	323	L323YDU	327	L327YKV
309	L309YDU	314	L314YDU	319	L319YDU	324	L324YDU	328	L328YKV
310	L310YDU	315	L315YDU	320	L320YDU	325	L325YDU	329	L329YKV
311	L311YDU	316	L316YDU	321	L321YDU	326	L326YKV	330	L330YKV
312	L312YDU	317	L317YDU	322	L322YDU				

351-360

Ford Transit 190D — Alexander AM — B16FT — 1985 — Ex Cheltenham & Gloucester, 1990

351w	C616SFH	353	C620SFH	355	C623SFH	357w	C625SFH	359	C646SFH
352	C619SFH	354	C622SFH	356	C624SFH	358w	C628SFH	360	C647SFH

361-365

Ford Transit 190D — Dormobile — B16F — 1986 — Ex East Kent, 1990-91

361	C702FKE	362	C703FKE	363	C713FKE	364	C714FKE	365	C720FKE

366-370

Ford Transit 190D — Carlyle — B16F — 1986 — Ex Alder Valley, 1991

366	D313WPE	367	D314WPE	368	D315WPE	369	D320WPE	370	D321WPE

371	C729JJO	Ford Transit 190D	Carlyle	B20F	1986	Ex City of Oxford, 1991

372-382

Ford Transit 190D — Dormobile — B16F* — 1986 — Ex East Kent, 1991-92
*377/81 are DP16F

372	C708FKE	375w	C722FKE	377	C707FKE	379w	C710FKE	381w	C717FKE
373	C718FKE	376	C706FKE	378w	C709FKE	380w	C711FKE	382	C719FKE
374w	C721FKE								

383	C618SFH	Ford Transit 190D	Alexander	B16F	1985	Ex Cheltenham & Gloucester, 1994
384	C627SFH	Ford Transit 190D	Alexander	B16F	1985	Ex Cheltenham & Gloucester, 1994

385	C629SFH	Ford Transit 190D	Alexander	B16F	1985	Ex Cheltenham & Gloucester, 1994
386	C716FKE	Ford Transit 190D	Dormobile	B16F	1986	Ex Stagecoach South, 1994
387	C634SFH	Ford Transit 190D	Alexander	B16F	1985	Ex Cheltenham & Gloucester, 1994
388	C635SFH	Ford Transit 190D	Alexander	B16F	1985	Ex Cheltenham & Gloucester, 1994
389	C638SFH	Ford Transit 190D	Alexander	B16F	1985	Ex Cheltenham & Gloucester, 1994
390	C705FKE	Ford Transit 190D	Dormobile	B16F	1986	Ex Stagecoach South, 1994
391	C715FKE	Ford Transit 190D	Dormobile	B16F	1986	Ex Stagecoach South, 1994
392	C724FKE	Ford Transit 190D	Dormobile	B16F	1986	Ex Stagecoach South, 1994
400	F71LAL	Mercedes-Benz 811D	Alexander AM	DP33F	1988	Ex Skills, Nottingham, 1991

401-418

Mercedes-Benz 811D   Wright   B33F*   1991   *402/4/7-12 are DP33F
     *405/6/13/7/8 are B31F

401	H401MRW	405	H495MRW	409	J409PRW	413	J413PRW	416	J416PRW
402	H402MRW	406	H406MRW	410	J410PRW	414	J414PRW	417	J417PRW
403	H403MRW	407	J407PRW	411	J411PRW	415	J415PRW	418	J418PRW
404	H404MRW	408	J408PRW	412	J412PRW

419	G115OGA	Mercedes-Benz 811D	Alexander AM	DP33F	1988	Ex Beaton, Blantyre, 1992

420-425

Mercedes-Benz 811D   Wright   B31F   1993

420	K420ARW	422	K422ARW	423	K423ARW	424	K424ARW	425	K425ARW
421	K421ARW

426	F846TLU	Mercedes-Benz 811D	Optare StarRider	C29F	1989	Ex Brents Coaches, Watford, 1993

451-456

Volvo B6-9.9M   Alexander Dash   B40F   1994

1451	L451YAC	453	L453YAC	454	L454YAC	455	L455YAC	456	L456YAC
1452	L452YAC

457-482

Freight Rover Sherpa   Rootes   B16F   1986-87

457w	D457CKV	461w	D461CKV	467w	D467CKV	478w	D478CKV	482w	D482CKV
460w	D460CKV	462w	D462CKV	476w	D476CKV

483	D273OOJ	Freight Rover Sherpa	Carlyle	B20F	1987	Ex Carlyle demonstrator, 1988
484	D271OOJ	Freight Rover Sherpa	Carlyle	B20F	1987	Ex Carlyle demonstrator, 1988
485	D735OOG	Freight Rover Sherpa	Carlyle	B20F	1987	Ex Carlyle demonstrator, 1988
486	D736OOG	Freight Rover Sherpa	Carlyle	B20F	1987	Ex Carlyle demonstrator, 1988
487	D755JUB	Freight Rover Sherpa	Dormobile	B20F	1986	Ex Yorkshire Rider, 1990
488	D762JUB	Freight Rover Sherpa	Dormobile	B20F	1986	Ex Yorkshire Rider, 1990

Six B6s with Alexander Dash bodywork and DP seating joined Midland Red during 1994 as the first new large buses into that fleet since 1980. Two of these are allocated to G&G where 1000 has been added to the fleet numbers. The remaining four work from Kenilworth, where 454, L454YAC was heading when photographed in the summer. *David Cole*

Typical of the vehicles acquired from Midland Red are the numerous Leyland Nationals, many of which have been refurbished in recent years. Photographed shortly after its repaint is 503, JOX503P, now allocated to Rugby. *David Cole*

502-590

							B49F*	1976-77 Ex Midland Red, 1981		
								582 is fitted with DAF engine; 504/90 are B49DL(variable)		
502	JOX502P	**506**	JOX506P	**571**	NOE571R		**579**	NOE579R	**586**	NOE586R
503	JOX503P	**567**	NOE568R	**577**	NOE577R		**581**	NOE581R	**589**	NOE589R
504	JOX504P	**568**	NOE568R	**578**	NOE578R		**582**	NOE582R	**590**	NOE590R
505	JOX505P	**570**	NOE570R							

591	YEU446Y	Leyland National 10351B/1R	B44F	1981	Ex Cheltenham & Gloucester, 1994
592	NOE551R	Leyland National 11351A/1R	B49F	1976	Ex Midland Red, 1981
593	KHT122P	Leyland National 11351/1R	B52F	1976	Ex Cheltenham & Gloucester, 1994
594	VAE502T	Leyland National 10351B/1R	B44F	1979	Ex Cheltenham & Gloucester, 1994
595	GOL426N	Leyland National 11351/1R	B49F	1975	Ex Cheltenham & Gloucester, 1994
596	GOL413N	Leyland National 11351/1R	B49F	1975	Ex Cheltenham & Gloucester, 1994
597	HEU122N	Leyland National 11351/1R	B52F	1975	Ex Cheltenham & Gloucester, 1994
598	KHT124P	Leyland National 11351/1R	B52F	1976	Ex Cheltenham & Gloucester, 1994
599	WFR392V	Leyland National 10351B/1R	B44F	1980	Ex Ribble, 1994

602-772

							B49F*	1977-80 Ex Midland Red, 1981		
								*624, 708 are B52F		
602	NOE602R	**622**	PUK622R	**627**	PUK627R		**708**	TOF708S	**755**	XOV755T
603	NOE603R	**623**	PUK623R	**628**	PUK628R		**709**	TOF709S	**756**	XOV756T
604	NOE604R	**624**	PUK624R	**629**	PUK629R		**710**	TOF710S	**760**	XOV760T
605	NOE605R	**625**	PUK625R	**664**	SOA664S		**753**	XOV753T	**771**	BVP771V
606	NOE606R	**626**	PUK626R	**707**	TOF707S		**754**	XOV754T	**772**	BVP772V
621	PUK621R									

816	BVP816V	Leyland National 2 NL116L11/1R (DAF)	B49F	1980	Ex Midland Red, 1981
817	BVP817V	Leyland National 2 NL116L11/1R (DAF)	B49F	1980	Ex Midland Red, 1981
818	BVP818V	Leyland National 2 NL116L11/1R (DAF)	B49F	1980	Ex Midland Red, 1981

834-848

			Iveco Daily 49.10		Robin Hood City Nippy	B19F	1986	Ex Rhondda, 1992-93

834	D34KAX	**843**	D43KAX	**845**	D45KAX	**847**	D47KAX	**848w** D48KAX
835w	D35KAX							

851-863

Iveco Daily 49.10		Robin Hood City Nippy	B19F*	1986-87	*852 is B21F

851	D851CKV	**854**	D854CKV	**857**	D857CKV	**860**	D860CKV	**862**	D862CKV
852	D852CKV	**855**	D855CKV	**858**	D858CKV	**861**	D861CKV	**863**	D863CKV
853	D853CKV	**856**	D856CKV	**859**	D859CKV				

864-868

Iveco Daily 49.10		Robin Hood City Nippy	B19F	1988	

864	F864PAC	**865**	F865PAC	**866**	F866PAC	**867**	F867PAC	**868**	F868PAC

871	F871UAC	Iveco Daily 49.10	Robin Hood City Nippy	B25F	1989
872	F872UAC	Iveco Daily 49.10	Robin Hood City Nippy	B25F	1989
873	G26XBK	Iveco Daily 49.10	Phoenix	B25F	1990	Ex Loftys, Bridge Trafford, 1993

882-888

Iveco Daily 49.10		Robin Hood City Nippy	DP19F*	1986	*882/3 are DP21F

882	D882CKV	**884**	D884CKV	**886**	D886CKV	**887**	D887CKV	**888**	D888CKV
883	D883CKV	**885**	D885CKV						

890w	E889HHP	Peugeot-Talbot Pullman	Talbot	B22F	1987	Ex Talbot demonstrator, 1988

902-912

Leyland Olympian ONLXB/1R		Eastern Coach Works	H45/32F	1983-84	

902	A542HAC	**904**	A544HAC	**906**	A546HAC	**910**	B910ODU	**912**	B912ODU
903	A543HAC	**905**	A545HAC	**907**	A547HAC	**911**	B911ODU		

928	LHT725P	Bristol VRT/SL3/501(6LXB)	Eastern Coach Works	H39/31F	1976	Ex Cheltenham & Gloucester, 1994
929	NHU672R	Bristol VRT/SL3/6LXB	Eastern Coach Works	H43/27D	1979	Ex Cheltenham & Gloucester, 1994
931	CBV11S	Bristol VRT/SL3/501(6LXB)	Eastern Coach Works	H43/31F	1977	Ex Ribble, 1994
932	CBV16S	Bristol VRT/SL3/501(6LXB)	Eastern Coach Works	H43/31F	1977	Ex Ribble, 1994
933	CBV20S	Bristol VRT/SL3/501(6LXB)	Eastern Coach Works	H43/31F	1977	Ex Ribble, 1994
934	DBV23W	Bristol VRT/SL3/6LXB	Eastern Coach Works	H43/31F	1980	Ex Ribble, 1994
935	DBV31W	Bristol VRT/SL3/6LXB	Eastern Coach Works	H43/31F	1980	Ex Ribble, 1994
936	URF661S	Bristol VRT/SL3/501	Eastern Coach Works	H43/31F	1977	Ex Ribble, 1994
937	DWF195V	Bristol VRT/SL3/6LXB	Eastern Coach Works	H43/31F	1980	Ex East Midland, 1994
938	DWF197V	Bristol VRT/SL3/6LXB	Eastern Coach Works	H43/31F	1980	Ex East Midland, 1994
939	DWF194V	Bristol VRT/SL3/6LXB	Eastern Coach Works	H43/31F	1980	Ex East Midland, 1994
940	PEU511R	Bristol VRT/SL3/6LXB	Eastern Coach Works	DPH43/31F	1977	Ex Badgerline, 1994
941	GTX746W	Bristol VRT/SL3/501	Eastern Coach Works	H43/31F	1980	Ex Red & White, 1993
943	GTX754W	Bristol VRT/SL3/501	Eastern Coach Works	H43/31F	1980	Ex Red & White, 1993
944	HUD475S	Bristol VRT/SL3/6LXB	Eastern Coach Works	H43/31F	1977	Ex City of Oxford, 1993
945	HUD480S	Bristol VRT/SL3/6LXB	Eastern Coach Works	H43/31F	1977	Ex City of Oxford, 1993
946	HUD479S	Bristol VRT/SL3/6LXB	Eastern Coach Works	H43/31F	1977	Ex City of Oxford, 1993
947	AET181T	Bristol VRT/SL3/6LXB	Eastern Coach Works	H43/31F	1979	Ex East Midland, 1994
948	VTV170S	Bristol VRT/SL3/6LXB	Eastern Coach Works	H43/31F	1978	Ex East Midland, 1994
949	DWF189V	Bristol VRT/SL3/6LXB	Eastern Coach Works	H43/31F	1980	Ex East Midland, 1994
952	OUC44R	Leyland Fleetline FE30AGR	MCW	H44/29F	1976	Ex Stevenson's, 1989
953	OJD241R	Leyland Fleetline FE30AGR	MCW	H44/29F	1977	Ex Stevenson's, 1989
954	OUC42R	Leyland Fleetline FE30AGR	MCW	H44/29F	1976	Ex Stevenson's, 1990
955	OJD136R	Leyland Fleetline FE30AGR	Park Royal	H44/29F	1976	Ex Stevenson's, 1990
959	YNA363M	Daimler Fleetline CRG6LXB	Northern Counties	H43/32F	1974	Ex Greater Manchester PTE, 1988
960	B960ODU	Leyland Olympian ONLXB/1R	Eastern Coach Works	DPH42/30F	1984	
961	B961ODU	Leyland Olympian ONLXB/1R	Eastern Coach Works	DPH42/30F	1984	
962	C962XVC	Leyland Olympian ONLXB/1RH	Eastern Coach Works	DPH42/29F	1986	
963	C963XVC	Leyland Olympian ONLXB/1RH	Eastern Coach Works	DPH42/29F	1986	
964	C964XVC	Leyland Olympian ONLXB/1RH	Eastern Coach Works	DPH42/29F	1986	
1008	KHP649N	Leyland Leopard PSU3B/4R	Duple Dominant	C53F	1975	Ex Tanners International, 1989
1009	NGU602P	Bedford YMT	Plaxton Supreme III	C53F	1976	Ex Tanners International, 1989
1010	NGU605P	Bedford YMT	Plaxton Supreme III	C53F	1976	Ex Tanners International, 1989
1015	YWK3S	Bedford YMT	Plaxton Supreme III	C53F	1978	Ex Tanners International, 1989
1017w	HCS817N	Leyland Leopard PSU3/3R	Alexander AY	B53F	1975	Ex Lothian Transit, Newtongrange, 1993
1019	A848VML	Leyland Leopard PSU3E/4R	Duple Dominant IV (1983)	C53F	1979	Ex Grey-Green, 1987
1020	TVC504W	Leyland Leopard PSU3E/4R	Eastern Coach Works	C53F	1981	
1021w	MUV837X	Leyland Leopard PSU5C/4R	Duple Dominant IV	C53F	1982	Ex Grey-Green, 1988
1029w	NAK29X	Leyland Leopard PSU3F/4R	Duple Dominant IV	C47F	1981	Ex East Midland, 1994
1051	KIB8140	Leyland National 10351A/2R		B22DL	1978	Ex London Buses, 1991
1052	AIB4053	Leyland National 10351A/2R		B22DL	1978	Ex London Buses, 1991
1053	PIB8019	Leyland National 10351A/2R		B22DL	1978	Ex London Buses, 1991

Midland Red South continued to use poppy red as the dominant colour of the livery long after its sale from NBC, though more grey and white were added. Many Iveco Daily 49-10s with Robin Hood City Nippy bodywork were delivered in the late 1980s including 855, D855CKV seen here in the old livery, but with Stagecoach names in the windscreen. *David Cole*

The last of the vehicles in non-corporate livery were transferred from the Ribble fleet during 1994, including some Bristol VRTs to Stagecoach Midland Red where they were placed service in with original Midland Red vinyls. Photographed shortly after its arrival 932, CBV16S, still shows its old fleet number. *David Cole*

1058	9984PG	Leyland Leopard PSU3E/4R	Duple Dominant II Express	C53F	1980	Ex Grey-Green, 1988
1059	E630KCX	DAF SB2305DHTD585	Duple 320	C53F	1988	Ex Gray, Hoyland Common, 1990
1068	WSU293	Volvo B10M-60	Plaxton Paramount 3200 III	C53F	1990	Ex Cheltenham & Gloucester, 1993
1086	CSV219	MCW Metroliner DR130/6	MCW	CH55/19FT	1985	Ex Go-Ahead Northern, 1992
1087	498FYB	Leyland Tiger TRCTL11/3R	Plaxton Paramount 3200	C50F	1983	Ex Cheltenham & Gloucester, 1993
1088	A8GGT	Leyland Tiger TRCTL11/3R	Plaxton Paramount 3200 E	C57F	1983	Ex Cheltenham & Gloucester, 1993
1089	A7GGT	Leyland Tiger TRCTL11/3RH	Plaxton Paramount 3200	C51F	1984	Ex Midland Red South, 1992
1412	GOL412N	Leyland National 11351/1R		B49F	1975	Ex Midland Red, 1981
1427	H912XGA	Mercedes-Benz 814D	Reeve Burgess Beaver	DP33F	1990	Ex Loftys, Bridge Trafford, 1993
1458w	D458CKV	Freight Rover Sherpa	Rootes	B16F	1986	Ex Midland Red South, 1992
1464w	D464CKV	Freight Rover Sherpa	Rootes	B16F	1986	Ex Midland Red South, 1992
1475w	D475CKV	Freight Rover Sherpa	Rootes	B16F	1986	Ex Midland Red South, 1990
1489	E77PUH	Freight Rover Sherpa	Carlyle Citybus 2	B20F	1987	Ex Red & White, 1991
1490	E95OUH	Freight Rover Sherpa	Carlyle Citybus 2	B20F	1987	Ex Red & White, 1991
1491	E99OUH	Freight Rover Sherpa	Carlyle Citybus 2	B20F	1987	Ex Red & White, 1991
1553	NOE553R	Leyland National 11351A/1R		B49F	1976	Ex Midland Red, 1981
1820	F660PWK	Leyland Lynx LX112L10ZR1R	Leyland	B51F	1988	
1821	F661PWK	Leyland Lynx LX112L10ZR1R	Leyland	B51F	1988	
1929w	AFY192X	Leyland Atlantean AN68B/1R	Willowbrook	H45/33F	1982	Ex Merseybus, 1989
1930	LHT724P	Bristol VRT/SL3/501(6LXB)	Eastern Coach Works	H43/31F	1976	Ex Swindon & District, 1992
1931	MAU145P	Bristol VRT/SL3/6LXB	Eastern Coach Works	H43/31F	1976	Ex Bluebird, 1993
1932	ONH846P	Bristol VRT/SL3/6LXB	Eastern Coach Works	H43/31F	1976	Ex Bluebird, 1993
1933	PEU516R	Bristol VRT/SL3/6LXB	Eastern Coach Works	H43/31F	1977	Ex Swindon & District, 1992
1934w	AUP713S	Bristol VRT/SL3/6LXB	Eastern Coach Works	H43/31F	1977	Ex United, 1993
1950w	WWM930W	Leyland Atlantean AN68B/1R	Willowbrook	H45/33F	1981	Ex Merseybus, 1989
1951w	WWM936W	Leyland Atlantean AN68B/1R	Willowbrook	H45/33F	1981	Ex Merseybus, 1989
1956	SDA651S	Leyland Fleetline FE30AGR	Park Royal	H43/33F	1978	Ex West Midlands Travel, 1990
1957	SDA715S	Leyland Fleetline FE30AGR	MCW	H43/33F	1978	Ex West Midlands Travel, 1990
1958	WDA994T	Leyland Fleetline FE30AGR	MCW	H43/33F	1979	Ex West Midlands Travel, 1990
2007	4012VC	Leyland Leopard PSU3E/4R	Plaxton Supreme IV Express	C53F	1980	Ex Premier Travel, 1991
2011w	FDV820V	Leyland Leopard PSU3E/4R	Willowbrook 003	C49F	1980	Ex Devon General, 1989
2012w	FDV822V	Leyland Leopard PSU3E/4R	Willowbrook 003	C49F	1980	Ex Devon General, 1989
2013	LOA838X	Leyland Leopard PSU3F/4R	Willowbrook 003	C49F	1982	Ex Tindall, Low Fell, 1991
2016	YBO16T	Leyland Leopard PSU3E/2R	East Lancashire	B51F	1979	Ex G & G, Leamington, 1993
2018	YBO18T	Leyland Leopard PSU3E/2R	East Lancashire	B51F	1979	Ex G & G, Leamington, 1993
2022w	DDM24X	Leyland Leopard PSU3F/4R	Willowbrook 003	C51F	1981	Ex Grimsby-Cleethorpes, 1989
2023w	DDM31X	Leyland Leopard PSU3F/4R	Willowbrook 003	C51F	1982	Ex Grimsby-Cleethorpes, 1989
2026	ELJ209V	Leyland Leopard PSU3E/4R	Plaxton Supreme IV Express	C49F	1979	Ex East Midland, 1994
2027	JWA27W	Leyland Leopard PSU3E/4R	Willowbrook 003	C47F	1981	Ex East Midland, 1994
2035	A35XBO	Dennis Lancet SD515	East Lancashire	B47F	1984	Ex National Welsh, 1992
2036	A36XBO	Dennis Lancet SD515	East Lancashire	B47F	1984	Ex National Welsh, 1992
2037	A37XBO	Dennis Lancet SD515	East Lancashire	B47F	1984	Ex National Welsh, 1992
2066	3063VC	Volvo B10M-60	Plaxton Paramount 3500 III	C49F	1990	Ex Wallace Arnold, 1993
2067	9258VC	Volvo B10M-60	Plaxton Paramount 3500 III	C49F	1990	Ex Wallace Arnold, 1993
2074	4828VC	Leyland Tiger TRCTL11/3R	Plaxton Paramount 3500 II	C51F	1985	Ex Sovereign, 1990
2075	9737VC	Leyland Tiger TRCTL11/3R	Plaxton Paramount 3500 II	C51F	1985	Ex Sovereign, 1990
2076	6253VC	Leyland Tiger TRCTL11/3R	Plaxton Paramount 3200 II	C51F	1986	Ex Thames Transit, 1991
2077	6804VC	Leyland Tiger TRCTL11/3R	Plaxton Paramount 3200 II	C51F	1986	Ex Thames Transit, 1991
2343w	C904LEW	Ford Transit 190D	Dormobile	B16F	1985	Ex Red & White, 1993
2344w	C53FDV	Ford Transit 190D	Robin Hood	B16F	1986	Ex Red & White, 1993
2345	C102HKG	Ford Transit 190D	Robin Hood	B16F	1986	Ex Red & White, 1993
2346w	C105HKG	Ford Transit 190D	Robin Hood	B16F	1986	Ex Red & White, 1993
2347w	C345GFJ	Ford Transit 190D	Robin Hood	B16F	1986	Ex Red & White, 1993
2348w	C352GFJ	Ford Transit 190D	Robin Hood	B16F	1986	Ex Red & White, 1993
2349w	C516BFB	Ford Transit 190D	Carlyle	B16F	1986	Ex Red & White, 1993
2507	XGR728R	Leyland National 11351A/1R (DAF)		B49F	1977	Ex United, 1993
2508	THX155S	Leyland National 10351A/2R		B36D	1978	Ex Scorpio, Harrow, 1991
2509	THX231S	Leyland National 10351A/2R		B36D	1978	Ex London Buses, 1991
2510	CBV780S	Leyland National 11351A/1R		B49F	1978	Ex Thames Transit, 1991
2511	CBV783S	Leyland National 11351A/1R		B49F	1978	Ex Thames Transit, 1991
2512	EMB365S	Leyland National 11351A/1R (Gardner)		B49F	1978	Ex Crosville Wales, 1991
2513	LMA411T	Leyland National 11351A/1R (Gardner)		B49F	1979	Ex Crosville Wales, 1991
2514w	LUP901T	Leyland National 11351A/1R (DAF)		B49F*	1979	Ex United, 1993
2808	BVP808V	Leyland National 2 NL116L11/1R		B49F	1980	Ex North Western, 1991
2809	SVV589W	Leyland National 2 NL116L11/1R		B49F	1980	Ex Luton & District, 1991

Many double deck buses have been transferred to Midland Red and its associated operations, G&G Travel and Vanguard, since the fleet became part of the Stagecoach group. One added to the G&G Travel operation is 1932, ONH846P, seen in Coventry with the latest fleetnames.
David Cole

Vanguard Travel Service ran from Bedworth with a mixed assortment of vehicles. Included in the bus fleet are three Dennis Lancets acquired from National Welsh in 1992. These were new to Taff Ely in 1984 and feature the functional East Lancashire design of bodywork.
David Cole

Previous Registrations:

230HUE	BVP786V	6253VC	YDK917, JPU817, C472CAP	AIB4053	THX186S
3063VC	G543LWU	6804VC	WVT618, C473CAP	BIW4977	A70KDU
3273AC	BVP788V	9258VC	G544LWU	CSV219	B231XEU
331HWD	BVP787V	9737VC	C212PPE	KHP649N	HNU123N, AIB4053
4012VC	KUB546V	9984PG	FYX815W	KIB8140	THX249S
420GAC	A211SAE	A75NAC	A190GVC, 420GAC	PIB8019	THX119S
4828VC	C211PPE	A76NAC	A191GVC, 491GAC	Q275UOC	JOX453P
491GAC	B73OKV	A7GGT	B72OKV	UFC190P	PCW683P, TIA6295
498FYB	CDG207Y	A848VML	FRA64V	WSU293	From New
552OHU	A201RHT	A8GGT	A202RHT		

Operating units:

G&G	30, 451/2, 484/6, 571, 902/3/34, 1019/20/58-89, 1427/89-91, 1820/1, 1930-3/56-8.
Vanguard	377, 597/8, 938/41, 2007/16/8/26/35-77, 2345, 2507-13, 2808/9.
Midland Red	Remainder.

RED & WHITE

Red & White Services Ltd, 1 St David's Road, Cwmbran, Gwent, NP44 1QX
The Valleys Bus Company Ltd, 1 St David's Road, Cwmbran, Gwent, NP44 1QX
Aberdare Bus Company Ltd, 1 St David's Road, Cwmbran, Gwent, NP44 1QX

Depots and outstations: Red & White - Mill Street, Abergavenny; Bishops Meadow, Brecon; Warwick Road, Brynmawr; Cinderford; Bulwark Road, Chepstow; Risca Road, Crosskeys; St David's Road, Cwmbran; Lydney; Ross on Wye; **The Valleys** - Dowlais Industrial Estate, Pant, Merthyr Tydfil; Commercial Street, Pengam; **Aberdare Bus** - Cwmbach New Road, Cwmbach, Aberdare.

10-14		Renault-Dodge S56		Northern Counties	DP25F	1988	Ex Cynon Valley, 1992
10	E291TAX	11	E292TAX	12	E293TAX	13	E294TAX	14	E295TAX

10	E291TAX	11	E292TAX	12	E293TAX	13	E294TAX	14	E295TAX

15	E896SDW	Renault-Dodge S56	East Lancashire	B29F	1987	Ex Cynon Valley, 1992
16	E897SDW	Renault-Dodge S56	East Lancashire	B29F	1987	Ex Cynon Valley, 1992
17	E898SDW	Renault-Dodge S56	East Lancashire	B29F	1987	Ex Cynon Valley, 1992
18	E899SDW	Renault-Dodge S56	East Lancashire	B29F	1987	Ex Cynon Valley, 1992
20	E931UBO	Renault-Dodge S56	Northern Counties	DP25F	1988	Ex Cynon Valley, 1992
21	E932UBO	Renault-Dodge S56	Northern Counties	DP25F	1988	Ex Cynon Valley, 1992
22	G21CSG	Renault-Dodge S56	Reeve Burgess Beaver	B25F	1989	Ex Fife Scottish, 1994
23	E929UBO	Renault-Dodge S56	Northern Counties	DP25F	1988	Ex Cynon Valley, 1992
24	E930UBO	Renault-Dodge S56	Northern Counties	DP25F	1988	Ex Cynon Valley, 1992
25	G24CSG	Renault-Dodge S56	Reeve Burgess Beaver	B25F	1989	Ex Fife Scottish, 1994
30	E275BRG	Renault-Dodge S56	Alexander AM	DP19F	1987	Ex Go-Ahead Northern, 1992

96-158		Freight Rover Sherpa (Ford)		Carlyle Citybus 2	B20F	1987	Ex National Welsh, 1991

96	E96OUH	100	E100OUH	115	E115RAX	122	E122RAX	158	E158RNY
97	E97OUH								

202	F202YKG	Freight Rover Sherpa (Ford)	Carlyle Citybus 2	B18F	1988	Ex National Welsh, 1991
237	C514BFB	Ford Transit 190D	Carlyle	B16F	1985	Ex Badgerline, 1993
239	C294MEG	Ford Transit 190D	Dormobile	B16F	1985	Ex National Welsh, 1991
240	C293MEG	Ford Transit 190D	Dormobile	B16F	1985	Ex National Welsh, 1991
242	C316OFL	Ford Transit 190D	Dormobile	B16F	1986	Ex National Welsh, 1991
243	C318OFL	Ford Transit 190D	Dormobile	B16F	1986	Ex National Welsh, 1991
245	C351GFJ	Ford Transit 190D	Robin Hood	B16F	1986	Ex Red Bus, 1991
247	C362GFJ	Ford Transit 190D	Dormobile	B16F	1986	Ex Red Bus, 1991
248	C364GFJ	Ford Transit 190D	Dormobile	B16F	1986	Ex Red Bus, 1991
255	C101HKG	Ford Transit 190D	Robin Hood	B16F	1986	Ex Rhondda, 1992
256	C103HKG	Ford Transit 190D	Robin Hood	B16F	1986	Ex Rhondda, 1992
257	C107HKG	Ford Transit 190D	Robin Hood	B16F	1986	Ex Rhondda, 1992
258	C108HKG	Ford Transit 190D	Robin Hood	B16F	1986	Ex Rhondda, 1992
261	C118HUH	Ford Transit 190D	Robin Hood	B16F	1986	Ex Rhondda, 1992
262	C111HKG	Ford Transit 190D	Robin Hood	B16F	1986	Ex Rhondda, 1992
263	C113HUH	Ford Transit 190D	Robin Hood	B16F	1986	Ex Rhondda, 1992
266	C106HKG	Ford Transit 190D	Robin Hood	B16F	1986	Ex Rhondda, 1993
267	C434BHY	Ford Transit 190D	Dormobile	B16F	1986	Ex City Line, 1993
268	C466BHY	Ford Transit 190D	Dormobile	B16F	1986	Ex City Line, 1993
269	C471BHY	Ford Transit 190D	Dormobile	B16F	1986	Ex City Line, 1993
270	C474BHY	Ford Transit 190D	Dormobile	B16F	1986	Ex City Line, 1993
272	C557TUT	Ford Transit 190D	Rootes	B16F	1986	Ex Stevensons, 1993
280	D948UDY	Mercedes-Benz L608D	Alexander	DP19F	1986	Ex Stagecoach South, 1994
281	D950UDY	Mercedes-Benz L608D	Alexander	DP19F	1986	Ex Stagecoach South, 1994
282	D544RCK	Mercedes-Benz L608D	Reeve Burgess	B20F	1986	Ex Ribble, 1994
283	D540RCK	Mercedes-Benz L608D	Reeve Burgess	B20F	1986	Ex Ribble, 1994
284	C595SHC	Mercedes-Benz L608D	PMT Hanbridge	B20F	1986	Ex Stagecoach South, 1994
285	C808SDY	Mercedes-Benz L608D	Alexander	B20F	1986	Ex Stagecoach South, 1994
286	C902HWF	Mercedes-Benz L608D	Reeve Burgess	DP19F	1985	Ex Bluebird, 1994
287	C820SDY	Mercedes-Benz L608D	Alexander	B20F	1986	Ex Stagecoach South, 1994

Opposite top: Several Leyland National 2s have been transferred from Fife Scottish to Red and White during the last year with examples of both lengths involved. Photographed in Blackwood is 507,WAS767V. Malc McDonald
Opposite bottom: Twenty-seven Mercedes-Benz minibuses have now been supplied to Red and White since it became a Stagecoach company, many displacing Ford Transits and Freight Rover Sherpas. With autumn colours in the background, 348, M348JBO, is seen in service shortly after delivery. John Jones

A major repaint programme has been undertaken at Red & White during 1994 as the corporate livery has been applied to the fleet. Seen here is Mercedes-Benz 709D 332, H556TUG, an example fitted with Dormobile Routemaker bodywork which was acquired from Graham's of Tredegar who sold their service and this vehicle shortly after Stagecoach purchased Red & White. *John Jones*

288	C596SHC	Mercedes-Benz L608D	PMT Hanbridge	B20F	1986	Ex Stagecoach South, 1994
289	C593SHC	Mercedes-Benz L608D	PMT Hanbridge	B20F	1986	Ex Stagecoach South, 1994
295	F958HTO	Iveco Daily 49.10	Robin Hood City Nippy	B23F	1988	Ex East Midland, 1994
296	G912KWF	Iveco Daily 49.10	Reeve Burgess Beaver	B25F	1989	Ex East Midland, 1994
297	G919KWF	Iveco Daily 49.10	Reeve Burgess Beaver	B25F	1989	Ex East Midland, 1994
298	G920KWF	Iveco Daily 49.10	Reeve Burgess Beaver	B25F	1989	Ex East Midland, 1994
299	G924KWF	Iveco Daily 49.10	Reeve Burgess Beaver	B25F	1989	Ex East Midland, 1994
300	H370PNY	Iveco Daily 49-10	Carlyle Dailybus	B25F	1991	Ex Cynon Valley, 1992
301	H301PAX	Mercedes-Benz 709D	PMT Ami	C25F	1991	
302	J302TUH	Mercedes-Benz 709D	PMT	B25F	1991	
303	J303TUH	Mercedes-Benz 709D	PMT	B25F	1991	

304-317

Mercedes-Benz 811D   Wright   B33F   1991-92

304	J304UKG	307	J307UKG	310	K310YKG	313	K313YKG	316	K316YKG
305	J305UKG	308	K308YKG	311	K311YKG	314	K314YKG	317	K317YKG
306	J306UKG	309	K309YKG	312	K312YKG	315	K315YKG		

318	K318YKG	Mercedes-Benz 709D	Wright	B25F	1992	
319	K319YKG	Mercedes-Benz 709D	Alexander Sprint	B25F	1992	
320	K320YKG	Mercedes-Benz 709D	Alexander Sprint	B25F	1992	
321	K321YKG	Mercedes-Benz 709D	Alexander Sprint	B25F	1992	
322	K322YKG	Mercedes-Benz 811D	Wright	B33F	1992	
323	K323YKG	Mercedes-Benz 811D	Wright	B33F	1992	
324	K324YKG	Mercedes-Benz 811D	Wright	B33F	1992	
325	K325YKG	Mercedes-Benz 811D	Wright	B33F	1993	
326	L326CHB	Mercedes-Benz 811D	Marshall C16	B33F	1993	
327	L327CHB	Mercedes-Benz 811D	Marshall C16	B33F	1993	
328	L328CHB	Mercedes-Benz 811D	Marshall C16	B33F	1993	
329	L329CHB	Mercedes-Benz 811D	Marshall C16	B33F	1993	
330	L685CDD	Mercedes-Benz 709D	Alexander Sprint	B25F	1994	Ex Red & White, 1994
331	L331CHB	Mercedes-Benz 811D	Marshall C16	B33F	1993	
332	H556TUG	Mercedes-Benz 709D	Dormobile Routemaker	DP25F	1990	Ex Graham's, Tredegar, 1994

Five Leyland Lynx operate with Red & White, all entering the fleet from Cynon Valley in 1992. Photographed while heading for Blaenavon is 396, E114SDW. *John Jones*

334-360

Mercedes-Benz 709D   Alexander Sprint   B25F   1994

334	L334FWO	**340**	L340FWO	**346**	M346JBO	**351**	M351JBO	**356** M356JBO
335	L335FWO	**341**	L341FWO	**347**	M347JBO	**352**	M352JBO	**357** M357JBO
336	L336FWO	**342**	L342FWO	**348**	M348JBO	**353**	M353JBO	**358** M358JBO
337	L337FWO	**343**	L343FWO	**349**	M349JBO	**354**	M354JBO	**359** M359JBO
338	L338FWO	**344**	M344JBO	**350**	M350JBO	**355**	M355JBO	**360** M360JBO
339	L339FWO	**345**	M345JBO					

362	WUH179T	Leyland Leopard PSU3E/4R	Plaxton Supreme III Express	C49F	1978	Ex National Welsh, 1991
368	WUH185T	Leyland Leopard PSU3E/4R	Plaxton Supreme III Express	C49F	1978	Ex National Welsh, 1991
391	GHB146N	Bristol RESL6L	Eastern Coach Works	B44F	1974	Ex Cynon Valley, 1992
392	HTG354N	Bristol RESL6L	Eastern Coach Works	B44F	1975	Ex Cynon Valley, 1992
393	GHB148N	Bristol RESL6L	Eastern Coach Works	B44F	1974	Ex Cynon Valley, 1992
394	D109NDW	Leyland Lynx LX112TL11ZR1	Leyland Lynx	B49F	1987	Ex Cynon Valley, 1992
395	E113RBO	Leyland Lynx LX112TL11ZR1	Leyland Lynx	B49F	1987	Ex Cynon Valley, 1992
396	E114SDW	Leyland Lynx LX112TL11ZR1	Leyland Lynx	B49F	1987	Ex Cynon Valley, 1992
397	E115SDW	Leyland Lynx LX112TL11ZR1	Leyland Lynx	B49F	1988	Ex Cynon Valley, 1992
398	F74DCW	Leyland Lynx LX2R11C15Z4R	Leyland Lynx 2	DP45F	1989	Ex Cynon Valley, 1992
413	KDW359P	Leyland National 11351/1R/SC		B48F	1975	Ex National Welsh, 1991

420-434

Leyland National 11351A/1R/SC   DP48F   1977   Ex National Welsh, 1991
427 is fitted with a DAF engine; 420/3/34 Volvo

420	NWO454R	**423**	NWO457R	**427**	NWO461R	**432** NWO466R	**434** NWO468R

435	LDW361P	Leyland National 10351/1R	B44F	1975	Ex Cynon Valley, 1992

439-449

Leyland National 10351A/1R   B44F   1977-80   Ex Cynon Valley, 1992

439	RHB307R	**441**	UTX725S	**444**	UTX728S	**448** DDW433V	**449** DDW434V
440	UTX724S	**442**	UTX726S	**447**	DDW432V		

469	YBO144T	Leyland National 10351A/1R	B44F	1979	Ex National Welsh, 1991
472	YBO147T	Leyland National 10351A/1R	B44F	1979	Ex National Welsh, 1991
482	BUH203V	Leyland National 10351A/1R	B44F	1979	Ex National Welsh, 1991

500	YSX934W	Leyland National 2 NL106L11/1R		B44F	1981	Ex Fife Scottish, 1994
501	RSG814V	Leyland National 2 NL116L11/1R		B52F	1980	Ex Fife Scottish, 1994
502	YSX932W	Leyland National 2 NL106L11/1R		B44F	1981	Ex Fife Scottish, 1994
503	YSX933W	Leyland National 2 NL106L11/1R		B44F	1981	Ex Fife Scottish, 1994
504	MSO13W	Leyland National 2 NL116L11/1R		B52F	1980	Ex Fife Scottish, 1994
505	RSG815V	Leyland National 2 NL116L11/1R		B52F	1980	Ex Fife Scottish, 1994
506	WAS765V	Leyland National 2 NL116L11/1R		B52F	1980	Ex Fife Scottish, 1994
507	WAS767V	Leyland National 2 NL116L11/1R		B52F	1980	Ex Fife Scottish, 1994
508	MSO14W	Leyland National 2 NL116L11/1R		B52F	1980	Ex Fife Scottish, 1994
509	YSX926W	Leyland National 2 NL106L11/1R		B44F	1981	Ex Fife Scottish, 1994
510	YSX935W	Leyland National 2 NL106L11/1R		B44F	1981	Ex Fife Scottish, 1994
512	RSG824V	Leyland National 2 NL116L11/1R		B52F	1980	Ex Fife Scottish, 1994
513	RSG825V	Leyland National 2 NL116L11/1R		B52F	1980	Ex Fife Scottish, 1994

559-649

Leyland National 11351A/1R   B49F*   1976-79 Ex National Welsh, 1991

*559/78 are B52F; 605/35/49 are fitted with Volvo engines, 619 DAF.

559	NWO475R	597	SKG907S	609	PKG741R	635	WUH168T	646	BUH211V
570	NWO486R	598	SKG908S	619	SKG923S	642	BUH207V	647	BUH212V
578	NWO494R	604	SKG914S	633	WUH166T	645	BUH210V	649	BUH214V
584	NWO500R	605	SKG915S	634	WUH167T				

650	HEU121N	Leyland National 11351/1R		B52F	1975	Ex Badgerline, 1991
651	NOE552R	Leyland National 11351A/1R		B49F	1976	Ex Cheltenham & Gloucester, 1991
652	NOE573R	Leyland National 11351A/1R(Volvo)		B49F	1976	Ex Midland Red South, 1992
653	NOE572R	Leyland National 11351A/1R(DAF)		B49F	1976	Ex Midland Red South, 1992
654	NOE576R	Leyland National 11351A/1R		B49F	1976	Ex Midland Red South, 1992
655	SGR555R	Leyland National 11351A/1R		B49F	1976	Ex Go-Ahead Northern, 1992
657	MGR948T	Leyland National 11351A/1R		B49F	1979	Ex Go-Ahead Northern, 1992
658	BPT903S	Leyland National 11351A/1R		B49F	1977	Ex Go-Ahead Northern, 1992
659	NWS903R	Leyland National 11351A/2R		B49F	1977	Ex City Line, 1992
660	XVV540S	Leyland National 11351A/1R		B49F	1978	Ex City Line, 1993
661	MFN114R	Leyland National 11351A/1R		B49F	1977	Ex City Line, 1993

701-712

Volvo B6-9.9M   Alexander Dash   B40F   1994

701	L701FWO	704	L704FWO	707	L707FWO	709	L709FWO	711	L711FWO
702	L702FWO	705	L705FWO	708	L708FWO	710	L710FWO	712	L712FWO
703	L703FWO	706	L706FWO						

803	SKG896S	Bristol VRT/SL3/501	Eastern Coach Works	H43/31F	1977	Ex National Welsh, 1991
814	XBO116T	Bristol VRT/SL3/501	Eastern Coach Works	H43/31F	1978	Ex National Welsh, 1991
825	TWS909T	Bristol VRT/SL3/6LXB	Eastern Coach Works	H43/28F	1979	Ex Cheltenham & Gloucester, 1992
826	HPT86N	Bristol VRT/SL2/6G	Eastern Coach Works	H43/31F	1975	Ex Cheltenham & Gloucester, 1992
827	A541HAC	Leyland Olympian ONLXB/1R	Eastern Coach Works	H43/31F	1983	Ex Midland Red South, 1993
828	A548HAC	Leyland Olympian ONLXB/1R	Eastern Coach Works	H43/31F	1983	Ex Midland Red South, 1993
829	A549HAC	Leyland Olympian ONLXB/1R	Eastern Coach Works	H43/31F	1983	Ex Midland Red South, 1993

No 708, L708FWO, seen with a full load as it heads for Merthyr, is one of twelve B6s which were allocated to Red & White during 1994. These have standard bus seats, and, as with all new Stagecoach vehicles, have dot matrix displays which simplifies movement between fleets and eliminates the cost of roller blinds. *John Jones*

830	AET185T	Bristol VRT/SL3/6LXB		Eastern Coach Works	H43/31F	1979	Ex East Midland, 1993	
831	DAK201V	Bristol VRT/SL3/501(6LXB)		Eastern Coach Works	H43/31F	1979	Ex East Midland, 1994	
832	CBV6S	Bristol VRT/SL3/501(6LXB)		Eastern Coach Works	H43/31F	1977	Ex Ribble, 1994	
833	DBV26W	Bristol VRT/SL3/6LXB		Eastern Coach Works	H43/31F	1980	Ex Ribble, 1994	

834-844

Bristol VRT/SL3/501 — Eastern Coach Works — H43/31F — 1980 — Ex National Welsh, 1991
835/6 are fitted with 6LXB engines

834	BUH232V	836	GTX738W	838	GTX743W	840	GTX747W	843	GTX750W
835	BUH237V	837	GTX742W	839	GTX744W	841	GTX748W	844	GTX753W

845	CBV8S	Bristol VRT/SL3/501(6LXB)	Eastern Coach Works	H43/31F	1977	Ex Ribble, 1994
861u	OSR206R	Bristol VRT/LL3/501	Alexander AL	H49/35F	1977	Ex National Welsh, 1991
862	OSR207R	Bristol VRT/LL3/501	Alexander AL	H49/35F	1977	Ex National Welsh, 1991
863	OSR208R	Bristol VRT/LL3/501	Alexander AL	H49/35F	1977	Ex National Welsh, 1991
864	OSR209R	Bristol VRT/LL3/501	Alexander AL	H49/35F	1977	Ex National Welsh, 1991
865	WDA1T	Leyland Titan TNLXB1RF	Park Royal	H47/26F	1978	Ex Selkent, 1994
866	WDA2T	Leyland Titan TNLXB1RF	Park Royal	H47/26F	1979	Ex Selkent, 1994
867	WDA5T	Leyland Titan TNLXB1RF	Park Royal	H47/26F	1979	Ex Selkent, 1994

898-915

Leyland Tiger TRCTL11/3R — Plaxton Paramount 3200 — C51F* — 1983 — Ex National Welsh, 1991
*906-9/12 are C46F

898	AAX450A	901	AAX466A	907u	AAL575A	911	AAL516A	914	AAX516A
899	AAX451A	902	AAX488A	909	AAL538A	912	AAX489A	915	AAX529A
900	AAX465A	906	AAL544A	910	AAL518A	913	AAX515A		

916	CYJ492Y	Leyland Tiger TRCTL11/3R	Plaxton Paramount 3200	C50F	1983	Ex Stagecoach South, 1994
917	CYJ493Y	Leyland Tiger TRCTL11/3R	Plaxton Paramount 3200	C50F	1983	Ex Stagecoach South, 1994
925	AKG197A	Leyland Tiger TRCTL11/3R	Duple Laser	C49F	1984	Ex National Welsh, 1991
925	AKG197A	Leyland Tiger TRCTL11/3R	Duple Laser	C49F	1984	Ex National Welsh, 1991
927	AKG214A	Leyland Tiger TRCTL11/3R	Duple Laser	C49F	1984	Ex National Welsh, 1991
931	AKG271A	Leyland Tiger TRCTL11/3R	Duple Laser	C49F	1984	Ex National Welsh, 1991
934	AKG296A	Leyland Tiger TRCTL11/3R	Duple Laser	C49F	1984	Ex National Welsh, 1991
935	A227MDD	Leyland Tiger TRCTL11/3R	Plaxton Paramount 3200	C51F	1984	Ex Cheltenham & Gloucester, 1994

940-951

Dennis Javelin 11SDA2133 — Plaxton Premiére Interurban DP47F — 1994

940	M940JBO	943	M943JBO	946	M946JBO	948	M948JBO	950	M950JBO
941	M941JBO	944	M944JBO	947	M947JBO	949	M949JBO	951	M951JBO
942	M942JBO	945	M945JBO						

Previous Registrations:

		A227MDO	A71KDO, 552OHU, A873MRW, YJU806		
AAL516A	SDW927Y	AAX451A	SDW915Y	AAX516A	SDW930Y
AAL518A	SDW926Y	AAX465A	SDW916Y	AAX529A	SDW931Y
AAL538A	SDW925Y	AAX466A	SDW917Y	AKG197A	A225VWO
AAL544A	SDW922Y	AAX488A	SDW918Y	AKG214A	A227VWO
AAL575A	SDW923Y	AAX489A	SDW928Y	AKG271A	A231VWO
AAX450A	SDW914Y	AAX515A	SDW929Y	AKG296A	A234VWO
CYJ492Y	XUF531X, 401DCD	CYJ493Y	XUF532X, 2880CD, 402DCD		

Transfers between fleets have included many double-deck buses arriving with Red & White. These have included the three single-doored Leyland Titans from Selkent as well as Bristol VRTs. Photographed in Cwmbran is 833, DBV26W which is one of the latter, in this case coming from Ribble.
John Jones

RIBBLE

Stagecoach Ribble, Frenchwood Avenue, Preston, Lancashire, PR1 4LU.
Stagecoach Manchester, Frenchwood Avenue, Preston,
Lancashire, PR1 4LU.

Depots : George Street, Blackburn; Goodwin Street, Bolton; Bredbury, (Stagecoach Manchester); Eaves Lane, Chorley; Pimlico Road, Clitheroe; Sidings Road, Fleetwood; Owen Road, Lancaster; Heysham Road, Morecambe and Selbourne Street, Preston. **Outstations:** Burnley; Garstang and Ingleton.

135	F135SPX		Dennis Javelin 11SDL1914		Duple 300		B63F	1989	Ex Hampshire Bus, 1991
136	F136SPX		Dennis Javelin 11SDL1914		Duple 300		B63F	1989	Ex Hampshire Bus, 1991
137	F137SPX		Dennis Javelin 11SDL1914		Duple 300		B63F	1989	Ex Hampshire Bus, 1991

138-144

Dennis Javelin 11SDA2129   Plaxton Premiére Interurban DP47F   1993

138	L138BFV	140	L140BFV	142	L142BFV	143	L143BFV	144	L144BFV
139	L139BFV	141	L141BFV						

145-161

Dennis Javelin 11SDA2133   Plaxton Premiére Interurban DP47F   1993

145	L145BFV	150	L150BFV	153	L153BFV	156	L156BFV	159	L159CCW
146	L146BFV	151	L151BFV	154	L154BFV	157	L157BFV	160	L160CCW
148	L148BFV	152	L152BFV	155	L155BFV	158	L158BFV	161	L161CCW
149	L149BFV								

162-168

Dennis Javelin 11SDA2133   Plaxton Premiére Interurban DP47F   1993   Ex Stagecoach South, 1994

162	L101SDY	164	L104SDY	166	L102SDY	167	L105SDY	168	L107SDY
163	L103SDY	165	L106SDY						

Ribble's services between Morecambe and Blackpool are operated as The Lancashire Coastliner with route-dedicated Interurban coaches based on the Dennis Javelin. Photographed in Lancaster is 139, L139BFV. *Roy Marshall*

Three Duple 300-bodied Dennis Javelin buses were transferred from Hampshire Bus to Ribble in 1991. These have spent most of their time allocated to the Garstang outstation though, during 1994, all three moved to Fleetwood for a short period. While there 137, F137SPX, was photographed at the ferry when working service 182.
Lee Whitehead

237-256

Volvo B6-9.9M — Alexander Dash — DP40F — 1993

237	L237CCW	**241**	L242CCK	**245**	L245CCK	**249**	L249CCK	**253**	L253CCK
238	L238CCW	**242**	L242CCK	**246**	L246CCK	**250**	L250CCK	**254**	L254CCK
239	L239CCW	**243**	L243CCK	**247**	L247CCK	**251**	L251CCK	**255**	L255CCK
240	L240CCW	**244**	L244CCK	**248**	L248CCK	**252**	L252CCK	**256**	L256CCK

257-265

Volvo B6-9.9M — Alexander Dash — DP40F — 1993 — Ex Fife Scottish, 1994

257	L667MSF	**259**	L669MSF	**261**	L661MSF	**263**	L663MSF	**265**	L665MSF
258	L668MSF	**260**	L660HKS	**262**	L662MSF	**264**	L664MSF		

277-283

Volvo B6-9.9M — Alexander Dash — B40F — 1993 — Ex Cumberland 1994

277	L277JAO	**278**	L278JAO	**279**	L279JAO	**281**	L281JAO	**283**	L283JAO

301	CHH214T	Leyland National 10351B/1R	B44F	1978	Ex Cumberland, 1993
303	SNS825W	Leyland National 2 NL116AL11/1R	B52F	1981	Ex Cumberland, 1993
305u	HHH371V	Leyland National 2 NL116L11/1R	B52F	1980	Ex Cumberland, 1993
311	AHH206T	Leyland National 10351B/1R	B44F	1978	Ex Cumberland, 1993
312	CHH210T	Leyland National 10351B/1R	B44F	1979	Ex Cumberland, 1993
318	AHH208T	Leyland National 10351B/1R	B44F	1978	Ex Cumberland, 1993
357	KHH377W	Leyland National 2 NL116L11/1R	B52F	1980	Ex Cumberland, 1993
358	OLS809T	Leyland National 10351B/1R	B44F	1978	Ex Cumberland, 1993
359	KHH375W	Leyland National 2 NL116L11/1R	B52F	1980	Ex Cumberland, 1993
367u	MAO367P	Leyland National 11351/1R	B52F	1976	Ex Cumberland, 1993
370	HHH370V	Leyland National 2 NL116L11/1R	B52F	1980	Ex Cumberland, 1993
371u	OLS807T	Leyland National 10351B/1R	B44F	1978	Ex Cumberland, 1993
372	HHH372V	Leyland National 2 NL116L11/1R	B52F	1980	Ex Cumberland, 1993
373u	HHH373V	Leyland National 2 NL116L11/1R	B52F	1980	Ex Cumberland, 1993
374	KHH374W	Leyland National 2 NL116L11/1R	B52F	1980	Ex Cumberland, 1993
375	AHH209T	Leyland National 10351B/1R	B44F	1978	Ex Cumberland, 1993
376	KHH376W	Leyland National 2 NL116L11/1R	B52F	1980	Ex Cumberland, 1993
378	KHH378W	Leyland National 2 NL116L11/1R	B52F	1980	Ex Cumberland, 1993
379u	NHH379W	Leyland National 2 NL116AL11/1R	B52F	1981	Ex Cumberland, 1993
380	NHH380W	Leyland National 2 NL116AL11/1R	B52F	1981	Ex Cumberland, 1993
381	NHH381W	Leyland National 2 NL116AL11/1R	B52F	1981	Ex Cumberland, 1993
383	RRM383X	Leyland National 2 NL116AL11/1R	DP52F	1982	Ex Cumberland, 1993
384	CHH211T	Leyland National 10351B/1R	B44F	1978	Ex Cumberland, 1993
385	RRM384X	Leyland National 2 NL116AL11/1R	DP52F	1982	Ex Cumberland, 1993

386-394

Leyland National 2 NL116AL11/1R — B52F — 1981-82 — Ex Cumberland, 1993

386	RRM386X	**390**	SHH390X	**392**	SHH392X	**393**	SHH393X	**394**	SHH394X
387	SHH387X	**391**	SHH391X						

395	RRM385X	Leyland National 2 NL116AL11/1R	B52F	1982	Ex Cumberland, 1993
396	WAO396Y	Leyland National 2 NL116HLXB/1R	B52F	1982	Ex Cumberland, 1993

Stagecoach Manchester have just one route, the 192 between Manchester centre and Hazel Grove, some six kilometres south-east of Stockport. The service started with new Volvo B6s as a high quality operation which has needed more, and larger, vehicles as patronage increased. The service is now operated by Volvo B10Ms and 403, L343KCK, is seen passing through Stockport on a short working to Stepping Hill. *Tony Wilson*

397	SNS831W	Leyland National 2 NL116AL11/1R		B52F	1981	Ex Cumberland, 1993	
398	WAO398Y	Leyland National 2 NL116HLXB/1R		B52F	1982	Ex Cumberland, 1993	
399	SHH388X	Leyland National 2 NL116AL11/1R		B52F	1982	Ex Cumberland, 1993	

401-429

	Volvo B10M-55		Alexander PS		DP48F	1994			
401	L341KCK	410	L340KCK	415	M415RRN	420	M420RRN	425	M425RRN
402	L342KCK	411	M411RRN	416	M416RRN	421	M421RRN	426	M426RRN
403	L343KCK	412	M412RRN	417	M417RRN	422	M422RRN	427	M427RRN
404	L344KCK	413	M413RRN	418	M418RRN	423	M423RRN	428	M782PRS
409	L339KCK	414	M414RRN	419	M419RRN	424	M424RRN	429	M783PRS

449	K449YCW	Optare MetroRider		Optare	B31F	1992	Ex Lancaster, 1993
450	K450YCW	Optare MetroRider		Optare	B31F	1992	Ex Lancaster, 1993

501-527

	Mercedes-Benz L608D		Reeve Burgess		DP19F*	1986	*524/7 are B20F		
							524/7 ex Cumberland, 1990-91		
501	D501RCK	506	D506RCK	510	D510RCK	515	D515RCK	524	D524RCK
502	D502RCK	507	D507RCK	512	D512RCK	516	D516RCK	527	D527RCK
505	D505RCK	508	D508RCK	513	D513RCK	521	D521RCK		

530	D672SHH	Mercedes-Benz 609D	Ribble/Cumbria Commercials	B20F	1986	

536-564

	Mercedes-Benz L608D		Reeve Burgess		B20F	1986	533/62 ex Cumberland, 1993/91		
536	D536RCK	545	D545RCK	550	D550RCK	554	D554RCK	562	D562RCK
537	D537RCK	546	D546RCK	551	D551RCK	555	D555RCK	563	D563RCK
541	D541RCK	548	D548RCK	552	D552RCK	556	D556RCK	564	D564RCK
542	D542RCK	549	D549RCK	553	D553RCK				

565-592

	Mercedes-Benz 709D		Alexander Sprint		B23F*	1990	579/80 ex Magicbus, 1990		
							*567-572 are DP25F		
565	G665PHH	571	G571PRM	577	G577PRM	583	G183PAO	588	G188PAO
566	G566PRM	572	G572PRM	578	G578PRM	584	G184PAO	589	G189PAO
567	G567PRM	573	G573PRM	579	G179PAO	585	G185PAO	590	G190PAO
568	G568PRM	574	G574PRM	580	G180PAO	586	G186PAO	591	G191PAO
569	G569PRM	575	G575PRM	581	G181PAO	587	G187PAO	592	G192PAO
570	G570PRM	576	G576PRM	582	G182PAO				

Opposite, top: **During 1993 and 1994 a shuffle of B6 stock saw highback-seated vehicles moved to Ribble and Western Scottish and bus-seated versions to Fife. Photographed in Blackburn while worling the Hyndburn circular is 261, L661MSF, formerly allocated to Fife. The recent deliveries of B6s have allowed more popular minibus services to be upgraded with 40-seaters at Fleetwood, Blackburn and Preston, the latter being branded as Zippy Plus.** *David Cole*

Opposite, bottom: **Two recent additions to Ribble's coaching fleet are Expressliner 2s based on the Volvo B10M-62. These examples delivered in 1994 replaced earlier models of the Expressliner which**

595-608 — Mercedes-Benz 709D — Alexander Sprint — B25F — 1993

595	K115XHG	598	K118XHG	600	K120XHG	604	K124XHG	607	L127DRN
596	K116XHG	599	L119DRN	602	L122DRN	605	L125DRN	608	L128DRN
597	K117XHG								

610-628 — Mercedes-Benz 709D — Alexander Sprint — B23F — 1992-93

610	K610UFR	614	K614UFR	617	K617UFR	620	K620UFR	625	K625UFR
611	K611UFR	615	K615UFR	618	K618UFR	621	K621UFR	627	K627UFR
612	K612UFR	616	K616UFR	619	K619UFR	624	K624UFR	628	K628UFR
613	K613UFR								

629-637 — Mercedes-Benz 709D — Alexander Sprint — B25F — 1993

629	L629BFV	631	L631BFV	633	L633BFV	635	L635BFV	637	K112XHG
630	L630BFV	632	L632BFV	634	L634BFV	636	L636BFV		

645	WAO645Y	Leyland Tiger TRCTL11/2R	Alexander TE	DP47F	1983	Ex Cumberland, 1991
646	WAO646Y	Leyland Tiger TRCTL11/2R	Alexander TE	DP47F	1983	Ex Cumberland, 1991
800	NCW800T	Leyland National LN113690/1R		B52F	1978	

801-812 — Leyland National 10351B/1R — B44F — 1977-79 — 801/2,6-12 ex Cumberland, 1992-93

801	GCW461S	806	TRN806V	808	TRN808V	809	TRN809V	812	TRN812V
802u	TRN802V	807	TRN807V						

813-843 — Leyland National 2 NL106L11/1R — B44F — 1980 — 813/4/42 ex Cumberland, 1993

813	YRN813V	820	YRN820V	828	DBV828W	834	DBV834W	839	DBV839W
814	YRN814V	822	YRN822V	829	DBV829W	835	DBV835W	840	DBV840W
815	YRN815V	823	BCW823V	830	DBV830W	836	DBV836W	841	DBV841W
817	YRN817V	824	BCW824V	831	DBV831W	837	DBV837W	842	DBV842W
818	YRN818V	825	BCW825V	832	DBV832W	838	DBV838W	843	DBV843W
819	YRN819V	826	BCW826V	833	DBV833W				

846-877 — Leyland National 2 NL106AL11/1R — B44F — 1981 — 856/7/60/1/3/72/3 ex Cumberland, 1993

846	JCK846W	857	LFR857X	861	LFR861X	868	LFR868X	872	LFR872X
847	JCK847W	858	LFR858X	863	LFR863X	870	LFR870X	873	LFR873X
848	JCK848W	859	LFR859X	866	LFR866X	871	LFR871X	877	LFR877X
856	LFR856X	860	LFR860X						

Chorley town service C9 is now operated by Mercedes-Benz 709Ds. Minibuses with Ribble carry the Zippy! name throughout the Ribble area, and new B6s for Preston carry Zippy Plus names. *Roy Marshall*

878-886   Leyland National 2 NL116AL11/1R   B52F   1982   881 ex Cumberland, 1993

878	RHG878X	880	RHG880X	881	RHG881X	884	RHG884X	886	RHG886X
879	RHG879X								

888-894   Leyland National 2 NL116HLXB/1R   B52F   1983   892 ex Cumberland, 1993

888	ARN888Y	890	ARN890Y	892	ARN892Y	893	ARN893Y	894	ARN894Y
889	ARN889Y	891	ARN891Y						

No.	Reg	Chassis	Body	Seating	Year	Notes
895	CEO720W	Leyland National 2 NL116L11/1R		B49F	1980	Ex Cumberland, 1993
896	CEO721W	Leyland National 2 NL116L11/1R		B49F	1980	Ex Cumberland, 1993
897	CEO722W	Leyland National 2 NL116L11/1R		B49F	1980	Ex Cumberland, 1993
898	CEO723W	Leyland National 2 NL116L11/1R		B49F	1980	Ex Cumberland, 1993
900	B900WRN	Leyland Tiger TRCTL11/1R	Duple Dominant	B49F	1984	
1150	A150LFR	Leyland Tiger TRCTL11/2R	Duple Dominant IV	C51F	1983	
1152	B152WRN	Leyland Tiger TRCTL11/2R	Duple Laser 2	C49F	1985	
1157	927GTA	Leyland Tiger TRCTL11/3R	Duple Laser 2	C53F	1985	
1158	B158WRN	Leyland Tiger TRCTL11/3R	Duple Laser 2	C53F	1985	
1159	LJY145	Volvo B10M-61	Plaxton Paramount 3500 III	C48FT	1987	Ex Cumberland, 1993
1160	YDG616	Volvo B10M-61	Plaxton Paramount 3500 III	C48FT	1987	Ex Cumberland, 1993
1163	IIL3507	Volvo B10M-60	Plaxton Paramount 3500 III	C50F	1989	Ex Cumberland, 1993
1164	M164SCK	Volvo B10M-62	Plaxton Expressliner 2	C46FT	1994	
1165	M165SCK	Volvo B10M-62	Plaxton Expressliner 2	C46FT	1994	
1166	H150CVU	Volvo B10M-60	Plaxton Expressliner	C46FT	1990	Ex Skyliner, Mossley, 1993
1167	H149CVU	Volvo B10M-60	Plaxton Expressliner	C46FT	1990	Ex Skyliner, Mossley, 1993
1200	TCK200X	Leyland Atlantean AN68D/2R	East Lancashire	H50/36F	1982	Ex Lancaster, 1993
1205	LFV205X	Leyland Atlantean AN68C/2R	East Lancashire	H50/36F	1981	Ex Lancaster, 1993
1206	LFV206X	Leyland Atlantean AN68C/2R	East Lancashire	H50/36F	1981	Ex Lancaster, 1993
1212	TCK212X	Leyland Atlantean AN68D/2R	East Lancashire	H50/36F	1982	Ex Lancaster, 1993
1213	WCK213Y	Leyland Atlantean AN68D/2R	East Lancashire	H50/36F	1982	Ex Lancaster, 1993
1214	A214MCK	Leyland Atlantean AN68D/2R	East Lancashire	H50/36F	1984	Ex Lancaster, 1993
1215	WCK215Y	Leyland Atlantean AN68D/2R	East Lancashire	H50/36F	1982	Ex Lancaster, 1993
1221	BFV221Y	Leyland Atlantean AN68D/2R	East Lancashire	DPH45/32F	1983	Ex Lancaster, 1993
1222	BFV222Y	Leyland Atlantean AN68D/2R	East Lancashire	DPH45/32F	1983	Ex Lancaster, 1993
1450	LEO735Y	Leyland Atlantean AN68D/1R	Northern Counties	H43/32F	1983	Ex Barrow, 1989
1451	LEO736Y	Leyland Atlantean AN68D/1R	Northern Counties	H43/32F	1983	Ex Barrow, 1989

1469-1485   Leyland Atlantean AN68A/1R   Eastern Coach Works   H43/31F   1979-80   Ex Cumberland, 1992-93

1469	TRN469V	1478	TRN478V	1481	TRN481V	1484	TRN484V	1485	TRN485V
1476	TRN476V	1480	TRN480V	1482	TRN482V				

Ten Leyland Atlanteans, all with East Lancashire bodywork were purchased from Lancaster City Transport . They were painted into corporate livery during 1994 and are all based at Preston. Pulling off Burnley bus station at the start of its journey home is 1200, TCK200X.
Roy Marshall

2021	CBV21S	Bristol VRT/SL3/501(6LXB)	Eastern Coach Works	H43/31F	1977	
2030	DBV30W	Bristol VRT/SL3/6LXB	Eastern Coach Works	H43/31F	1980	
2034	URF662S	Bristol VRT/SL3/501(6LXB)	Eastern Coach Works	H43/31F	1977	Ex Potteries, 1982
2040	FDV813V	Bristol VRT/SL3/6LXB	Eastern Coach Works	H43/31F	1980	Ex Magicbus, 1990
2042	RRP858R	Bristol VRT/SL3/501	Eastern Coach Works	H43/31F	1977	Ex United Counties, 1990
2043	FDV817V	Bristol VRT/SL3/6LXB	Eastern Coach Works	H43/31F	1980	Ex Magicbus, 1990
2044	FDV833V	Bristol VRT/SL3/6LXB	Eastern Coach Works	H43/31F	1980	Ex Magicbus, 1990
2045	FDV784V	Bristol VRT/SL3/6LXB	Eastern Coach Works	H43/31F	1980	Ex Magicbus, 1990
2051	LFJ882W	Bristol VRT/SL3/6LXC	Eastern Coach Works	H43/31F	1980	Ex United Counties, 1993
2052	LFJ883W	Bristol VRT/SL3/6LXC	Eastern Coach Works	H43/31F	1980	Ex United Counties, 1993
2053	LFJ858W	Bristol VRT/SL3/6LXB	Eastern Coach Works	H43/31F	1980	Ex United Counties, 1993
2054	LFJ859W	Bristol VRT/SL3/6LXB	Eastern Coach Works	H43/31F	1980	Ex United Counties, 1993
2055	LFJ885W	Bristol VRT/SL3/6LXC	Eastern Coach Works	H43/31F	1980	Ex United Counties, 1993
2056	LFJ866W	Bristol VRT/SL3/6LXB	Eastern Coach Works	H43/31F	1980	Ex United Counties, 1993
2057	LFJ861W	Bristol VRT/SL3/6LXB	Eastern Coach Works	H43/31F	1980	Ex United Counties, 1993
2058	LFJ884W	Bristol VRT/SL3/6LXC	Eastern Coach Works	H43/31F	1980	Ex United Counties, 1993
2075	XRR175S	Bristol VRT/SL3/6LXB	Eastern Coach Works	O43/31F	1980	Ex East Midland, 1994
2076	UWV622S	Bristol VRT/SL3/6LXB	Eastern Coach Works	O43/31F	1980	Ex East Kent, 1994
2100u	DBV100W	Leyland Olympian B45.02	Eastern Coach Works	H45/33F	1980	

2101-2137
Leyland Olympian ONLXB/1R* Eastern Coach Works H45/32F 1981-83 *2124-30 are ONLXBT/1R

2101	GFR101W	2108	JFR8W	2115	OFV15X	2122	OFV22X	2128	VRN828Y
2102	JFR2W	2109	JFR9W	2116	OFV16X	2123	OFV23X	2129	VRN829Y
2103	JFR3W	2110	JFR10W	2117	OFV17X	2124	SCK224X	2130	VRN830Y
2104	JFR4W	2111	JFR11W	2118	OFV18X	2125	SCK225X	2131	DBV131Y
2105	JFR5W	2112	JFR12W	2119	OFV19X	2126	SCK226X	2132	DBV132Y
2106	JFR6W	2113	JFR13W	2120	OFV20X	2127	VRN827Y	2137	DBV137Y
2107	JFR7W	2114	OFV14X	2121	OFV21X				

2138-2152
Leyland Olympian ONLXB/1R Eastern Coach Works H45/32F 1984

2138	A138MRN	2142	A142MRN	2143	A143MRN	2145	A145MRN	2152	B152TRN

2156-2179
Leyland Olympian ONLXB/1R Eastern Coach Works DPH41/26F 1984-85

2156	A156OFR	2159	A159OFR	2171	C171ECK	2173	C173ECK	2178	C178ECK
2157	A157OFR	2170	C170ECK	2172	C172ECK	2174	C174ECK	2179	C179ECK
2158	A158OFR								

2180-2189
Leyland Olympian ON2R50G16Z4 Alexander RL DPH51/31F 1989

2180	G180JHG	2182	G182JHG	2184	G184JHG	2186	G186JHG	2188	G188JHG
2181	G181JHG	2183	G183JHG	2185	G185JHG	2187	G187JHG	2189	G189JHG

2191-2197
Leyland Olympian ON2R50G16Z4 Alexander RL H47/30F 1990

2191	H191WFR	2193	H193WFR	2195	H195WFR	2196	H196WFR	2197	H197WFR
2192	H192WFR	2194	H194WFR						

2198-2210
Leyland Olympian ON2R56G13Z4 Alexander RL DPH47/27F 1991

2198	J198HFR	2202	J202HFR	2205	J205HFR	2207	J207HFR	2209	J209HFR
2199	J199HFR	2203	J203HFR	2206	J206HFR	2208	J208HFR	2210	J210HFR
2201	J201HFR	2204	J204HFR						

2211-2223
Leyland Olympian ONLXB/1R Alexander RL H45/32F 1984-85 Ex Highland Scottish, 1991

2211	A975OST	2214	A979OST	2217	B893UAS	2220	B896UAS	2222	B898UAS
2212	A977OST	2215	B891UAS	2218	B894UAS	2221	B897UAS	2223	B899UAS
2213	A978OST	2216	B892UAS	2219	B895UAS				

Previous Registrations:

927GTA	B157WRN	K449YCW	K300LCT	LJY145	D205LWX
IIL3507	F410DUG	K450YCW	K200LCT	YDG616	D206LWX

Operating Companies:
Stagecoach Manchester: 249/50, 401-4/9-27, 553

SELKENT

South East London and Kent Bus Company, Riverdale Offices, 68 Molesworth Street, Lewisham, London, SE13 7EU

Depots : Hastings Road, Bromley; Bromley Road, Catford; Nugent Industrial Estate, Orpington and Plumstead Road, Plumstead.

DM948u GHV948N	Daimler Fleetline CRG6	Park Royal	O44/27D	1978	Ex London Buses, 1994
DM1102uGHV102N	Daimler Fleetline CRG6	Park Royal	O44/27D	1978	Ex London Buses, 1994

DT28-55

						Dennis Dart 8.5SDL3003		Carlyle Dartline		B28F	1990	Ex London Buses, 1994

28	49CLT	32	G32TGW	35	G35TGW	38	G38TGW	40	G40TGW
30	G30TGW	33	G33TGW	36	G36TGW	39	G39TGW	55	WLT575
31	G31TGW	34	G34TGW	37	G37TGW				

DW59-71

Dennis Dart 8.5SDL3003 · Wright Handy-bus · B28F · 1991 · Ex London Buses, 1994

59	JDZ2359	61	JDZ2361	63	JDZ2363	65	JDZ2365	71	JDZ2371
60	JDZ2360	62	JDZ2362	64	JDZ2364				

FM1-10

Iveco Daily 49.10 · Marshall C29 · B23F · 1993 · Ex London Buses, 1994

1	K521EFL	3	K523EFL	5	K525EFL	7	K527EFL	9	K529EFL
2	K522EFL	4	K524EFL	6	K526EFL	8	K528EFL	10	K530EFL

L7-145

Leyland Olympian ONLXB/1RH · Eastern Coach Works · H42/26D · 1986 · Ex London Buses, 1994

7	C807BYY	53	C53CHM	76	C76CHM	107	C107CHM	125	D125FYM
9	C809BYY	54	C54CHM	77	C77CHM	108	C108CHM	126	D126FYM
10	C810BYY	55	C55CHM	80	C80CHM	109	C109CHM	127	D127FYM
11	C811BYY	57	C57CHM	81	C81CHM	110	C110CHM	128	D128FYM
12	C812BYY	60	C60CHM	82	C82CHM	111	C111CHM	129	D129FYM
15	C815BYY	61	C61CHM	83	C83CHM	112	C112CHM	130	D130FYM
18	C818BYY	62	C62CHM	86	C86CHM	114	C114CHM	131	D131FYM
19	C819BYY	64	C64CHM	87	C87CHM	115	C115CHM	132	D132FYM
23	C23CHM	67	C67CHM	91	C91CHM	116	C116CHM	133	D133FYM
28	C28CHM	68	C68CHM	92	C92CHM	117	C117CHM	134	D134FYM
29	C29CHM	69	C69CHM	94	C94CHM	118	C118CHM	136	D136FYM
30	C30CHM	70	C70CHM	97	C97CHM	119	C119CHM	137	D137FYM
42	C42CHM	71	C71CHM	98	C98CHM	120	C120CHM	141	D141FYM
43	C43CHM	72	C72CHM	103	C103CHM	121	C121CHM	142	D142FYM
44	C44CHM	73	C73CHM	104	C104CHM	122	C122CHM	144	D144FYM
48	C43CHM	74	C74CHM	105	C105CHM	123	D123FYM	145	D145FYM
51	C51CHM	75	C75CHM	106	C106CHM	124	D124FYM		

Roundabout is the marketing name of the Orpington network on which DT39, G39TGW, is seen on LRT tendered service R1 to Bromley Common. Thirteen of these Carlyle Dartline-bodied examples were taken over from London Buses with the Selkent operation.
Malc MacDonald

Certain services operated by East London and Selkent which operate into central London are required to use vehicles in a 'red livery'. However, it has been decided that the two fleets should operate in a unified scheme, though training and ancilliary vehicles will receive corporate livery. One of the early repaints into all-red, and complete with Selkent vinyls is L263, VLT9, a Leyland Olympian and one of three with high-back seating. It is seen in Parliament Square on route 53. *Colin Lloyd*

L260	VLT20	Leyland Olympian ONLXB/1RH	Eastern Coach Works	DPH42/26D	1986	Ex London Buses, 1994
L262	VLT14	Leyland Olympian ONLXB/1RH	Eastern Coach Works	DPH42/26D	1986	Ex London Buses, 1994
L263	VLT9	Leyland Olympian ONLXB/1RH	Eastern Coach Works	DPH42/26D	1986	Ex London Buses, 1994

LA1-16

Dennis Lance 11SDA3101   Alexander PS   B39D   1992   Ex London Buses, 1994

1	J101WSC	5	J105WSC	8	J108WSC	11	J111WSC	14	J114WSC
2	J102WSC	6	J106WSC	9	J109WSC	12	J112WSC	15	J115WSC
3	J103WSC	7	J107WSC	10	J110WSC	13	J113WSC	16	J116WSC
4	J104WSC								

LV1-12

Dennis Lance 11SDA3112   Plaxton Verde   B42D   1994   Ex London Buses, 1994

1	L201YAG	4	L204YAG	7	L207YAG	9	L209YAG	11	L211YAG
2	L202YAG	5	L205YAG	8	L208YAG	10	L210YAG	12	L212YAG
3	L203YAG	6	L206YAG						

MA9-41

Mercedes-Benz 811D   Alexander AM   B28F   1988-89   Ex London Buses, 1994

9	F609XMS	16	F616XMS	20	F620XMS	25	F625XMS	31	F631XMS
14	F614XMS	17	F617XMS	21	F621XMS	29	F629XMS	41	F641XMS
15	F615XMS	19	F619XMS	24	F624XMS	30	F630XMS		

MC1-5

Mercedes-Benz 811D   Carlyle   B28F   1990   Ex London Buses, 1994

| 1 | WLT491 | 2 | H882LOX | 3 | H883LOX | 4 | WLT400 | 5 | H885LOX |

| MR27 | E127KYW | MCW MetroRider MF150/38 | MCW | B25F | 1987 | Ex London Buses, 1994 |
| MR46 | E146KYW | MCW MetroRider MF150/38 | MCW | B25F | 1987 | Ex London Buses, 1994 |

Two batches of Dennis Lance are operated by Stagecoach Selkent each with different bodywork. These carried a livery where the red was relieved by more white while operating with London Buses. Members of class LA - represented by LA7, J107WSC - carry Alexander PS-type bodywork while the LVs - represented by LV6, L206YAG (Below) - are fitted with Plaxton Verde bodywork. *Tony Wilson*

Thirty-one 25-seat Optare MetroRiders are operated by Selkent on various services to the south east of London,. Photographed in Eltham on service 314 is MRL166, H166WWT. Selkent have now dispersed the coach fleet, though three double-deck opentops are still owned, being parked at a Cumberland depot for the winter. *Malc MacDonald*

MRL141-176

Optare MetroRider — Optare — B26F — 1990-91 Ex London Buses, 1994

141	H141UUA	148	H148UUA	154	H154UUA	165	H165WWT	171	H171WWT
142	H142UUA	149	H149UUA	160	H160WWT	166	H166WWT	172	H172WWT
143	H143UUA	150	H150UUA	161	H161WWT	167	H167WWT	173	H173WWT
144	H144UUA	151	H151UUA	162	H162WWT	168	H168WWT	174	H174WWT
145	H145UUA	152	H152UUA	163	H163WWT	169	H169WWT	175	H175WWT
146	H146UUA	153	H153UUA	164	H564WWR	170	H170WWT	176	H176WWT
147	H147UUA							

MT4	F394DHL	Mercedes-Benz 709D	Reeve Burgess Beaver	B20FL	1988	Ex London Buses, 1994

MW1-16

Mercedes-Benz 811D — Wright — B26F — 1989 Ex London Buses, 1994

1	HDZ2601	5	HDZ2605	8	HDZ2608	11	HDZ2611	14	HDZ2614
2	HDZ2602	6	HDZ2606	9	HDZ2609	12	HDZ2612	15	HDZ2615
3	HDZ2603	7	HDZ2607	10	HDZ2610	13	HDZ2613	16	HDZ2616
4	HDZ2604							

RH1	C501DYM	Iveco Daily 49.10	Robin Hood City Nippy	DP21F	1986	Ex London Buses, 1994
RH5	C505DYM	Iveco Daily 49.10	Robin Hood City Nippy	B21F	1986	Ex London Buses, 1994
RH22	D522FYL	Iveco Daily 49.10	Robin Hood City Nippy	B21F	1986	Ex London Buses, 1994
RH46	E46MRP	Iveco Daily 49.10	Robin Hood City Nippy	B23F	1988	Ex United Counties, 1994 (On loan)
RH47	E47MRP	Iveco Daily 49.10	Robin Hood City Nippy	B23F	1988	Ex United Counties, 1994 (On loan)
RH49	E49MRP	Iveco Daily 49.10	Robin Hood City Nippy	B23F	1988	Ex United Counties, 1994 (On loan)
RH50	E50MRP	Iveco Daily 49.10	Robin Hood City Nippy	B23F	1988	Ex United Counties, 1994 (On loan)
RM1515	u515CLT	AEC Routemaster R2RH	Park Royal	O36/28R	1960	Ex London Buses, 1994

T49-250

Leyland Titan TNLXB2RRSp   Park Royal   H44/26D   1979-80 Ex London Buses, 1994

49	WYV49T	130	CUL130V	179	CUL179V	209	CUL209V	236	EYE236V
56	WYV56T	137	CUL137V	180	CUL180V	215	CUL215V	237	EYE237V
79	WYV79T	142	CUL142V	189	CUL189V	224	CUL224V	238	EYE238V
86	WYV86T	163	CUL163V	190	CUL190V	225	CUL225V	240	EYE240V
98	WYV98T	168	CUL168V	198	CUL198V	229	EYE229V	244	EYE244V
114	WYV114T	169	CUL169V	208	CUL208V	233	EYE233V	250	EYE250V
120	WYV120T								

T267	GYE267W	Leyland Titan TNLXB2RR	Park Royal/Leyland	H44/24D	1981	Ex London Buses, 1994

T282-523

Leyland Titan TNLXB2RR   Leyland   H44/24D   1981-82 Ex London Buses, 1994
T345 is type TNTL112RR

282	KYN282X	348	KYV348X	410	KYV410X	451	KYV451X	487	KYV486X
288	KYN288X	361	KYV361X	420	KYV420X	455	KYV455X	511	KYV511X
305	KYN305X	368	KYV368X	442	KYV442X	474	KYV474X	523	KYV523X
345	KYN345X	397	KYV397X	447	KYV447X				

T594-674

Leyland Titan TNLXB2RR   Leyland   H44/24D   1982   Ex London Buses, 1994

594	NUW594Y	611	NUW611Y	616	NUW616Y	618	NUW618Y	674	NUW674Y
596	NUW596Y								

T680-999

Leyland Titan TNLXB2RR   Leyland   H44/24D   1983-84 Ex London Buses, 1994
T877/80 are type TNTL112RR

680	OHV680Y	797	OHV797Y	823	A823SUL	848	A848SUL	882	A882SUL
700	OHV700Y	800	OHV800Y	824	A824SUL	850	A850SUL	883	A883SUL
710	OHV710Y	801	OHV801Y	825	A825SUL	854	A854SUL	885	A885SUL
714	OHV714Y	804	OHV804Y	828	A828SUL	855	A855SUL	918	A918SYE
721	OHV721Y	805	OHV805Y	829	A829SUL	856	A856SUL	925	A925SYE
728	OHV728Y	809	OHV809Y	830	A830SUL	857	A857SUL	926	A926SYE
740	OHV740Y	810	OHV810Y	834	A834SUL	858	A858SUL	950	A950SYE
748	OHV748Y	812	OHV812Y	837	A837SUL	859	A859SUL	951	A951SYE
762	OHV762Y	814	OHV814Y	838	A838SUL	866	A866SUL	961	A961SYE
770	OHV770Y	815	OHV815Y	841	A841SUL	868	A868SUL	976	A976SYE
771	OHV771Y	816	RYK816Y	842	A842SUL	874	A874SUL	978	A978SYE
772	OHV772Y	818	RYK818Y	843	A843SUL	877	A877SUL	988	A988SYE
780	OHV780Y	820	RYK820Y	845	A845SUL	880	A880SUL	996	A996SYE
785	OHV785Y	821	RYK821Y	847	A847SUL	881	A881SUL	999	A999SYE
791	OHV791Y	822	RYK822Y						

T1003-1077

Leyland Titan TNLXB2RR   Leyland   H44/24D   1984   Ex London Buses, 1994

1003	A603THV	1028	A628THV	1033	A632THV	1045	A645THV	1066	A66THX
1007	A607THV	1029	A629THV	1033	A634THV	1048	A648THV	1067	A67THX
1013	A613THV	1030	A630THV	1033	A635THV	1052	A652THV	1076	A76THX
1025	A625THV	1031	A631THV	1033	A636THV	1065	A65THX	1077	A77THX
1027	A627THV								

T1079-1125

Leyland Titan TNLXB2RR   Leyland   H44/24D   1984   Ex London Buses, 1994

1079	B79WUV	1092	B92WUV	1101	B101WUV	1113	B113WUV	1119	B119WUV
1081	B81WUV	1093	B93WUV	1103	B103WUV	1114	B114WUV	1121	B121WUV
1083	B83WUV	1096	B96WUV	1106	B106WUV	1115	B115WUV	1122	B122WUV
1084	B84WUV	1097	B97WUV	1108	B108WUV	1116	B116WUV	1124	B124WUV
1089	B89WUV	1099	B99WUV	1110	B110WUV	1117	B117WUV	1125	B125WUV
1091	B91WUV	1100	B100WUV	1112	B112WUV	1118	B118WUV		

Previous Registrations:

49CLT	G29TGW	VLT20	D260FYL	WLT491	H881LOX
515CLT	From new	VLT9	D263FYL	WLT575	G41TGW
VLT14	D262FYL	WLT400	H884LOX		

Livery: Red

STAGECOACH SOUTH

Stagecoach (South) Ltd, Lewes Enterprise Centre, 112 Malling Street,
Lewes, East Sussex, BN7 2RB
Sussex Coastline Buses; Hampshire Bus; South Coast Buses;
Hants & Surrey; East Kent Road Car Co;
Lewes Enterprise Centre, 112 Malling Street,
Lewes, East Sussex, BN7 2RB

Depots and outstations: Halimote Road, Aldershot; Mill Lane, Alton; Livingstone Road, Andover; Station Road, Ashford; New Market Square, Basingstoke; Abbey Mill, Bishops Waltham; St Stephen's Road, Canterbury; Southgate, Chichester; South Street, Deal; Russell Street, Dover; Cavendish Place, Eastbourne; Kent Road, Cheriton, Folkestone; Beaufort Road, Silverhill, Hastings; Elm Lane, Havant; Henfield; High Street, Herne Bay; London Road, Hindhead; Eastgate Street, Lewes; Littlehampton; Marlborough; Littlestone Road, New Romney; Bedford Road, Petersfield; Station Approach, Rye; Claremont Road, Seaford; Hazeldown Farm, Stockbridge; Margate Road, Westwood, Thanet; Uckfield; The Broadway, Winchester and Library Place, Worthing.

1	H101EKR	Iveco Daily 49.10	Phoenix	B23F	1991	Ex East Kent, 1993	
2	H102EKR	Iveco Daily 49.10	Phoenix	B23F	1991	Ex East Kent, 1993	
3	H103EKR	Iveco Daily 49.10	Phoenix	B23F	1991	Ex East Kent, 1993	
4	H104EKR	Iveco Daily 49.10	Phoenix	B23F	1991	Ex East Kent, 1993	
5	D935EBP	Iveco Daily 49.10	Robin Hood City Nippy	B19F	1986	Ex East Kent, 1993	
6	D226VCD	Iveco Daily 49.10	Robin Hood City Nippy	B21F	1986	Ex East Kent, 1993	
10	D230VCD	Iveco Daily 49.10	Robin Hood City Nippy	B21F	1986	Ex East Kent, 1993	
11	J121LKO	Iveco Daily 49.10	Dormobile Routemaker	B23F	1991	Ex East Kent, 1993	
12	J112LKO	Iveco Daily 49.10	Carlyle Dailybus	B23F	1991	Ex East Kent, 1993	
13	J113LKO	Iveco Daily 49.10	Carlyle Dailybus	B23F	1991	Ex East Kent, 1993	
14	J114LKO	Iveco Daily 49.10	Carlyle Dailybus	B23F	1991	Ex East Kent, 1993	

15-20

		Iveco Daily 49.10	Dormobile Routemaker	B23F	1991	Ex East Kent, 1993	
15	J115LKO	17	J117LKO	18	J118LKO	19	J119LKO	20	J120LKO
16	J116LKO						

21-26

		Iveco Daily 49.10	Robin Hood City Nippy	B23F	1989	Ex Stagecoach, 1990	
21	F21PSL	22	F22PSL	23	F23PSL	25	F25PSL	26	F26PSL

30	G30PSR	Iveco Daily 49.10	Phoenix	B23F	1989	Ex Stagecoach, 1990	
31	F61AVV	Iveco Daily 49.10	Robin Hood City Nippy	B25F	1989	Ex United Counties, 1989	
32	F62AVV	Iveco Daily 49.10	Robin Hood City Nippy	B25F	1989	Ex United Counties, 1989	
33	E233JRF	Iveco Daily 49.10	Phoenix	B25F	1987		

34-39

		Iveco Daily 49.10	Phoenix	B23F	1989	Ex Stagecoach, 1990	
						35 ex East Midland, 1993	
34	G34PSR	36	G36SSR	37	G37SSR	38	G38SSR	39	G39SSR
35	G35PSR						

41	D231VCD	Iveco Daily 49.10	Robin Hood City Nippy	B21F	1986	Ex East Kent, 1993	
42	G42SSR	Iveco Daily 49.10	Phoenix	B23F	1989	Ex Stagecoach, 1990	
43	G43SSR	Iveco Daily 49.10	Phoenix	B23F	1989	Ex Stagecoach, 1990	
45	E65BVS	Iveco Daily 49.10	Robin Hood City Nippy	B23F	1988		
46	G446VKK	Iveco Daily 49.10	Carlyle Dailybus	B23F	1990	Ex East Kent, 1993	
47	G447VKK	Iveco Daily 49.10	Carlyle Dailybus	B23F	1990	Ex East Kent, 1993	

51-70

		Iveco Daily 49.10	Robin Hood City Nippy	B23F	1987	Ex East Kent, 1993	
51	E151UKR	55	E155UKR	59	E159UKR	63	E163UKR	67	E167UKR
52	E152UKR	56	E156UKR	60	E160UKR	64	E164UKR	68	E168UKR
53	E153UKR	57	E157UKR	61	E161UKR	65	E165UKR	69	E169UKR
54	E154UKR	58	E158UKR	62	E162UKR	66	E166UKR	70	E170UKR

71-75

		Iveco Daily 49.10	Robin Hood City Nippy	B23F	1989	Ex East Kent, 1993	
71	F71FKK	72	F72FKK	73	F73FKK	74	F74FKK	75	F75FKK

76	J416TGM	Iveco Daily 49.10	Reeve Burgess Beaver	B25F	1991	Ex Alder Valley, 1992	

80-87

80-87		Iveco Daily 49.10		Robin Hood City Nippy		B19F	1987	Ex East Kent, 1993	
80	E580TKJ	**82**	E582TKJ	**84**	E584TKJ	**86**	E586TKJ	**87**	E587TKJ
81	E581TKJ	**83**	E583TKJ	**85**	E585TKJ				

91	G491RKK	Iveco Daily 49.10	Carlyle Dailybus	B23F	1990	Ex East Kent, 1993
92	G492RKK	Iveco Daily 49.10	Carlyle Dailybus	B23F	1990	Ex East Kent, 1993
93	G493RKK	Iveco Daily 49.10	Carlyle Dailybus	B23F	1990	Ex East Kent, 1993
94	G494RKK	Iveco Daily 49.10	Carlyle Dailybus	B23F	1990	Ex East Kent, 1993
95	G95SKR	Iveco Daily 49.10	Phoenix	B23F	1990	Ex East Kent, 1993
96	G96SKR	Iveco Daily 49.10	Phoenix	B23F	1990	Ex East Kent, 1993
97	G97SKR	Iveco Daily 49.10	Phoenix	B23F	1990	Ex East Kent, 1993
98	G98SKR	Iveco Daily 49.10	Phoenix	B23F	1990	Ex East Kent, 1993

100-118

100-118		Leyland National 11351A/1R				B52F*	1979	106 ex Hampshire Bus, 1992 *106 is B49F	
100	AYJ100T	**104**	AYJ104T	**109**	ENJ909V	**113**	ENJ913V	**116**	ENJ916V
101	AYJ101T	**105**	AYJ105T	**110**	ENJ910V	**114**	ENJ914V	**117**	ENJ917V
102	AYJ102T	**106**	DRU6T	**111**	ENJ911V	**115**	ENJ915V	**118**	ENJ918V
103	AYJ103T	**107**	AYJ107T	**112**	ENJ912V				

119-126

119-126		Leyland National 2 NL116L11/1R				B52F	1980		
119	GYJ919V	**121**	GYJ921V	**123**	HFG923V	**125**	OUF262W	**126**	SYC852
120	GYJ920V	**122**	GYJ922V	**124**	JNJ194V				

127	FDV830V	Leyland National 2 NL116L11/1R	B52F	1980
128	FDV831V	Leyland National 2 NL116L11/1R	B52F	1980

129-138

129-138		Leyland National 2 NL116AL11/1R				B49F*	1982	*129/32 are B45F	
129	415DCD	**131**	411DCD	**133**	420DCD	**135**	405DCD	**137**	407DCD
130	400DCD	**132**	YLJ332	**134**	HUF451X	**136**	406DCD	**138**	410DCD

139	FDV829V	Leyland National 2 NL116L11/1R	B52F	1980	
140	CPO98W	Leyland National 2 NL106L11/1R	B41F	1980	Ex Portsmouth, 1990
141	CPO99W	Leyland National 2 NL106L11/1R	DP40F	1980	Ex Portsmouth, 1990
142	CPO100W	Leyland National 2 NL106L11/1R	DP40F	1980	Ex Portsmouth, 1990
143	ERV115W	Leyland National 2 NL106AL11/1R	B41F	1981	Ex Portsmouth, 1990
144	ERV116W	Leyland National 2 NL106AL11/1R	B41F	1981	Ex Portsmouth, 1990
145	ERV117W	Leyland National 2 NL106AL11/1R	B41F	1981	Ex Portsmouth, 1990
146	ERV118W	Leyland National 2 NL106AL11/1R	B41F	1981	Ex Portsmouth, 1990
147	BCW827V	Leyland National 2 NL116L11/1R	B44F	1980	Ex Ribble, 1994
148	UFG48S	Leyland National 11351A/2R	B52F	1977	
149	JCK849W	Leyland National 2 NL106AL11/1R	B44F	1981	Ex Ribble, 1994
151	WPR151S	Leyland National 11351A/1R	B49F	1978	
152	WPR152S	Leyland National 11351A/1R	B49F	1978	

Early repaints into corporate livery with Stagecoach South had three non-standard stripes incorporated across the vehicle at mid-deck height. On the Leyland Nationals this was confined to the panels each side of the destination box as shown in this picture of 152, VOD625S, seen outside Eastbourne's Arndale Centre while allocated to South Coast Buses.

154	VOD604S	Leyland National 11351A/1R		B52F	1978	Ex Devon General, 1987
155	VOD605S	Leyland National 11351A/1R		B52F	1978	Ex Devon General, 1987
157	UHG757R	Leyland National 11351A/1R		B49F	1977	Ex Ribble, 1986
159	YRN816V	Leyland National 2 NL106L11/1R		B44F	1980	Ex Ribble, 1994
160	YRN821V	Leyland National 2 NL106L11/1R		B44F	1980	Ex Ribble, 1994
161	TRN811V	Leyland National 10351B/1R		B44F	1979	Ex Magicbus, 1991
162	FPR62V	Leyland National 11351A/1R		B49F	1980	
163	PCD73R	Leyland National 11351A/1R		B49F	1976	
164	VFX984S	Leyland National 11351A/1R		B49F	1978	
165	VOD625S	Leyland National 11351A/1R		B52F	1978	
166	MLJ922P	Leyland National 11351/1R		B49F	1976	Ex Devon General, 1987
167	MLJ917P	Leyland National 11351/1R		B49F	1976	
168	WYJ168S	Leyland National 11351A/2R		B48F	1978	
169	WYJ169S	Leyland National 11351A/2R(DAF)		B48F	1978	
171	WYJ171S	Leyland National 11351A/2R		B44D	1978	
172	PCD82R	Leyland National 11351A/1R		B49F	1977	
173	YCD73T	Leyland National 11351A/2R		B52F	1978	
174	YCD74T	Leyland National 11351A/2R		B48F	1978	
176	YCD76T	Leyland National 11351A/2R		B48F	1978	
177	YCD77T	Leyland National 11351A/2R		B48F	1978	
178	PCD78R	Leyland National 11351A/1R		B49F	1976	
179	PCD79R	Leyland National 11351A/1R		B49F	1977	
180	PCD80R	Leyland National 11351A/1R		B49F	1977	
181	XRR581M	Leyland National 1151/1R/0403		B49F	1973	Ex East Midland, 1993
182	YCD82T	Leyland National 11351A/2R		B48F	1978	
183	UFX853S	Leyland National 11351A/1R		B49F	1977	
184	CBV784S	Leyland National 11351A/1R		B49F	1978	Ex Ribble, 1986
186	CBV776S	Leyland National 11351A/1R		B49F	1978	Ex Ribble, 1986
187	YCD87T	Leyland National 11351A/2R		B48F	1978	
188	CBV798S	Leyland National 11351A/1R		B49F	1978	Ex Ribble, 1986
189	AYJ89T	Leyland National 11351A/1R		B52F	1979	
190	TEL490R	Leyland National 11351A/1R		DP48F	1977	
191	AYJ91T	Leyland National 11351A/1R		B52F	1979	
192	AYJ92T	Leyland National 11351A/1R		B52F	1979	
194	AYJ94T	Leyland National 11351A/1R		B52F	1979	
195	AYJ95T	Leyland National 11351A/1R		B52F	1979	
196	RJT146R	Leyland National 11351A/1R		B49F	1977	
197	AYJ97T	Leyland National 11351A/1R		B52F	1979	
198	AYJ98T	Leyland National 11351A/1R		B52F	1979	

201-206

Leyland Olympian ON2R56G13Z4 Alexander RL   H51/36F   1988

201	F601MSL	203	F603MSL	204	F604MSL	205	F605MSL	206	F606MSL
202	F602MSL								

207-214

Leyland Olympian ON2R56G13Z4 Alexander RL   DPH51/31F 1989

207	G807RTS	209	G809RTS	211	G211SSL	213	G213SSL	214	G214SSL
208	G808RTS	210	G210SSL	212	G212SSL				

**The longer version of the Olympian is used in several fleets, and the 1995 order for the Volvo version is to include both lengths of this product.
Photographed in Southsea is 224, J624GCR.**
Tony Wilson

215-219

Leyland Olympian ON2R56G13Z4 Alexander RL   H51/34F   1990

215	H815CBP	216	H816CBP	217	H817CBP	218	H818CBP	219	H819CBP

220	J720GAP	Leyland Olympian ON2R56G13Z4 Alexander RL	DPH47/27F	1992
221	J721GAP	Leyland Olympian ON2R56G13Z4 Alexander RL	DPH47/27F	1992
222	J722GAP	Leyland Olympian ON2R56G13Z4 Alexander RL	DPH47/27F	1992
223	J623GCR	Leyland Olympian ON2R56G13Z4 Alexander RL	H47/30F	1991
224	J624GCR	Leyland Olympian ON2R56G13Z4 Alexander RL	H47/30F	1991

225-234

Leyland Olympian ON2R56G13Z4 Alexander RL   H51/34F   1990

225	G705TCD	227	G707TCD	229	G709TCD	231	G701TCD	233	G703TCD
226	G706TCD	228	G708TCD	230	G710TCD	232	G702TCD	234	G704TCD

235-240

Leyland Olympian ON2R50G13Z4 Alexander RL   DPH43/27F   1992

235	K235NHC	237	K237NHC	238	K238NHC	239	K239NHC	240	K240NHC
236	K236NHC								

241-250

Volvo Olympian YN2RV18Z4   Northern Counties Palatine II   DPH43/25F   1993

241	L241SDY	243	L243SDY	245	L245SDY	247	L247SDY	249	L249SDY
242	L242SDY	244	L244SDY	246	L246SDY	248	L248SDY	250	L250SDY

254	K714ASC	Leyland Olympian ON2R50G13Z4 Alexander RL	H47/32F	1992	Ex Fife Scottish, 1994
255	K715ASC	Leyland Olympian ON2R50G13Z4 Alexander RL	H47/32F	1992	Ex Fife Scottish, 1994
256	K716ASC	Leyland Olympian ON2R50G13Z4 Alexander RL	H47/32F	1992	Ex Fife Scottish, 1994
257	K717ASC	Leyland Olympian ON2R50G13Z4 Alexander RL	H47/32F	1992	Ex Fife Scottish, 1994

301-309

Volvo Citybus B10M-50   Northern Counties   DPH43/33F   1989

301	F301MYJ	303	F303MYJ	305	F305MYJ	307	F307MYJ	309	F309MYJ
302	F302MYJ	304	F304MYJ	306	F306MYJ	308	F308MYJ		

315	GLJ467N	Bristol VRT/SL2/6LXB	Eastern Coach Works	H43/31F	1974	
321	VTV171S	Bristol VRT/SL3/6LXB	Eastern Coach Works	H43/31F	1978	Ex East Midland, 1993
322	VTV172S	Bristol VRT/SL3/6LXB	Eastern Coach Works	H43/31F	1978	Ex East Midland, 1993
323	XRR173S	Bristol VRT/SL3/6LXB	Eastern Coach Works	O43/31F	1978	Ex East Midland, 1993
324	XAP644S	Bristol VRT/SL3/6LXB	Eastern Coach Works	H43/31F	1978	
327	LHG437T	Bristol VRT/SL3/501(6LXB)	Eastern Coach Works	H43/31F	1978	Ex Ribble, 1986
328	LHG438T	Bristol VRT/SL3/501(6LXB)	Eastern Coach Works	H43/31F	1978	Ex Ribble, 1986
336	XAP636S	Bristol VRT/SL3/6LXB	Eastern Coach Works	H43/31F	1978	
347	AAP647T	Bristol VRT/SL3/6LXB	Eastern Coach Works	H43/31F	1978	
348	AAP648T	Bristol VRT/SL3/6LXB	Eastern Coach Works	H43/31F	1978	
349	AAP649T	Bristol VRT/SL3/6LXB	Eastern Coach Works	H43/31F	1978	

Twelve Northern Counties-bodied Volvo Citybuses were delivered to Southdown in 1989, three of which are now allocated to Fife Scottish. These feature high-back seating and were prominent on the 701 limited stop Coastline Buses service. Seen passing through Southsea is 304, F304MYJ.
Siegmund de Reuther

The Bristol VRT is still operated in significant numbers within the group, though many have been replaced with new single-deck vehicles to enhance customer appeal. Typical of the type is 351, JWV251W, seen heading for Leigh Park.
Siegmund de Reuther

351-358

		Bristol VRT/SL3/6LXB		Eastern Coach Works		H43/31F*	1980	*351/3 are DPH43/31F

351	JWV251W	**353**	JWV253W	**355**	JWV255W	**356**	JWV256W	**358**	JWV258W
352	JWV252W								

359	DBV29W	Bristol VRT/SL3/6LXB	Eastern Coach Works	DPH43/31F	1980	Ex Ribble, 1986
360	AAP660T	Bristol VRT/SL3/6LXB	Eastern Coach Works	H43/31F	1978	
362	AAP662T	Bristol VRT/SL3/6LXB	Eastern Coach Works	H43/31F	1978	
365	DBV25W	Bristol VRT/SL3/6LXB	Eastern Coach Works	DPH43/31F	1980	Ex Ribble, 1986
366	JWV266W	Bristol VRT/SL3/680(6LXB)	Eastern Coach Works	H43/31F	1981	
367	JWV267W	Bristol VRT/SL3/680(6LXB)	Eastern Coach Works	DPH43/27F	1981	
368	JWV268W	Bristol VRT/SL3/680(6LXB)	Eastern Coach Works	H43/31F	1981	
369	JWV269W	Bristol VRT/SL3/680(6LXB)	Eastern Coach Works	DPH43/31F	1981	
372	AAP672T	Bristol VRT/SL3/6LXB	Eastern Coach Works	H43/31F	1978	
374	JWV274W	Bristol VRT/SL3/680(6LXB)	Eastern Coach Works	H43/31F	1981	
375	JWV275W	Bristol VRT/SL3/680	Eastern Coach Works	H43/31F	1981	
376	JWV976W	Bristol VRT/SL3/680(6LXB)	Eastern Coach Works	H43/31F	1981	
377	EAP977V	Bristol VRT/SL3/6LXB	Eastern Coach Works	H43/31F	1979	
380	EAP980V	Bristol VRT/SL3/6LXB	Eastern Coach Works	H43/31F	1979	
382	EAP982V	Bristol VRT/SL3/6LXB	Eastern Coach Works	H43/31F	1979	

391-397

		Bristol VRT/SL3/6LXB		Eastern Coach Works		H43/31F	1978	

391	VPR490S	**393**	VPR492S	**395**	YEL2T	**396**	YEL3T	**397**	YEL4T
392	VPR491S	**394**	HFG193T						

400	M490BFG	Volvo B6-9.9M	Alexander Dash	B35F	1994
401	M401BFG	Volvo B6-9.9M	Alexander Dash	B35F	1994
402	M402BFG	Volvo B6-9.9M	Alexander Dash	B35F	1994
403	M403BFG	Volvo B6-9.9M	Alexander Dash	B31F	1994

422-450

		Bristol VRT/SL3/6LXB		Eastern Coach Works		H43/31F	1979-81	

422	FDV818V	**435**	FDV839V	**440**	KRU840W	**446**	LFJ874W	**449**	LFJ875W
432	ELJ212V	**438**	KRU838W	**441**	KRU841W	**447**	LFJ881W	**450**	LFJ880W
433	FDV834V	**439**	KRU839W	**444**	KRU844W	**448**	LFJ870W		

460-467

		Iveco Daily 49.10		Reeve Burgess Beaver	B23F*	1989	Ex East Midland, 1993
							*460 is B25F

460	G910KWF	**461**	G911KWF	**463**	G913KWF	**464**	G914KWF	**467**	G917KWF

469-476

		Iveco Daily 49.10		Robin Hood City Nippy	B21F	1986	Ex Alder Valley, 1992

469	D469WPM	**470**	D470WPM	**471**	D471WPM	**473**	D473WPM	**476**	D476WPM

In addition to Volvo B6s, Stagecoach also operate the Dennis Dart in significant numbers. Seen at Eastbourne is 521, J521GCD, one of the large number allocated to Stagecoach South during 1992.
Tony Wilson

477	E201EPB	Iveco Daily 49.10	Robin Hood City Nippy	B25F	1987	Ex Alder Valley, 1992
478	E202EPB	Iveco Daily 49.10	Robin Hood City Nippy	B25F	1987	Ex Alder Valley, 1992
479	E203EPB	Iveco Daily 49.10	Robin Hood City Nippy	B25F	1987	Ex Alder Valley, 1992
480	E204EPB	Iveco Daily 49.10	Robin Hood City Nippy	B25F	1987	Ex Alder Valley, 1992
481	G921KWF	Iveco Daily 49.10	Reeve Burgess Beaver	B23F	1989	Ex East Midland, 1993
482	G922KWF	Iveco Daily 49.10	Reeve Burgess Beaver	B23F	1990	Ex East Midland, 1993
483	G923KWF	Iveco Daily 49.10	Reeve Burgess Beaver	B23F	1990	Ex East Midland, 1993
485	F695OPA	Iveco Daily 49.10	Carlyle Dailybus 2	B23F	1988	Ex Alder Valley, 1992

488-492
Iveco Daily 49.10 — Phoenix — B23F — 1990

488	G418RYJ	489	G419RYJ	490	G420RYJ	491	G421RYJ	492	G422RYJ

494	G864BPD	Iveco Daily 49.10	Carlyle Dailybus 2	B23F	1989	Ex Alder Valley, 1992

501-580
Dennis Dart 9.8SDL3017 — Alexander Dash — B41F* — 1991-92 — *535-80 are B40F

501	J501GCD	517	J517GCD	533	J533GCD	549	J549GCD	565	K565NHC
502	J502GCD	518	J518GCD	534	J534GCD	550	J550GCD	566	K566NHC
503	J503GCD	519	J519GCD	535	J535GCD	551	J551GCD	567	K567NHC
504	J504GCD	520	J520GCD	536	J536GCD	552	J552GCD	568	K568NHC
505	J505GCD	521	J521GCD	537	J537GCD	553	K553NHC	569	K569NHC
506	J506GCD	522	J522GCD	538	J538GCD	554	K554NHC	570	K570NHC
507	J507GCD	523	J523GCD	539	J539GCD	555	K655NHC	571	K571NHC
508	J508GCD	524	J524GCD	540	J540GCD	556	K556NHC	572	K572NHC
509	J509GCD	525	J525GCD	541	J541GCD	557	K557NHC	573	K573NHC
510	J510GCD	526	J526GCD	542	J542GCD	558	K558NHC	574	K574NHC
511	J511GCD	527	J527GCD	543	J543GCD	559	K559NHC	575	K575NHC
512	J512GCD	528	J528GCD	544	J544GCD	560	K660NHC	576	K576NHC
513	J513GCD	529	J529GCD	545	J545GCD	561	K561NHC	577	K577NHC
514	J514GCD	530	J530GCD	546	J546GCD	562	K562NHC	578	K578NHC
515	J515GCD	531	J531GCD	547	J547GCD	563	K563NHC	579	K579NHC
516	J516GCD	532	J532GCD	548	J548GCD	564	K564NHC	580	K580NHC

581	J701YRM	Dennis Dart 9.8DL3017	Alexander Dash	B41F	1991	Ex Cumberland, 1992
582	J702YRM	Dennis Dart 9.8DL3017	Alexander Dash	B41F	1991	Ex Cumberland, 1992
583	J703YRM	Dennis Dart 9.8DL3017	Alexander Dash	B41F	1992	Ex Cumberland, 1992

584-588
Dennis Dart 9.8DL3017 — Alexander Dash — B40F* — 1992 — *584 is B41F

584	K584ODY	585	K585ODY	586	K586ODY	587	K587ODY	588	K588ODY

The 1994 Showbus event at Duxford was the highlight of the bus rally season. Stagecoach was represented by many immaculate vehicles including Stagecoach South's 605, L605VCD, a Northern Counties-bodied B10M. Stagecoach vehicles received a number of awards at the show.
Phillip Stephenson

601-605

Volvo B10M-55 — Northern Counties Paladin — DP49F — 1994

601	L601VCD	602	L602VCD	603	L603VCD	604	L604VCD	605	L605VCD

606-658

Volvo B10M-55 — Alexander PS — DP48F — 1994 — 656-8 ex Ribble, 1994

606	L606TDY	613	M613APN	620	L620TDY	627	L627TDY	633	L633TDY
607	L607TDY	614	M614APN	621	L621TDY	628	L628TDY	634	L634TDY
608	L608TDY	615	M615APN	622	L622TDY	629	L629TDY	635	L635TDY
609	L609TDY	616	L616TDY	623	L623TDY	630	L625TDY	656	L346KCK
610	M610APN	617	L617TDY	624	L624TDY	631	L626TDY	657	L347KCK
611	M611APN	618	L618TDY	625	L625TDY	632	L627TDY	658	L338KCK
612	M612APN	619	L619TDY	626	L626TDY						

659	K789DAO	Volvo B10M-55	Alexander PS	DP48F	1993	Ex Cumberland, 1994
660	K790DAO	Volvo B10M-55	Alexander PS	DP48F	1993	Ex Cumberland, 1994
661	K791DAO	Volvo B10M-55	Alexander PS	DP48F	1993	Ex Cumberland, 1994
665	L345KCK	Volvo B10M-55	Alexander PS	DP48F	1994	Ex Ribble, 1994
668	AAP668T	Bristol VRT/SL3/6LXB	Eastern Coach Works	H43/28F	1979	
670	AAP670T	Bristol VRT/SL3/6LXB	Eastern Coach Works	H43/28F	1979	
671	AAP671T	Bristol VRT/SL3/6LXB	Eastern Coach Works	H43/28F	1979	

673-692

Bristol VRT/SL3/6LXB — Eastern Coach Works — H43/31F — 1979-80

673	EAP973V	684	EAP984V	686	EAP986V	688	EAP988V	691	EAP991V
678	EAP978V	685	EAP985V	687	EAP987V	690	EAP990V	692	EAP992V

693	ELJ213V	Bristol VRT/SL3/6LXB	Eastern Coach Works	H43/31F	1979	
696	EAP996V	Bristol VRT/SL3/6LXB	Eastern Coach Works	H43/31F	1980	
729	WKO129S	Bristol VRT/SL3/6LXB	Eastern Coach Works	H43/31F	1978	Ex Hastings & District, 1989
730	WKO130S	Bristol VRT/SL3/6LXB	Eastern Coach Works	H43/31F	1978	Ex Hastings & District, 1989
749	BKE849T	Bristol VRT/SL3/6LXB	Eastern Coach Works	H43/31F	1979	Ex Hastings & District, 1989
750	BKE850T	Bristol VRT/SL3/6LXB	Eastern Coach Works	H43/31F	1979	Ex Hastings & District, 1989
751	BKE851T	Bristol VRT/SL3/6LXB	Eastern Coach Works	H43/31F	1979	Ex Hastings & District, 1989
758	BKE858T	Bristol VRT/SL3/6LXB	Eastern Coach Works	H43/31F	1979	Ex Hastings & District, 1989
759	BKE859T	Bristol VRT/SL3/6LXB	Eastern Coach Works	H43/31F	1979	Ex Hastings & District, 1989

Representing the new single-deck scene on the south coast are *top,* 658, L338KCK, one of three B10Ms with Alexander PS bodywork intended for Manchester, but delivered new to Cumberland before being allocated to Chichester where they operate upgraded service X60 to Guildford. The identification of this mark 4 version of the B10M can be seen from the radiator grill, now mounted immediately behind the nearside front wheel, the 12-metre example being redesignated B10M-62. Stagecoach East Kent recently won the contract to operate the Canterbury park & ride service. Photographed shortly after its entry into service is 1405, M405DKM, one of five Dennis Lances, which features a Berkhof 2000 NLF 'compromise' low floor body, so called because the 340mm low floor extends approximately 70% of the vehicle length. The bus features a very broad isle and is equipped with an extendible platform to aid boarding for disabled passengers. *Malc McDonald/Nick Coleman*

760	BKE860T	Bristol VRT/SL3/6LXB	Eastern Coach Works	H43/31F	1979	Ex Hastings & District, 1989
761	RJT151R	Bristol VRT/SL3/6LXB	Eastern Coach Works	H43/31F	1977	
762	BKE862T	Bristol VRT/SL3/6LXB	Eastern Coach Works	H43/34F	1979	Ex Hastings & District, 1989
780	BAU180T	Bristol VRT/SL3/6LXB	Eastern Coach Works	H43/34F	1978	Ex East Midland, 1993
782	AET182T	Bristol VRT/SL3/6LXB	Eastern Coach Works	H43/34F	1979	Ex East Midland, 1993
786	AET186T	Bristol VRT/SL3/6LXB	Eastern Coach Works	H43/34F	1979	Ex East Midland, 1993
787	AET187T	Bristol VRT/SL3/6LXB	Eastern Coach Works	H43/34F	1979	Ex East Midland, 1993
800	C800SDY	Mercedes-Benz L608D	Alexander AM	B20F	1986	Ex Hastings & District, 1989
828	D228UHC	Mercedes-Benz L608D	Alexander AM	B20F	1986	Ex Hastings & District, 1989
830	D230UHC	Mercedes-Benz L608D	Alexander AM	B20F	1986	Ex Hastings & District, 1989

841-850

Mercedes-Benz 709D — Alexander Sprint — B23F* — 1990 — *841-3 are DP25F

841	G71APO	843	G73APO	845	G975ARV	847	G977ARV	849	H679BTP
842	G72APO	844	G974ARV	846	G976ARV	848	G978ARV	850	H680BTP

853-888

Mercedes-Benz 709D — Alexander Sprint — B25F — 1993

853	K853ODY	861	K861ODY	868	K868ODY	875	K875ODY	882	L882SDY
854	K854ODY	862	K862ODY	869	K869ODY	876	K876ODY	883	L883SDY
855	K855ODY	863	K863ODY	870	K870ODY	877	K877ODY	884	L884SDY
856	K856ODY	864	K864ODY	871	K871ODY	878	K878ODY	885	L885SDY
857	K857ODY	865	K865ODY	872	K872ODY	879	K879ODY	886	L886SDY
858	K858ODY	866	K866ODY	873	K873ODY	880	K880ODY	887	L887SDY
859	K859ODY	867	K867ODY	874	K874ODY	881	L881SDY	888	L188SDY
860	K860ODY								

950-985

Bristol VRT/SL3/6LXB — Eastern Coach Works — H43/31F — 1978-80 Ex Alder Valley, 1992

950	TPE156S	961	GGM81W	966	WJM826T	972	WJM832T	982	CJH142V
953	VPF283S	962	GGM82W	967	WJM827T	977	CJH117V	985	CJH145V
955	GGM85W	964	WJM824T	968	WJM828T	979	CJH119V	988	KKK888V
956	GGM86W	965	WJM825T	969	WJM829T	980	CJH120V	995	GGM105W
960	GGM80W								

1003	403DCD	Leyland Tiger TRCTL11/3R	Plaxton Paramount 3200	C50F	1983	
1004	BYJ919Y	Leyland Tiger TRCTL11/3R	Plaxton Paramount 3200	C50F	1983	
1005	UWP105	Leyland Tiger TRCTL11/3R	Plaxton Paramount 3200	C50F	1983	
1006	896HOD	Volvo B10M-61	Plaxton Paramount 3500 II	C40FT	1985	Ex Fife Scottish, 1991
1007	495FFJ	Volvo B10M-61	Plaxton Paramount 3500 II	C52F	1985	Ex Fife Scottish, 1991
1017	NFX667	Leyland Leopard PSU5E/4R	Plaxton Supreme V	C50F	1982	
1064	VSV564	Leyland Tiger TRCTL11/3R	Plaxton Paramount 3200 E	C49F	1983	Ex Hastings & District, 1989
1066	MSU466	Leyland Tiger TRCTL11/3RH	Duple 340	C53FT	1987	Ex Fife Scottish, 1991
1072	USV672	Leyland Tiger TRCTL11/3R	Plaxton Paramount 3200 E	C49F	1983	Ex Hastings & District, 1989
1084	C84PRP	Leyland Tiger TRCTL11/3R	Plaxton Paramount 3500 II	C46FT	1986	Ex United Counties, 1993
1094	GPJ894N	Leyland National 11351/1R		B49F	1975	Ex Alder Valley, 1992
1115	MFN115R	Leyland National 11351A/1R		B49F	1976	Ex East Kent, 1993
1118	MFN118R	Leyland National 11351A/1R		B49F	1976	Ex East Kent, 1993

1160-1166

Volvo B10M-62 — Plaxton Premiére Interurban DP51F — 1994

1160	M160CCD	1162	M162CCD	1164	M164CCD	1165	M165CCD	1166	M166CCD
1161	M161CCD	1163	M163CCD						

1170	ELJ208V	Leyland Leopard PSU3E/4R	Plaxton Supreme IV Express	C53F	1979	
1176	NPJ476R	Leyland National 11351A/1R		B49F	1976	Ex Alder Valley, 1992
1180	UMO180N	Leyland National 11351/1R		B49F	1974	Ex Alder Valley, 1992

1181-1189

Leyland National 11351A/1R — DP48F — 1977 Ex East Kent, 1993

1181	NFN81R	1183	NFN83R	1186	NFN86R	1188	NFN88R	1189	NFN89R
1182	NFN82R	1184	NFN84R	1187	NFN87R				

1193	YEL93Y	Leyland Leopard PSU5E/4R	Eastern Coach Works B51	DP52F	1982	
1194	YEL94Y	Leyland Leopard PSU5E/4R	Eastern Coach Works B51	DP55F	1982	

1201-1218

Leyland National 11351/1R — B49F — 1975 Ex Alder Valley, 1992

1201	HPK503N	1214	KPA365P	1215	KPA366P	1217	KPA368P	1218	KPA369P
1203	HPK505N								

1221	NEL121P	Leyland National 11351A/1R				B49F	1976	Ex East Midland, 1993
1223	KPA374P	Leyland National 11351/1R				B49F	1975	Ex Alder Valley, 1992
1227	KPA378P	Leyland National 11351/1R				B49F	1975	Ex Alder Valley, 1992
1228	KPA379P	Leyland National 11351/1R				B49F	1975	Ex Alder Valley, 1992
1232	KPA383P	Leyland National 11351/1R				B49F	1974	Ex Alder Valley, 1992
1236	KPA387P	Leyland National 11351A/1R				B49F	1976	Ex Alder Valley, 1992
1237	KPA388P	Leyland National 11351A/1R				B49F	1976	Ex Alder Valley, 1992
1238	KPA389P	Leyland National 11351A/1R				B49F	1976	Ex Alder Valley, 1992
1247	LPF605P	Leyland National 11351/1R/SC				B49F	1976	Ex Alder Valley, 1992

1253-1273		Leyland National 11351A/1R				B49F	1976-77	Ex Alder Valley, 1992
1253	NPJ474R	**1259**	NPJ480R	**1264**	NPJ485R	**1272**	TPE149S	**1273** TPE150S
1256	NPJ477R	**1261**	NPJ482R	**1271**	TPE148S			

1276	TPE169S	Leyland National 11351A/1R			DP45F	1978	Ex Alder Valley, 1992
1298	SGS504W	Leyland Tiger TRCTL11/3R	Plaxton Supreme IV		C50F	1981	Ex Alder Valley, 1992
1299	XGS762X	Leyland Tiger TRCTL11/3R	Plaxton Supreme IV		C51F	1981	Ex Alder Valley, 1992
1344	PJJ344S	Leyland National 10351A/1R			B41F	1977	Ex East Kent, 1993
1345	PJJ345S	Leyland National 10351A/1R			B41F	1977	Ex East Kent, 1993
1346	PJJ346S	Leyland National 10351A/1R			B41F	1977	Ex East Kent, 1993
1401	J401LKO	DAF SB220LC550	Optare Delta		B49F	1991	Ex East Kent, 1993
1402	J402LKO	DAF SB220LC550	Optare Delta		B49F	1991	Ex East Kent, 1993
1403	J403LKO	DAF SB220LC550	Optare Delta		B49F	1991	Ex East Kent, 1993

1404-1408		Dennis Lance 11SDA3201	Berkhof		B40F	1994	
1404	M404OKM	**1405**	M405OKM	**1406**	M406OKM	**1407** M407OKM	**1408** M408OKM

1546	GFN546N	Leyland National 10351/1R		B40F	1975	Ex East Kent, 1993
1552	GFN552N	Leyland National 10351/1R		B37F	1975	Ex East Kent, 1993
1559	NOE559R	Leyland National 11351A/1R		B30D	1976	Ex East Kent, 1993
1851	LFB851P	Leyland National 11351A/2R		B30D	1976	Ex East Kent, 1993

Seen in Canterbury Park & Ride livery is Optare Delta 1401, J401LKO, allocated to the East Kent operation. Until the East London operation joined Stagecoach these were the only Deltas operated by the group. *Phillip Stephenson*

1890-1900

Leyland National 11351A/1R — B49F — 1976 — Ex East Kent, 1993

1890	JJG890P	1893	JJG893P	1895	JJG895P	1898	JJG898P	1900	JJG900P
1892	JJG892P								

No.	Reg	Type	Body	Seats	Year	Notes
2701	C701FKE	Ford Transit 190D	Dormobile	B16F	1986	Ex East Kent, 1993
2712	C712FKE	Ford Transit 190D	Dormobile	B16F	1986	Ex East Kent, 1993
2742	C742HKK	Freight Rover Sherpa	Dormobile	B16F	1986	Ex East Kent, 1993
2891	G91VMM	Leyland Swift LBM6T/2RA	Wadham Stringer Vanguard	B34FL	1989	On loan from East Sussex CC
2892	G92VMM	Leyland Swift LBM6T/2RA	Wadham Stringer Vanguard	B34FL	1989	On loan from East Sussex CC
2901	F561HPP	MCW MetroRider MF158/9	MCW	B33F	1988	
2902	F562HPP	MCW MetroRider MF158/9	MCW	B33F	1988	
2903	F563HPP	MCW MetroRider MF158/9	MCW	B33F	1988	
2904	F564HPP	MCW MetroRider MF158/9	MCW	B33F	1988	
2906	416DCD	MCW MetroRider MF158/10	MCW	B31F	1988	
2907	417DCD	MCW MetroRider MF154/1	MCW	B31F	1988	
2908	418DCD	MCW MetroRider MF158/3	MCW	DP33F	1988	
2909	419DCD	MCW MetroRider MF154/16	MCW	DP28F	1988	

7016-7024

Bristol VRT/SL3/6LXB — Willowbrook — H43/31F — 1977-78 — Ex East Kent, 1993

7016	PJJ16S	7021	PJJ21S	7022	PJJ22S	7023	PJJ23S	7024	PJJ24S

No.	Reg	Type	Body	Seats	Year	Notes
7042	MFN42R	Bristol VRT/SL3/6LXB	Eastern Coach Works	H43/31F	1976	Ex East Kent, 1993
7043	MFN43R	Bristol VRT/SL3/6LXB	Eastern Coach Works	H43/31F	1976	Ex East Kent, 1993
7046	MFN46R	Bristol VRT/SL3/6LXB	Eastern Coach Works	H43/31F	1976	Ex East Kent, 1993

7604-7623

Bristol VRT/SL3/6LXB — Eastern Coach Works — CO43/31F — 1977-78

7604	UWV604S	7611	UWV611S	7614	UWV614S	7621	UWV621S	7623	UWV623S
7607	UWV607S	7613	UWV613S						

7650-7685

Bristol VRT/SL3/6LXB — Eastern Coach Works — H43/31F — 1980-81 — Ex East Kent, 1993
7655 was rebodied 1983

7650	XJJ650V	7658	XJJ658V	7665	XJJ665V	7672	BJG672V	7679	CJJ679W
7651	XJJ651V	7659	XJJ659V	7666	XJJ666V	7673	BJG673V	7680	SKL680X
7652	XJJ652V	7660	XJJ660V	7667	XJJ667V	7674	BJG674V	7681	SKL681X
7653	XJJ653V	7661	XJJ661V	7668	XJJ668V	7675	BJG675V	7682	SKL682X
7654	XJJ654V	7662	XJJ662V	7669	XJJ669V	7676	CJJ676W	7683	SKL683X
7655	XJJ655V	7663	XJJ663V	7670	XJJ670V	7677	CJJ677W	7684	SKL684X
7657	XJJ657V	7664	XJJ664V	7671	BJG671V	7678	CJJ678W	7685	SKL685X

7746-7755

MCW Metrobus Mk2 DR132/11 — MCW — H46/31F — 1988 — Ex East Kent, 1993

7746	E746SKR	7748	E748SKR	7750	E750SKR	7752	E752SKR	7754	E754UKR
7747	E747SKR	7749	E749SKR	7751	E751SKR	7753	E753SKR	7755	E755UKR

Photographed in Chichester is MCW MetroRider 2908, 418DCD, which has an index number previously carried by one of the famous Queen Mary class of Leyland Titan convertible open-top buses once operated by Southdown.
Phillip Stephenson

7761-7767

MCW Metrobus Mk2 DR132/15   MCW   DPH43/27F   1989   Ex East Kent, 1993

7761	F761EKM	7763	F763EKM	7765	F765EKM	7766	F766EKM	7767	F767EKM
7762	F762EKM	7764	F764EKM						

7771-7775

MCW Metrobus Mk2 DR132/14   MCW   H46/31F   1989   Ex East Kent, 1993

7771	F771EKM	7772	F772EKM	7773	F773EKM	7774	F774EKM	7775	F775EKM

7781	F781KKP	Scania N113DRB	Alexander RH	H47/33F	1989	Ex East Kent, 1993
7782	F782KKP	Scania N113DRB	Alexander RH	H47/33F	1989	Ex East Kent, 1993

7801-7810

Leyland Olympian ON2R56C16Z4 Northern Counties   H51/34F   1990   Ex East Kent, 1993

7801	H801BKK	7803	H803BKK	7805	H805BKK	7807	H807BKK	7809	H809BKK
7802	H802BKK	7804	H804BKK	7806	H806BKK	7808	H808BKK	7810	H810BKK

7811	J811NKK	Leyland Olympian ON2R50C13Z4	Northern Counties	H47/30F	1992	Ex East Kent, 1993
7812	J812NKK	Leyland Olympian ON2R50C13Z4	Northern Counties	H47/30F	1992	Ex East Kent, 1993
7813	J813NKK	Leyland Olympian ON2R50C13Z4	Northern Counties	H47/30F	1992	Ex East Kent, 1993
7814	J814NKK	Leyland Olympian ON2R50C13Z4	Northern Counties	H47/30F	1992	Ex East Kent, 1993

7821-7830

Leyland Olympian ON2R50C13Z4 Northern Counties   H47/30F   1993   7821-5 ex East Kent, 1993

7821	K821TKP	7823	K823TKP	7825	K823TKP	7827	L827BKK	7829	L829BKK
7822	K822TKP	7824	K824TKP	7826	L826BKK	7828	L828BKK	7830	L830BKK

7982	TFN982T	Bristol VRT/SL3/6LXB	Willowbrook	H43/31F	1978	Ex East Kent, 1993
7983	EAP983V	Bristol VRT/SL3/6LXB	Eastern Coach Works	H43/31F	1980	
7988	TFN988T	Bristol VRT/SL3/6LXB	Willowbrook	H43/31F	1978	Ex East Kent, 1993
8192	XSU912	MCW Metroliner HR131/2	MCW	C49FT	1984	Ex East Kent, 1993
8211	D211VEV	Scania K112CRB	Berkhof Esprite 350	C41DT	1987	Ex East Kent, 1993
8243	SIB8243	Volvo B10M-60	Plaxton Paramount 3500 III	C53F	1990	Ex East Kent, 1993
8245	LDZ3145	MCW Metroliner HR131/6	MCW	C49FT	1985	Ex East Kent, 1993
8246	XYK976	MCW Metroliner HR131/6	MCW	C49FT	1985	Ex East Kent, 1993
8399	XDU599	MCW Metroliner HR131/1	MCW	C49FT	1983	Ex East Kent, 1993
8831	UKE831X	Leyland Leopard PSU3G/4R	Eastern Coach Works B51	DP47F	1982	Ex East Kent, 1993
8837	BKR837Y	Leyland Leopard PSU3G/4R	Eastern Coach Works B51	DP47F	1982	Ex East Kent, 1993

8838-8842

Leyland Tiger TRCTL11/3R   Plaxton Paramount 3200 E   C53F*   1983   *8842 is DP51F; Ex East Kent, 1993

8838	TSU638	8839	TSU639	8840	TSU640	8841	TSU641	8842	TSU642

8850	WSU450	MCW Metroliner CR126/8	MCW	C51F	1984	Ex East Kent, 1993
8851	WSU451	MCW Metroliner CR126/8	MCW	C51F	1984	Ex East Kent, 1993
8852	WSU452	MCW Metroliner CR126/8	MCW	C51F	1984	Ex East Kent, 1993
8854	E854UKR	MCW Metroliner HR131/12	MCW	C51F	1988	Ex East Kent, 1993
8855	E855UKR	MCW Metroliner HR131/12	MCW	C51F	1988	Ex East Kent, 1993
8856	J856NKK	Scania K93CRB	Plaxton Paramount 3500 III	C49FT	1992	Ex East Kent, 1993

There are 146 MCW products in the Stagecoach group and almost 60% are MetroRiders. Metrobuses, 25 at Hull and 22 with East Kent form the next largest number. One of East Kent's Mark 2 Metrobuses photographed while working a rail replacement service.
Nick Coleman

8901-8908

8901-8908		Volvo B10M-60		Plaxton Expressliner		C49FT	1989	Ex East Kent, 1993	
8901	G901PKK	8903	G903PKK	8905	G905PKK	8907	G907PKK	8908	G908PKK
8902	G902PKK	8904	G904PKK	8906	G906PKK				

8909	J909NKP	Volvo B10M-60	Plaxton Expressliner	C46FT	1992	Ex East Kent, 1993
8910	K910TKP	Volvo B10M-60	Plaxton Expressliner 2	C49FT	1993	Ex East Kent, 1993
8911	M911WJK	Volvo B10M-60	Plaxton Expressliner 2	C49FT	1994	
8996	PFN873	Bova FHD12.280	Bova Futura	C49FT	1986	Ex East Kent, 1993

Special Events Vehicles:

0135	CD7045	Leyland G7	Short	O27/24R	1922	
0409	409DCD	Leyland Titan PD3/4	Northern Counties	FCO39/30F	1964	
0424	424DCD	Leyland Titan PD3/4	Northern Counties	FCO39/30F	1964	
0770	HKE690L	Bristol VRT/SL2/6LXB	Eastern Coach Works	O43/34F	1973	Ex Hastings & District, 1989
0813	UF4813	Leyland Titan TD1	Brush	O27/24R	1929	
0946	MFN946F	AEC Regent V 3D3RA	Park Royal	H40/32F	1967	Ex Hastings & District, 1989

Operating Companies:

Coastline: 5, 31/4/45, 120/2-32/5/9, 209/20-4/8-34/7-40/3-5, 304-9/36/47/51/5/6/9/65/7/8/72/5/6, 460/78/9/88-92, 551-69/74/9, 610-5/21-31/5/56-8/62/70/8-87/90-2/6, 787, 953, 1006, 1193/4, 1298, 2901-8, 7604/7/14

East Kent: 1-4/6-20/35/41/6-98, 149/61, 225-7/54-7, 461-7/81-3, 632-4/59-61, 1115/8/81-9, 1344-5, 1401-7, 1552, 1890-8, 1900, 2742, 7016-22/43, 7613/50-85, 7746-82, 7801-30, 7982/3, 8192, 8211/43-6, 8399, 8838-56, 8901-96

Hampshire Bus: 21-30/6-9/42/3, 100/4/6/19/52/4/64/6-8/86/90-2/6, 201-8/10-9/46-50, 321-3/53/8/66/9/74/7-82/91-7, 400-3/22-50, 524-40/2-50, 841-3/6-50, 950/6/65/6/77/88, 1003-5/17, 1160-6/70/6, 1221/47.

Hants & Surrey: 32/3, 162/89/94, 235/6, 469-77/80/5/94, 522/3/70-3/5-8/80-2/4-8, 759/80/2, 853-80, 955/60/2/8-72/9-85/95, 1007/94, 1180, 1201/3/5/8/23-38/53-76/99, 2712, 7611.

South Coast Buses: 101-3/5/7-18/40-8/55/57-60/3/5/9/72-80/2/95/7, 241/2, 301-3/24-8/48/52/60, 501-21/41/83, 601-9/16-20/68/71/3/88/93, 749-58/61/2/86, 800/28/30/44/5/81-88, 963/7, 1008-13/64-84, 1214/21, 2891/2, 2909, 7024, 7621/3.

Previous Registrations:

400DCD	RUF430X	420DCD	RUF433X, MSV533	TSU641	FKK841Y
401DCD	#	424DCD	424DCD, AOR158B	TSU642	FKK842Y
402DCD	#	495FFJ	B193CGA	USV672	FKL172Y
403DCD	XUF533Y	896HOD	B192CGA	UWP105	XUF535Y
405DCD	RUF435X	BYJ919Y	XUF534Y, 404DCD	VSV564	FKL171Y
406DCD	RUF436X	JNJ194V	HFG924V, DSV943	WSU448	A848OKK
407DCD	RUF437X	LDZ3144	B244JVA	WSU450	B850TKL
408DCD	#	LDZ3145	B245JVA	WSU451	B851TKL
410DCD	RUF438X	MSU466	D526ESG	WSU452	B852TKL
411DCD	RUF431X	NFX667	HHC367Y	WSU453	B853TKL
412DCD	#	OUF262W	JWV125W, LYJ145	XDU599	A543WOB, ABM399A
413DCD	#	PFN873	C996FKM	HUS451X	RUF434X, XLD244
415DCD	RUF429X	SIB8243	H826AHS	XMW285	A849OKK
416DCD	F816CWJ	SYC852	JWV126W	XSU912	B192JVA
417DCD	F817DWG	TSU638	FKK838Y	XSU913	A513HBC
418DCD	E518YWF	TSU639	FKK839Y	XYK976	B246JVA
419DCD	F565HPP	TSU640	FKK840Y	YLJ332	RUF432X

Recently replaced on vehicles but not yet re-assigned

Stagecoach South and its predecessors have a long history of providing open-top services to holidaymakers. The tradition continues as seen at Eastbourne Pier where 621, UWV621S was photographed while heading for Beachy Head. *Mike Harris*

UNITED COUNTIES

United Counties Omnibus Co Ltd, Rothersthorpe Avenue,
Northampton, NN4 9UT

Depots : St Johns, Bedford; Station Road, Corby; Stukeley Road, Huntingdon; Northampton Road, Kettering and Rothersthorpe Avenue, Northampton. **Outstations** : Daventry; Desborough; Higham Ferrers; Husbands Bosworth; Little Paxton; Milton Keynes; Nether Hayford; Stamford; Thrapston; Uppingham; Wellingborough; Wymington and Yardley Hastings.

46	E46MRP	Iveco Daily 49.10	Robin Hood City Nippy	B23F	1988	On loan to Selkent
47	E47MRP	Iveco Daily 49.10	Robin Hood City Nippy	B23F	1988	On loan to Selkent
49	E49MRP	Iveco Daily 49.10	Robin Hood City Nippy	B23F	1988	On loan to Selkent
50	E50MRP	Iveco Daily 49.10	Robin Hood City Nippy	B23F	1988	On loan to Selkent
54	F491NTR	Iveco Daily 49.10	Robin Hood City Nippy	B25F	1988	Ex Hampshire Bus, 1988
55	F492NTR	Iveco Daily 49.10	Robin Hood City Nippy	B25F	1988	Ex Hampshire Bus, 1988
56	F493NTR	Iveco Daily 49.10	Robin Hood City Nippy	B25F	1988	Ex Hampshire Bus, 1988
57	F57AVV	Iveco Daily 49.10	Robin Hood City Nippy	B23F	1989	
58	F58AVV	Iveco Daily 49.10	Robin Hood City Nippy	B23F	1989	
59	F59AVV	Iveco Daily 49.10	Robin Hood City Nippy	B23F	1989	
60	F60AVV	Iveco Daily 49.10	Robin Hood City Nippy	B23F	1989	

61-75

	Iveco Daily 49.10	Phoenix	B23F	1989	68-75 ex Magicbus, 1990

61	G61JVV	64	G64JVV	67	G67LVV	70	G27PSR	73	G33SSR
62	G62JVV	65	G65JVV	68	G28PSR	71	G31PSR	74	G40SSR
63	G63JVV	66	G66JVV	69	G29PSR	72	G32PSR	75	G41SSR

81	WLT682	Leyland Tiger TRCTL11/3RZ	Plaxton Paramount 3500 II	C46FT	1986	
82	WLT908	Leyland Tiger TRCTL11/3RZ	Plaxton Paramount 3500 II	C46FT	1986	
83	83CBD	Leyland Tiger TRCTL11/3RZ	Plaxton Paramount 3500	C48FT	1983	Ex Stagecoach Malawi, 1994
85	647DYE	Leyland Tiger TRCTL11/3RZ	Plaxton Paramount 3500 II	C46FT	1986	

92-96

	Volvo B10M-60	Plaxton Premiére 350	C49F	1992	Ex Park's, Hamilton, 1993
					94/5 ex Rainworth Travel, 1993

92	J430HDS	93	J439HDS	94	J445HDS	95	J446HDS	96	J450HDS

102	NBD102Y	Leyland Tiger TRCTL11/3R	Plaxton Paramount 3200 E	C53F	1983	
103	NBD103Y	Leyland Tiger TRCTL11/3R	Plaxton Paramount 3200 E	C53F	1983	
104	NBD104Y	Leyland Tiger TRCTL11/3R	Plaxton Paramount 3200 E	C53F	1983	
105	RBD397Y	Leyland Tiger TRCTL11/3R	Plaxton Paramount 3200 E	C53F	1983	

United Counties 114, A114TRP, is one of seven Leyland Tigers delivered in 1983 for express work from Northamptonshire, these feature Plaxton bodies with the express door. Now resplendent in Stagecoach corporate livery, and with Coachlinks names, is is seen heading for Northampton on service X61.

108-114

Leyland Tiger TRCTL11/3RH — Plaxton Paramount 3200 E — C50FT — 1983

108	A108TRP	110	A110TRP	112	A112TRP	113	A113TRP	114	A114TRP
109	A109TRP	111	A111TRP						

115	MSU465	Leyland Tiger TRCTL11/3RH	Duple 340	C46FT	1987	Ex Fife Scottish, 1992
116	VLT255	Leyland Tiger TRCTL11/3RZ	Duple Laser 2	C44FT	1985	Ex Stagecoach Malawi, 1993
120	C120PNV	Leyland Tiger TRCTL11/3RZ	Plaxton Paramount 3200 IIE	C57F	1986	
121	C121PNV	Leyland Tiger TRCTL11/3RZ	Plaxton Paramount 3200 IIE	C57F	1986	
122	C122PNV	Leyland Tiger TRCTL11/3RZ	Plaxton Paramount 3200 IIE	C57F	1986	
125	A729ANH	Volvo B10M-61	Plaxton Paramount 3200 E	C48F	1983	Ex Stagecoach, 1988
126	A728ANH	Volvo B10M-61	Plaxton Paramount 3200 E	C48F	1983	Ex Stagecoach, 1988

130-135

Volvo B10M-61 — Plaxton Paramount 3200 III — C53F* — 1988 — *133 is C57F

130	E130ORP	132	E132ORP	133	E133ORP	134	E134ORP	135	F135URP
131	E131ORP								

150-162

Volvo B10M-60 — Plaxton Premiére Interurban — DP53F* — 1993 — *155-162 are DP51F

150	K150DNV	153	K153DNV	156	L156JNH	159	L159JNH	161	L161JNH
151	K151DNV	154	K154DNV	157	L157JNH	160	L160JNH	162	L162JNH
152	K152DNV	155	L155JNH	158	L158JNH				

301-313

Iveco Daily 49.10 — Robin Hood City Nippy — B13F — 1987 — Ex Ribble, 1990-91

301	D406FRV	304	D728YBV	307	D735YBV	310	D610BCK	312	D619BCK
302	D724YBV	305	D729YBV	308	D859FOT	311	D616BCK	313	D725YBV
303	D726YBV	306	D731YBV	309	D613BCK				

314	D938ECR	Iveco Daily 49.10	Robin Hood City Nippy	B13F	1986	Ex Stagecoach, 1992
315	D22WNH	Iveco Daily 49.10	Robin Hood City Nippy	B13F	1986	Ex Bluebird, 1991
316	D771MUR	Iveco Daily 49.10	Robin Hood City Nippy	B13F	1986	Ex Bluebird, 1991
317	D26BVV	Iveco Daily 49.10	Robin Hood City Nippy	B13F	1987	Ex Bluebird, 1991

332-349

Mercedes-Benz 709D — Alexander Sprint — B25F — 1994

332	M332DRP	337	M337DRP	341	M341DRP	344	M344DRP	347	M347DRP
334	M334DRP	338	M338DRP	342	M342DRP	345	M345DRP	348	M348DRP
335	M335DRP	339	M339DRP	343	M343DRP	346	M346DRP	349	M349DRP
336	M336DRP	340	M340DRP						

350-383

Mercedes-Benz 709D — Alexander Sprint — B25F — 1992-93

350	K350ANV	357	K357ANV	364	L364JBD	371	L371JBD	378	L378JBD
351	K351ANV	358	K358ANV	365	L365JBD	372	L372JBD	379	L379JBD
352	K352ANV	359	K359ANV	366	L366JBD	373	L373JBD	380	L380JBD
353	K353ANV	360	L360JBD	367	L367JBD	374	L374JBD	381	L381NBD
354	K354ANV	361	L361JBD	368	L368JBD	375	L375JBD	382	L382NBD
355	K355ANV	362	L362JBD	369	L369JBD	376	L376JBD	383	L383NBD
356	K356ANV	363	L363JBD	370	L370JBD	377	L377JBD		

401-422

Volvo B6-9.9M — Alexander Dash — B40F — 1993

401	L401JBD	406	L406JBD	411	L411JBD	415	L415JBD	419	L419JBD
402	L402JBD	407	L407JBD	412	L412JBD	416	L416JBD	420	L420JBD
403	L403JBD	408	L408JBD	413	L413JBD	417	L417JBD	421	L421JBD
404	L404JBD	409	L409JBD	414	L414JBD	418	L418JBD	422	L422MVV
405	L405JBD	410	L410JBD						

423-430

Volvo B6-9.9M — Alexander Dash — B40F — 1994

423	L423XVV	425	L425XVV	427	L427XVV	429	M429BNV	430	M430BNV
424	L424XVV	426	L426XVV	428	L428XVV				

500	LFR862X	Leyland National 2 NL106AL11/1R	B44F	1981	Ex Cumberland, 1993
501	LFR864X	Leyland National 2 NL106AL11/1R	B44F	1982	Ex Cumberland, 1993

United Counties provide the commuter with many services in the northern reaches of the Home Counties, many using the Plaxton Interurban coach designed to meet Stagecoach's needs for this type of vehicle. Seen in Rushden High Street, while heading for Kettering is 157, L157JNH. *A Fulcherr*

1993 saw many new buses delivered to United Counties including 22 Volvo B6s with several being allocated to Bedford. Photographed at the bus station at in that town is 409, L409JBD. *Keith Grimes.*

Three tri-axle Leyland Olympians are operated by Stagecoach, two with high-back seating work from Cumberland's Barrow depot, while the third has bus seats and works with United Counties. Here 600, F110NES is seen with Stagecoach Holdings transfers. *Tony Wilson*

600	F110NES	Leyland Olympian ON6LXCT/5RZ Alexander RL		H66/44F	1989	Ex East Midland, 1992

601-611

Leyland Olympian ONLXB/1R   Eastern Coach Works   H45/32F*   1981   *601 is DPH45/27F *602/6 are DPH41/27F

601	ARP601X	604	ARP604X	606	ARP606X	608	ARP608X	610	ARP610X
602	ARP602X	605	ARP605X	607	ARP607X	609	ARP609X	611	ARP611X

612	WLT528	Leyland Olympian ONLXB/1RV	Alexander RL	H43/30F	1987	Ex Bluebird, 1991
613	D383XRS	Leyland Olympian ONLXB/1RV	Alexander RL	H43/30F	1987	Ex Bluebird, 1991
614	WLT512	Leyland Olympian ONLXB/1RV	Alexander RL	H47/30F	1987	Ex Bluebird, 1991
615	685DYE	Leyland Olympian ONLXB/1RV	Alexander RL	H47/30F	1987	Ex Bluebird, 1991
616	GSO6V	Leyland Olympian ONLXB/1RV	Alexander RL	H47/30F	1987	Ex Bluebird, 1991
617	GSO7V	Leyland Olympian ONLXB/1RV	Alexander RL	H47/30F	1987	Ex Bluebird, 1991
618	GSO2V	Leyland Olympian ONLXB/1RV	Alexander RL	H47/30F	1986	Ex Bluebird, 1994

620-649

Leyland Olympian ONLXB/2RZ   Alexander RL   H51/36F*   1988-89   *635-644 are H51/34F *645-9 are DPH51/31F

620	F620MSL	626	F626MSL	632	F632MSL	638	F638YRP	644	G644EVV
621	F621MSL	627	F627MSL	633	F633MSL	639	G639EVV	645	G645EVV
622	F622MSL	628	F628MSL	634	F634MSP	640	G640EVV	646	G646EVV
623	F623MSL	629	F629MSL	635	F635YRP	641	G641EVV	647	G647EVV
624	F624MSL	630	F630MSL	636	F636YRP	642	G642EVV	648	G648EVV
625	F625MSL	631	F631MSL	637	F637YRP	643	G643EVV	649	G649EVV

650-654

Leyland Olympian ON2R56G13Z4 Alexander RL   H51/34F   1990

650	H650VVV	651	H651VVV	652	H652VVV	653	H653VVV	654	H654VVV

655-670

Leyland Olympian ON2R50G13Z4 Northern Counties Palatine   H47/29F   1992

655	K655UNH	658	K658UNH	661	K661UNH	664	K664UNH	668	K668UNH
656	K656UNH	659	K659UNH	662	K662UNH	665	K665UNH	669	K669UNH
657	K657UNH	660	K660UNH	663	K663UNH	667	K667UNH	670	K670UNH

Electronic destination equipment fitted to early Leyland Olympians at United Counties feature a shallow name box, and small route number indicator. The arrangement is seen in this picture of 604, APR604X, taken in St Paul's Square, Bedford. *Mike Harris*

671-685

Volvo Olympian YN2RV18Z4   Alexander RL   H47/29F   1993

671	L671HNV	674	L674HNV	677	L677HNV	680	L680HNV	683	L683HNV
672	L672HNV	675	L675HNV	678	L678HNV	681	L681HNV	684	L684HNV
673	L673HNV	676	L676HNV	679	L679HNV	682	L682HNV	685	L685JBD

708-713

Leyland Olympian ON2R56C13Z4 Alexander RL   H47/32F   1992   Ex Fife Scottish, 1994

708	J808WFS	710	K710ASC	711	K711ASC	712	K712ASC	713	K713ASC
709	K709ASC							

714	J620GCR	Leyland Olympian ON2R56G13Z4	Alexander RL	H47/30F	1991	Ex Bluebird, 1994
715	J621GCR	Leyland Olympian ON2R56G13Z4	Alexander RL	H47/30F	1991	Ex Bluebird, 1994
716	J622GCR	Leyland Olympian ON2R56G13Z4	Alexander RL	H47/30F	1991	Ex Bluebird, 1994

721-740

Bristol VRT/SL3/6LXB   Eastern Coach Works   H43/31F   1980-81 Ex Devon General, 1988-89

721	LFJ862W	725	LFJ854W	732	FDV838V	735	LFJ864W	738	FDV835V
722	LFJ863W	726	LFJ855W	733	LFJ868W	736	LFJ865W	739	LFJ869W
723	LFJ853W	727	LFJ879W	734	FDV812V	737	FDV811V	740	FDV832V
724	LFJ852W	731	FDV809V					

744	LFJ878W	Bristol VRT/SL3/6LXC	Eastern Coach Works	H43/31F	1981	Ex Devon General, 1989
750	FAO417V	Bristol VRT/SL3/6LXB	Eastern Coach Works	H43/31F	1980	Ex Cumberland, 1992
751	FAO418V	Bristol VRT/SL3/6LXB	Eastern Coach Works	H43/31F	1980	Ex Cumberland, 1992
752	FAO419V	Bristol VRT/SL3/6LXB	Eastern Coach Works	H43/31F	1980	Ex Cumberland, 1992
794	GRP794L	Bristol VRT/SL2/6LX	Eastern Coach Works	H39/31F	1973	
839	LBD839P	Bristol VRT/SL3/6LX	Eastern Coach Works	H43/31F	1975	

849-891

Bristol VRT/SL3/6LXB   Eastern Coach Works   H43/31F   1976-78

849	OVV849R	870	TNH870R	876	WBD876S	885	XNV885S	889	XNV889S
856	OVV856R	871	TNH871R	878	XNV878S	886	XNV886S	890	XNV890S
862	RRP862R	872	TNH872R	879	XNV879S	887	XNV887S	891	XNV891S
863	RRP863R	873	TNH873R	880	XNV880S	888	XNV888S		

900	BAU178T	Bristol VRT/SL3/6LXB	Eastern Coach Works	H43/31F	1978	Ex East Midland, 1993	
901	BAU179T	Bristol VRT/SL3/6LXB	Eastern Coach Works	H43/31F	1978	Ex East Midland, 1993	

902-967

Bristol VRT/SL3/6LXB — Eastern Coach Works — H43/31F — 1978-81

902	CBD902T	915	HBD915T	930	SNV930W	944	URP944W	954	VVV954W
903	CBD903T	916	HBD916T	931	SNV931W	945	URP945W	961	VVV961W
908	FRP908T	917	HBD917T	935	SNV935W	948	VVV948W	962	VVV962W
909	FRP909T	919	HBD919T	936	SNV936W	949	VVV949W	963	VVV963W
910	FRP910T	920	LBD920V	937	SNV937W	950	VVV950W	965	VVV965W
911	FRP911T	921	LBD921V	939	URP939W	952	VVV952W	966	VVV966W
912	FRP912T	923	LBD923V	940	URP940W	953	VVV953W	967	VVV967W
914	HBD914T	926	ONH926V	941	URP941W				

970-974

Bristol VRT/SL3/6LXB — Eastern Coach Works — H43/31F — 1980 — Ex Hampshire Bus, 1988

970	KRU843W	971	KRU845W	972	KRU846W	973	KRU847W	974	KRU852W

Previous Registrations:

647DYE	C85PRP	GSO7V	D377XRS
685DYE	D379XRS	MSU465	D525ESG
83CBD	A294ANH	RBD397Y	NBD105Y, 83CBD
A728ANH	A800TGG, 4009SC, A332SNH, WLT908	VLT255	B357KNH, Malawi ?,
A729ANH	A798TGG, 7878SC, A320SNH, 647DYE	WLT512	D384XRS
D859FOT	D856FOT	WLT528	D382XRS
GSO2V	C472SSO	WLT682	C81PRP
GSO6V	D376XRS	WLT908	C82PRP

Livery variations: National Express: 92-6, 115.

Representing the United Counties Bristol VRTs is 750, FAO417V, an example transferred from Cumberland in 1992. *David Cole*

WESTERN

Western Scottish Buses Ltd, Nursery Avenue, Kilmarnock, KA1 3JD

Depots :Waggon Road, Ayr; Ayr Road, Cumnock; Eastfield Road, Dumfries; Argyll Road, Dunoon; Vicarton Street, Girvan; Nursery Avenue, Kilmarnock; Kirkcudbright; Brodick; Isle of Arran; Pointhouse, Rothesay; Lewis Street, Stranraer; Whithorn.

S100u	PSG842P	Seddon Pennine 7	Alexander AT	C24DL	1976	
R101u	XSJ656T	Leyland Fleetline FE30AGR	Northern Counties	O44/31F	1978	
R102u	HDS566H	Daimler Fleetline CRG6LX	Alexander D	O44/31F	1970	Ex Clydeside Scottish, 1989
H105	VLT81	Duple 425 SDAK1503	Duple	C51FT	1986	
H106	VLT206	Duple 425 SDAK1503	Duple	C54FT	1986	
H107	VLT54	Duple 425 SDAK1503	Duple	C54FT	1985	
H108	J8WSB	Plaxton 425	Lorraine	C53F	1992	
N111	803DYE	Dennis Javelin 12SDA2105	Plaxton Paramount 3200 III	C50F	1991	
N113	J13WSB	Dennis Javelin 12SDA1929	Plaxton Paramount 3200 III	C53F	1992	
N114	J14WSB	Dennis Javelin 12SDA1919	Plaxton Paramount 3200 III	C53F	1992	
N115	J15WSB	Dennis Javelin 12SDL2102	Plaxton Premiére 320	C53F	1992	

N116-120

		Dennis Dorchester SDA811	Alexander TC	C55F	1987	

N116	WLT526	N117	FSU737	N118	WLT415	N119	VLT73	N120	WLT447

N142	VLT272	Dennis Dorchester SDA810	Plaxton Paramount 3500 II	C55F	1985	
L170	G262EHD	DAF SB2305DHTD585	Plaxton Paramount 3200 III	C57F	1989	Ex Arran Coaches, 1994
L172	13CLT	Leyland Tiger TRCTL11/3RZ	Duple 340	C49FT	1987	Ex Kelvin Central, 1990
L173	WLT546	Leyland Tiger TRCTL11/3RZ	Duple 340	C49FT	1987	Ex Kelvin Central, 1990

V191-197

		Volvo B10M-61	Plaxton Paramount 3500	C44FT*	1985	*Seating varies

V191	VCS391	V194	VLT37	V195	WLT978	V196	WLT465	V197	WLT697

V198	WLT720	Volvo B10M-61	Berkhof Esprite	C53F	1985	
F200u	B764DEG	Ford Transit 150	Dormobile	B16F	1985	Ex Arran Coaches, 1994

Z201-218

		Mercedes-Benz L608D	Alexander AM	B21F	1986	Ex Kelvin Scottish, 1987

Z201	C101KDS	Z207	D107NUS	Z210	D110NUS	Z213	D113NUS	Z216	D116NUS
Z204	C104KDS	Z208	D108NUS	Z211	D111NUS	Z214	D114NUS	Z217	D117NUS
Z205	C105KDS	Z209	D109NUS	Z212	D112NUS	Z215	D115NUS	Z218	D118NUS
Z206	C106KDS								

Z219	L882LFS	Mercedes-Benz 709D	Alexander Sprint	B25F	1993	
Z220	L883LFS	Mercedes-Benz 709D	Alexander Sprint	B25F	1993	
Z221	G574FSD	Mercedes-Benz 709D	Reeve Burgess Beaver	B25F	1990	Ex Arran Coaches, 1994

Western Scottish was the one member of the Scottish Bus group to be registered as an English company, a legacy of English ownership of its predecessor company in the 1920s! Since purchase by Stagecoach the registered office has moved to Ribble's headquarters at Preston. A variety of vehicle types were included in the fleet at the time of takeover, including Renault-Dodge S56s that have now been supplemented by further examples from Fife Scottish. Seen in Dumfries is DD281, D301SDS. *Andrew Hamilton*

D222-260

Renault-Dodge S56 — Alexander AM — B25F* — 1987 — *D258 is DP25F

D222	D222NCS	**D230**	D230NCS	**D238**	D238NCS	**D246**	D246NCS	**D254** D254NCS
D223	D223NCS	**D231**	D231NCS	**D239**	D239NCS	**D247**	D247NCS	**D255** D255NCS
D224	D224NCS	**D232**	D232NCS	**D240**	D240NCS	**D248**	D248NCS	**D256** D256NCS
D225	D225NCS	**D233**	D233NCS	**D241**	D241NCS	**D249**	D249NCS	**D257** D257NCS
D226	D226NCS	**D234**	D234NCS	**D242**	D242NCS	**D250**	D250NCS	**D258** D258NCS
D227	D227NCS	**D235**	D235NCS	**D243**	D243NCS	**D251**	D251NCS	**D259** D259NCS
D228	D228NCS	**D236**	D236NCS	**D244**	D244NCS	**D252**	D252NCS	**D260** D260NCS
D229	D229NCS	**D237**	D237NCS	**D245**	D245NCS	**D253**	D253NCS	

Z262-271

Mercedes-Benz L608D — Alexander AM — B21F* — 1986 — Ex Kelvin Scottish, 1987
*Z271 is DP21F

Z262	D122NUS	**Z264**	D124NUS	**Z268**	D128NUS	**Z270**	D130NUS	**Z271** D121NUS
Z263	D123NUS	**Z266**	D136NUS	**Z269**	D129NUS			

Z272	E638YUS	Mercedes-Benz 609D	Reeve Burgess	C19F	1988	Ex Arran Coaches, 1994
T273	D94EKV	Peugeot-Talbot Freeway	Talbot	DP12FL	1987	Ex Sochulbus, Ashford, 1992

T274-278

Peugeot-Talbot Freeway — Talbot — DP12FL — 1989-90

T274	F334JHS	**T275**	F335JHS	**T276**	F336JHS	**T277**	G825VGA	**T278** G831VGA

Z279	L577NSB	Mercedes-Benz 709D	Dormobile Routemaker	B12FL	1993	Ex Arran Coaches, 1994
Z280	L578NSB	Mercedes-Benz 709D	Dormobile Routemaker	B12FL	1993	Ex Arran Coaches, 1994

D281-289

Renault-Dodge S56 — Alexander AM — B25F* — 1987 — Ex Clydeside Scottish, 1989
*D281 is DP25F

D281	D301SDS	**D283**	D303SDS	**D285**	D305SDS	**D287**	D307SDS	**D289** D309SDS
D282	D302SDS	**D284**	D304SDS	**D286**	D306SDS			

D290-296

Renault-Dodge S46 — Dormobile — B25F — 1987 — Ex Fife Scottish, 1994

D290	E634DCK	**D292**	E637DCK	**D294**	E643DCK	**D295**	E644DCK	**D296** E646DCK
D291	E636DCK	**D293**	E640DCK					

N301-310

Dennis Dart 9.8SDL3017 — Alexander Dash — B40F — 1992

N301	J301BRM	**N303**	J303BRM	**N305**	J305BRM	**N307**	J307BRM	**N309** J309BRM
N302	J302BRM	**N304**	J304BRM	**N306**	J306BRM	**N308**	J308BRM	**N310** J310BRM

V312-341

Volvo B6-9.9M — Alexander Dash — DP40F — 1994

V312	M772BCS	**V321**	M721BCS	**V326**	M726BCS	**V334**	M734BSJ	**V338** M738BSJ
V313	M773BCS	**V322**	M722BCS	**V327**	M727BCS	**V335**	M735BSJ	**V339** M739BSJ
V318	M718BCS	**V323**	M723BCS	**V332**	M732BSJ	**V336**	M736BSJ	**V340** M740BSJ
V319	M719BCS	**V324**	M724BCS	**V333**	M733BSJ	**V337**	M737BSJ	**V341** M741BSJ
V320	M720BCS	**V325**	M725BCS					

V351-358

Volvo B6-9.9M — Alexander Dash — B40F — 1994

V351	M674SSX	**V353**	M676SSX	**V355**	M678SSX	**V357**	M680SSX	**V358** M681SSX
V352	M675SSX	**V354**	M677SSX	**V356**	M679SSX			

N399	L208PSB	Dennis Dart	Marshall C36	B39F	1994	Ex Arran Coaches, 1994

N403-410

Dennis Dorchester SDA801 — Plaxton Paramount 3200 Ex — C49F — 1983 — N404/5/7-10 ex Clydeside, 1989

N403	703DYE	**N405**	WLT727	**N407**	WLT830	**N409**	WLT444	**N410** WLT874
N404	VLT104	**N406**	WLT794	**N408**	VCS376			

N411-420

Dennis Dorchester SDA810 — Plaxton Paramount 3500 — C55F* — 1985 — N416-20 ex Clydeside 2000, 1993
*N413/4 are C51F

N411	WLT441	**N413**	YSV730	**N415**	VLT245	**N417**	B986EGG	**N419** B981EGG
N412	VLT226	**N414**	YSV735	**N416**	B987EGG	**N418**	B985EGG	**N420** B979EGG

Western Scottish operate both Dennis Darts and Volvo B6s, all with Alexander Dash bodywork. Ten Dennis' were delivered in 1992 while the Volvos have arrived during 1994 and can be found on Kilmarnock town services. Examples of both types are RN306, J306BRM seen in Dunoon, and KV356, M679SSX. *Murdoch Currie*

One of the early repaints into Stagecoach livery is AN407, WLT830 seen in Renfield Street, Glasgow. It is a Dennis Dorchester with Plaxton Paramount 3200 bodywork. Outside the Western Scottish operation the only other Dorchesters are a pair operating at Hull. *Murdoch Currie*

N421	WLT501	Dennis Dorchester SDA811	Alexander TC	C55F	1987	
V423	WLT439	Volvo B10M-61	Duple Dominant IV	C51F	1981	
V424	WLT416	Volvo B10M-61	Duple Dominant IV	C55F	1981	Ex Clydeside Scottish, 1989
V426u	TOS524X	Volvo B10M-61	Duple Dominant IV	C55F	1982	Ex Clydeside Scottish, 1989
V427	TOS550X	Volvo B10M-61	East Lancashire (1994)	DP51F	1982	
V428	FSU739	Volvo B10M-61	Duple Dominant IV	C46FT	1982	
V429u	VLT219	Volvo B10M-61	Duple Dominant IV	C46FT	1981	Ex Clydeside Scottish, 1989
V430	VLT154	Volvo B10M-61	Duple Dominant IV	C55F	1981	Licenced to Scottish Citylink
V431	WGB646W	Volvo B10M-61	East Lancashire (1994)	DP51F	1981	
V432u	WGB645W	Volvo B10M-61	Duple Dominant IV	C51F	1981	Ex Clydeside Scottish, 1989

S434-482

		Seddon Pennine 7	Alexander AT	C49F*	1979-80	*S438/9 are C45F, S470 is DP53F
						S436/7/9/40/57-72/9 are ex Clydeside Scottish, 1988-89

S434	DSD934V	**S444**	DSD944V	**S452**	DSD952V	**S462**	DSD962V
S435	DSD935V	**S445**	DSD945V	**S453**	DSD953V	**S464**	DSD964V
S436	DSD936V	**S447**	DSD947V	**S454**	DSD954V	**S470**	DSD970V
S437	DSD937V	**S448**	DSD948V	**S455**	DSD955V	**S472**	DSD972V
S439	WGA908V	**S449**	DSD949V	**S456**	DSD956V	**S473**	DSD973V
S440	DSD940V	**S450**	DSD950V	**S457**	DSD957V	**S474**	DSD974V
S442	DSD942V	**S451**	DSD951V	**S460**	DSD960V	**S475**	DSD975V
S443	DSD943V						

S476	DSD976V
S477	DSD977V
S478	DSD978V
S479	DSD979V
S480	DSD980V
S481	DSD981V
S482	DSD982V

V486-491

		Volvo B10M-61	Duple Goldliner IV	C46FT*	1982-83 *V488/9 are C53F

V486	TOS720X	**V488**	WLT538	**V489**	WLT774	**V490**	WLT809	**V491**	WLT915
V487	GSU950						

S518-546

		Seddon Pennine 7	Alexander AY	B53F*	1978-80 *S526 is DP49F

S518w	YSD818T	**S525**w	ASD825T	**S531**w	ASD831T	**S535**w	ASD835T
S519w	YSD819T	**S526**w	ASD826T	**S532**w	ASD832T	**S536**w	ASD836T
S520w	YSD820T	**S527**w	ASD827T	**S533**w	ASD833T	**S537**w	ASD837T
S522w	YSD822T	**S529**w	ASD829T	**S534**w	ASD834T	**S542**w	ASD842T

S543w	ASD843T
S544w	ASD844T
S545w	DSD983V
S546w	DSD984V

One of the Duple-bodied Volvo B10Ms was rebodied in 1994 with an East Lancashire bus body. Now re-registered TOS550X, AV427 is seen in Aye at the end of August 1994. *Murdoch Currie*

S551-564

				Seddon Pennine 7		Alexander AY	DP49F	1979	

S551u	BSD851T	S553u	BSD853T	S558u	BSD858T	S560u	BSD860T	S563u	BSD863T
S552u	BSD852T	S556u	BSD856T	S559u	BSD859T	S562u	BSD862T	S564u	BSD864T

E571	HCS350N	Bedford YRQ	Plaxton Derwent	DP45F	1975	Ex Arran Coaches, 1994
E572	CCS459T	Bedford YMT	Duple Dominant Express	C53F	1979	Ex Arran Coaches, 1994
E573	MCS139W	Bedford YLQ	Duple Dominant II	C45F	1981	Ex Arran Coaches, 1994
E574	MCS138W	Bedford YMT	Duple Dominant II Express	C53F	1981	Ex Arran Coaches, 1994
E575	FCY284W	Bedford YMQ	Duple Dominant	DP45F	1980	Ex Arran Coaches, 1994
E576	FCY286W	Bedford YMQ	Duple Dominant	DP45F	1980	Ex Arran Coaches, 1994
E577	FCY294W	Bedford YMQ	Duple Dominant	B45F	1981	Ex Arran Coaches, 1994
E578	HVY132X	Bedford YMT	Plaxton Bustler	B55F	1982	Ex Arran Coaches, 1994
E579	D167TRA	Bedford YMT	Duple Dominant	B55F	1986	Ex Arran Coaches, 1994
E580	D917GRU	Bedford YMT	Plaxton Derwent	B53F	1987	Ex Arran Coaches, 1994
E581	D799USB	Bedford YMT	Duple Dominant	B55F	1987	Ex Arran Coaches, 1994
E582	D918GRU	Bedford YMT	Plaxton Derwent	B53F	1987	Ex Arran Coaches, 1994
E583	E849AAO	Bedford YNV	Plaxton Paramount 3200 III	C53F	1987	Ex Arran Coaches, 1994
L601	C802KBT	Leyland Cub CU435	Optare	DP33F	1986	Ex Arran Coaches, 1994
L629	GMS285S	Leyland Leopard PSU3E/4R	Alexander AYS	B53F	1978	Ex Kelvin Scottish, 1987
L630	GMS292S	Leyland Leopard PSU3D/4R	Alexander AYS	B53F	1978	Ex Kelvin Scottish, 1987

L633-699

		Leyland Leopard PSU3E/4R*	Alexander AY	B53F*	1977-80	*L637 is DP49F

*L667/70/1/6/8-80/5/91-3 are PSU3D/4R; L633/95-7 ex Clydeside Scottish, 1989

L633	GCS33V	L649	GCS49V	L662	GCS62V	L678	TSJ78S	L693	TSJ33S
L637	GCS37V	L651	GCS51V	L665	GCS65V	L679	TSJ79S	L695	BSJ895T
L638	GCS38V	L653	GCS53V	L667	TSJ67S	L680	TSJ80S	L696	BSJ896T
L641	GCS41V	L657	GCS57V	L669	GCS69V	L685	TSJ85S	L697	BSJ917T
L645	GCS45V	L658	GCS58V	L670	TSJ70S	L691	TSJ31S	L698	BSJ930T
L647	GCS47V	L660	GCS60V	L671	TSJ71S	L692	TSJ32S	L699	BSJ931T
L648	GCS48V	L661	GCS61V	L676	TSJ76S				

L701	UIB3541	Leyland National 11351A/1R		B48F	1978	Ex Kelvin Central, 1989

L702-706 Leyland National 11351A/3R   B48F 1978-79 Ex British Airways, Heathrow, 1993

L702	UIB3542	**L703**	UIB3543	**L704**	OIW7024	**L705**	OIW7025	**L706**	UIB3076

L707w	MHD336L	Leyland National 1151/1R/0501	B50F	1972	Ex Arran Coaches, 1994
L708w	PTF732L	Leyland National 1151/2R/0402	B52F	1973	Ex Arran Coaches, 1994
L709w	NHA256M	Leyland National 1151/1R/2501	B51F	1973	Ex Arran Coaches, 1994

L771-791 Leyland National 2 NL116L11/1R   B52F*   1980-81 Ex Kelvin Scottish, 1988
*L774-7/80/5/7-91 are B48F

L771	WAS771V	**L776**	MDS866V	**L780**	YFS308W	**L784**	RFS584V	**L788**	WAS768V
L773	RFS583V	**L777**	MDS859V	**L781**	MSO18W	**L785**	NLS985W	**L789**	NLS989W
L774	YFS304W	**L778**	MDS858V	**L782**	RFS582V	**L786**	SNS826W	**L790**	YFS310W
L775	MDS865V	**L779**	RFS579V	**L783**	NLS983W	**L787**	MSO17W	**L791**	YFS309W

L792	KRS540V	Leyland National 2 NL106L11/1R		B41F	1980	Ex Bluebird, 1993
L793	KRS542V	Leyland National 2 NL106L11/1R		B41F	1980	Ex Bluebird, 1993
L795	MSO10W	Leyland National 2 NL106L11/1R		B41F	1980	Ex Bluebird, 1993
L796	NLP388V	Leyland National 2 NL106L11/3R		B48F	1980	Ex British Airways, Heathrow, 1993
L797	JTF971W	Leyland National 2 NL106AL11/1R		B52F	1981	Ex Mitchell, Plean, 1994
A800	UNA853S	Leyland Atlantean AN68A/1R	Park Royal	H43/32F	1977	Ex GM Buses, 1991
A801	UNA863S	Leyland Atlantean AN68A/1R	Park Royal	H43/32F	1977	Ex GM Buses, 1991
A802	WVM884S	Leyland Atlantean AN68A/1R	Park Royal	H43/32F	1978	Ex GM Buses, 1991
A804	ANA211T	Leyland Atlantean AN68A/1R	Northern Counties	H43/32F	1978	Ex GM Buses, 1991
A805	BNC936T	Leyland Atlantean AN68A/1R	Park Royal	H43/32F	1979	Ex GM Buses, 1991
A806	RJA702R	Leyland Atlantean AN68A/1R	Northern Counties	H43/32F	1977	Ex GM Buses, 1991
A807	UNA772S	Leyland Atlantean AN68A/1R	Northern Counties	H43/32F	1977	Ex GM Buses, 1991
A808	RJA801R	Leyland Atlantean AN68A/1R	Park Royal	H43/32F	1977	Ex GM Buses, 1992
A809	VBA161S	Leyland Atlantean AN68A/1R	Northern Counties	H43/32F	1978	Ex GM Buses, 1992
A810	UNA824S	Leyland Atlantean AN68A/1R	Park Royal	H43/32F	1977	Ex GM Buses, 1992
A811	UNA840S	Leyland Atlantean AN68A/1R	Park Royal	H43/32F	1977	Ex GM Buses, 1992
A812	WVM888S	Leyland Atlantean AN68A/1R	Park Royal	H43/32F	1978	Ex GM Buses, 1992
R828	LMS160W	Leyland Fleetline FE30AGR	Alexander AD	H44/31F	1980	Ex Kelvin Central, 1989

**The newest double-deck buses at Western are four Volvo B10M Citybuses with Alexander express
bodywork for use on the Ayr-Glasgow service. Photographed at the Glasgow end is AV896,
E866RCS.** *Tony Wilson*

R832-837

R832-837		Leyland Fleetline FE30AGR		Eastern Coach Works	H43/32F	1978	Ex Northern Scottish, 1987		
R832	ASA22T	**R833**	ASA33T	**R834**w	ASA24T	**R836**w	ASA26T	**R837**	ASA27T

R839w	ULS669T	Leyland Fleetline FE30AGR	Eastern Coach Works	H43/32F	1978	Ex Kelvin Central, 1989
R840	ULS660T	Leyland Fleetline FE30AGR	Eastern Coach Works	H43/32F	1978	Ex Kelvin Central, 1989
R842w	OSG59V	Leyland Fleetline FE30AGR	Eastern Coach Works	H43/32F	1978	Ex Kelvin Central, 1989

R848-889

Leyland Fleetline FE30AGR   Northern Counties   H44/31F   1978-79
R859-6/9/80/5/7/9 ex Clydeside Scottish, 1988-89

R848w	XSJ648T	**R858**	XSJ658T	**R866**	XSJ666T	**R876**	ECS876V	**R883** ECS883V
R851	XSJ651T	**R859**	XSJ659T	**R867**	XSJ667T	**R877**	ECS877V	**R885** ECS885V
R853	XSJ653T	**R860**u	XSJ660T	**R868**	XSJ668T	**R878**	ECS878V	**R887** ECS887V
R854	XSJ654T	**R861**	XSJ661T	**R869**	XSJ669T	**R879**	ECS879V	**R888** BCS865T
R855	XSJ655T	**R862**	XSJ662T	**R870**	BCS870T	**R880**	ECS880V	**R889** BCS869T
R857	XSJ657T	**R865**w	XSJ665T	**R871**	BCS871T	**R882**	ECS882V	

V894	E864RCS	Volvo Citybus B10M-50	Alexander RV	DPH41/25F	1987	
V895	E865RCS	Volvo Citybus B10M-50	Alexander RV	DPH45/35F	1987	
V896	E866RCS	Volvo Citybus B10M-50	Alexander RV	DPH45/35F	1987	
V897	E867RCS	Volvo Citybus B10M-50	Alexander RV	DPH45/33F	1987	
L1059	YSD350L	Leyland Leopard PSU3/3R	Alexander AY	B41F	1972	
W1074	YYS174	Bedford C5Z1	Duple Vista	C21FM	1960	Ex David MacBrayne, 1970
D1684	RCS382	Leyland Titan PD3A/3	Alexander AM	L35/32RD	1961	
N1795	UCS659	Albion Lowlander LR3	Alexander AM	H40/31F	1963	

Previous Registrations:

13CLT	D317SGB	UIB3541	EGB89T	WLT439	NCS123W
703DYE	TSD153Y	UIB3542	EGT451T	WLT441	B201CGA
803DYE	H661UWR	UIB3543	WGY589S	WLT444	TSD159Y
B660EGG	B176FFS, WLT444	VCS376	TSD158Y, WLT652	WLT447	D220NCS
B979EGG	B409OSB, VLT204	VCS391	B191CGA	WLT465	B196CGA
B981EGG	B407OSB, 407CLT	VLT104	TSD154Y	WLT501	D221NCS
B985EGG	B403OSB, WLT364	VLT154	NCS115W	WLT526	D216NCS
B986EGG	B402OSB, 32CLT	VLT206	C206HSD	WLT538	TSD148Y
B987EGG	B401OSB, WLT471	VLT219	NCS119W	WLT546	D318SGB
FSU737	D217NCS	VLT226	B200CGA	WLT697	B197CGA
FSU739	GGE128X	VLT245	B199CGA	WLT720	B198CGA
GSU950	GGE131X	VLT272	B202CGA	WLT727	TSD155Y
HDS566H	SMS402H, 703DYE	VLT37	B194CGA	WLT774	TSD149Y
KRS540V	GSO6V	VLT54	C207HSD	WLT794	TSD156Y
KRS542V	GSO8V	VLT73	D219NCS	WLT809	TSD150Y
OIW7024	GLP433T	VLT81	C205HSD	WLT830	TSD157Y
OIW7025	GLP427T	WGA908V	DSD939V, WLT652	WLT874	TSD152Y
PSG842P	MSJ370P, 803DYE	WGB645W	NCS118W, VLT73	WLT915	TSD151Y
TOS524X	GGE126X, WLT526	WGB646W	NCS121W, WLT415	WLT978	B195CGA
TOS550X	GGE127X, FSU737	WLT415	D218NCS	YSV730	B203CGA
TOS720X	GGE130X, ESU435	WLT416	NCS114W	YSV735	B204CGA
UIB3076	EGT458T, WGY598S				

Livery: Yellow and blue (Scottish Citylink) H108, N113-5, L172/3, V191; red, green and cream (MacBrayne) W1074; red & cream (Western SMT) D1684, N1795.

HONG KONG

Stagecoach Hong Kong Ltd, Suite 1606, 16/F, Sha Tin Galleria Building
18-24 Shan Mei Street, Fo Tan, New Territories, Hong Kong.

1	FW6766	Volvo B10M-56	Alexander PS	DP50F	1994
2	FW6555	Volvo B10M-56	Alexander PS	DP50F	1994
3L	FW6832	Volvo B10M-56	Alexander PS	DP50F	1994
4L	FW8231	Volvo B10M-56	Alexander PS	DP50F	1994
5L	FW7894	Volvo B10M-56	Alexander PS	DP50F	1994

On order: Six tri-axle Volvo Olympians with Alexander coachwork.

As the first edition of the Stagecoach Bus Handbook went to press, the first five Volvo B10ms for Hong Kong were onboard ship bound for the island. The service on which they operate is residents service 801R which runs from Central to the district of Shatin Cpok Hong. These buses are fully air-conditioned and three of the vehicles feature a longer rear overhang and carry the suffix L. *Opposite:* The multi-story residential areas of the New Territories can be seen in the pictures of 3L, FW6832 and 1, FW6766. During 1995 six tri-axle Volvo Olympians will join the fleet, these too being employed on service 801R. *Stagecoach International*

Stagecoach Kenya Bus continue to receive ERF Trailblazers with locally-built Labh Singh bodywork. Photographed with the new corporate names and showing fleet numbers 390 and 391 *Stagecoach Kenya Bus*

KENYA BUS

Kenya Bus Services Ltd, General Waruingi Street, Eastleigh,
P O Box 41001, Nairobi, Kenya.

Depots: Mombasa and Nairobi.

301-320 ERF Trailblazer 6LXB   Suleman   B47D   1983-85

301	KUW565	305	KUY829	309	KWE549	313	KWP182	317	KWQ651
302	KUW634	306	KUZ807	310	KWE764	314	KWP609	318	KWQ673
303	KUY279	307	KUZ834	311	KWG808	315	KWP640	319	KWQ732
304	KUY289	308	KWC094	312	KWH535	316	KWQ159	320	KWT363

321-331 ERF Trailblazer 6LXB   Labh Singh   B49D*   1986-88   *330 is B43D, 331 is B46D
334-8 are B47D, 325 is B51F

321	KXQ484	324	KXR388	326	KYD117	328	KYV458	330	KYY078
322	KXR065	325	KYD116	327	KYW205	329	KYV457	331	KYW206
323	KXR282								

332-340 ERF Trailblazer 6LXB   Suleman   B53D*   1986-87

332	KYE173	334	KYH176	336	KYM857	338	KYS305	340	KYU693
333	KYE579	335	KYH535	337	KYN019	339	KYU264		

341-399 ERF Trailblazer 6LXB MkII   Labh Singh   B45D*   1993-94   *347 is B46D, 378 is B48D

341	KAC649X	353	KAD535A	365	KAD743D	377	KAD117G	389	KAD822K
342	KAC929X	354	KAD619A	366	KAD737D	378	KAD194G	390	KAD889Y
343	KAC023Y	355	KAD841A	367	KAD779D	379	KAD233G	391	KAD902Y
344	KAC022Y	356	KAD902A	368	KAD826D	380	KAD589H	392	KAD932Y
345	KAC021Y	357	KAD535A	369	KAD899D	381	KAD641H	393	KAD938Y
346	KAC287Y	358	KAD126C	370	KAD994D	382	KAD846H	394	KAD105Z
347	KAC290Y	359	KAD127C	371	KAD021E	383	KAD947H	395	KAD135Z
348	KAC289Y	360	KAD158C	372	KAD261E	384	KAD075J	396	KAD688A
349	KAC288Y	361	KAD225C	373	KAD360E	385	KAD199J	397	KAE689Y
350	KAD527A	362	KAD368C	374	KAD407E	386	KAD386J	398	KAE918A
351	KAD521A	363	KAD447C	375	KAD860F	387	KAD378J	399	KAE919A
352	KAD528A	364	KAD553C	376	KAD147G	388	KAD659K		

400-449 ERF Trailblazer 6LXB MkII   Labh Singh   B52D   1994-95

400	KAE660C	410		420		430		440	
401	KAE	411		421		431		441	
402	KAE	412		422		432		442	
403	KAE	413		423		433		443	
404	KAE	414		424		434		444	
405	KAE	415		425		435		445	
406	KAE	416		426		436		446	
407	KAE	417		427		437		447	
408	KAE	418		428		438		448	
409	KAE	419		429		439		449	

601	KAA128N	DAF TB2100DHT	Labh Singh	B47D	1990
602	KAA351N	DAF TB2100DHT	Labh Singh	B47D	1990
603	KAA330N	DAF TB2100DHT	Labh Singh	B47D	1990
604	KAA313Q	DAF TB2100DHT	Labh Singh	B47D	1990

605-616 DAF TB2100DHT   Labh Singh   B43D   1992

605	KAC145H	608	KAC253H	611	KAC592J	613	KAC865J	615	KAC519L
606	KAC146H	609	KAC447H	612	KAC672J	614	KAC887J	616	KAC243K
607	KAC252H	610	KAC485J						

701-720

Leyland Victory J MkII | Labh Singh | B49D* | 1979-80 | *710 is B47D,
*711 is B56D, 713 is B48D

701	KVR629	705	KVR866	709	KVS307	713	KVT703	717	KVU018
702	KVR652	706	KVR952	710	KVS284	714	KVT857	718	KVU079
703	KVR787	707	KVR995	711	KVS328	715	KVT909	719	KVU211
704	KVR818	708	KVS025	712	KVT664	716	KVT973	720	KVU156

721-736

Leyland Victory J MkII | Labh Singh | B49D* | 1980-82 | *722 is B44D,
*730 is B42D, 731 is B41D,

721	KVU237	725	KVW013	728	KVY046	731	KVY237	734	KVZ919
722	KVU369	726	KVX651	729	KVY074	732	KVZ671	735	KSJ158
723	KVV809	727	KVX664	730	KVY316	733	KVZ703	736	KSJ265
724	KVV957								

737-745

Leyland Victory J MkII | Suleman | B49D | 1979-80

737	KVU147	739	KTE936	741	KTE554	743	KSH120	745	KSP840
738	KTE826	740	KTE447	742	KSH004	744	KSH443		

746-779

Leyland Victory J MkII | Labh Singh | B49D* | 1980-82 | *747 are B48D,
*755 is B59D, 767 is B47D, 778 is B46D

746	KSP338	753	KSW895	760	KTG376	767	KTP917	774	KTR553
747	KSP339	754	KSW879	761	KTJ159	768	KTQ004	775	KTR630
748	KSP337	755	KTF528	762	KTJ235	769	KTQ164	776	KTR678
749	KSW894	756	KTF527	763	KTK846	770	KTQ249	777	KTT617
750	KSW877	757	KTF834	764	KTM915	771	KTQ287	778	KTT881
751	KSW876	758	KTF809	765	KTM946	772	KTQ398	779	KTV814
752	KSW875	759	KTG230	766	KTN216	773	KTR405		

780-796

Leyland Victory J MkII | Suleman | B53D* | 1981-82 | *Seating varies

780	KSW663	784	KTN321	788	KTU010	791	KTY066	794	KUE168
781	KSZ136	785	KTN339	789	KTU064	792	KUD378	795	KUF305
782	KSY974	786	KTR094	790	KTW693	793	KUE121	796	KUF366
783	KTN313	787	KTR124						

797-824

Leyland Victory J MkII | Labh Singh | B49D* | 1980-82 | *Seating varies

797	KTW268	803	KUG560	809	KUG938	815	KUJ874	820	KUJ890
798	KTW190	804	KUH104	810	KUG978	816	KUJ638	821	KUM688
799	KTY110	805	KUG585	811	KUH141	817	KUJ998	822	KUM870
800	KUF144	806	KUJ641	812	KUH254	818	KUJ889	823	KUM534
801	KUG599	807	KUG850	813	KUH275	819	KUK083	824	KUK271
802	KUG474	808	KUG860	814	KUJ561				

825-830

Leyland Victory J MkII | Suleman | B53D* | 1982 | *Seating varies

825	KUF947	827	KUK402	828	KUK427	829	KUK494	830	KUK979
826	KUK401								

831-850

Leyland Victory J MkII | Labh Singh | B49D* | 1983-84 | *Seating varies

831	KUY105	835	KWA577	839	KWB295	843	KWK134	847	KWM059
832	KWA562	836	KWA574	840	KWC826	844	KWK144	848	KWM145
833	KWA575	837	KWB994	841	KWE920	845	KWL823	849	KWM189
834	KWA576	838	KWB286	842	KWE971	846	KWL923	850	KWN536

851-874

Leyland Victory J MkII | Labh Singh | B49D* | 1984-85 | *870 is B45D

851	KWP262	856	KWR077	861	KWS725	866	KWT169	871	KWX948
852	KWQ584	857	KWR105	862	KWS971	867	KWT337	872	KWY155
853	KWQ808	858	KWR140	863	KWS985	868	KWV976	873	KWY371
854	KWQ914	859	KWS524	864	KWT030	869	KWX587	874	KXA037
855	KWQ946	860	KWS690	865	KWT146	870	KWX892		

875	KXD749	Leyland Victory J MkIII	Suleman	B48D	1986

876-900

	Leyland Victory J MkII		Labh Singh		B49D*	1985-86	*Seating varies		
876	KXD797	881	KXG262	886	KXH624	891	KXJ173	896	KXM065
877	KXK017	882	KXG278	887	KXH875	892	KXJ369	897	KXN855
878	KXK503	883	KXH320	888	KXH896	893	KXJ474	898	KXN982
879	KXD761	884	KXH321	889	KXH993	894	KXK610	899	KXP038
880	KXD781	885	KXH623	890	KXJ010	895	KXK708	900	KXP187

906-924

	Leyland Victory J		Labh Singh		B48D*	1974-75	*921/4 are B47D		
906	KPW130	920	KQC946	921	KQD110	922	KQD302	924	KQF075
915	KQB978								

931-942

	Leyland Victory J		Labh Singh		B47D*	1976-78	*935 is B41D, 936 B50D, 940 B46D		
931	KQV346	934	KQW802	937	KQX875	939	KRP967	941	KRQ083
932	KQW687	935	KQW958	938	KRP893	940	KRP995	942	KRQ125
933	KQW743	936	KQW994						

946-959

	Leyland Victory J		Labh Singh		B49D	1979			
946	KVK649	949	KVK823	952	KVL108	954	KVL266	957	KVN055
947	KVK708	950	KVK941	953	KVL232	956	KVM733	959	KVN137
948	KVK751	951	KVK993						

961	KUF067	Leyland Victory J	Labh Singh	B49D	1982 Rebuild
962	KUG695	Leyland Victory J	Labh Singh	B45D	1982 Rebuild
963	KUT967	Leyland Victory J	Labh Singh	B49D	1983 Rebuild
964	KNY401	Leyland Victory J	Labh Singh	B47D	1985 Rebuild
965	KUT615	Leyland Victory J	Labh Singh	B47D	1985 Rebuild
966	KZF894	Leyland Victory J	Labh Singh	B49D	1988 Rebuild
967	KQB925	Leyland Victory J	Labh Singh	B48D	1974 Rebuild
968	KQD250	Leyland Victory J	Labh Singh	B48D	1975 Rebuild
969	KPW753	Leyland Victory J	Labh Singh	B48D	1974 Rebuild
970	KPW294	Leyland Victory J	Labh Singh	B45D	1974 Rebuild
971	KUR801	Leyland Victory J MkII	Labh Singh	B45D	1983
972	KUR811	Guy Victory J MkII	Labh Singh	B42D	1983
973	KUS386	Leyland Victory J MkII	Labh Singh	B50D	1983
974	KUT208	Leyland Victory J MkII	Labh Singh	B35D	1983
981	KWY053	ERF Trailblazer 6LX	Suleman	B47F	1985
982	KWY095	ERF Trailblazer 6LX	Suleman	B47F	1985
983	KWY472	ERF Trailblazer 6LX	Suleman	B47F	1985
984	KXA410	ERF Trailblazer 6LX	Suleman	B47F	1985

991-997

	Leyland Victory J MkII		Labh Singh		B49D*	1979	*991 is B43D		
991	KZC129	993	KZA013	995	KYZ546	996	KZD894	997	KZB481
992	KZC481	994	KZF416						

Operating Companies:
Kenya Bus Services (Mombasa): 302/6-9/11-8, 332/3/5/9/40/92/3/5/7, 737-45/80-96, 825-30/75, 965/73/4/81-4.
KBS Companies A+B+C (Nairobi): Remainder.

The latest arrival at Kenya bus is 400, KAE660C, the first of the 12m ERF Trailblazers for this fleet. It is seen in December 1994 and shows its correct registration, unlike 390/1 on page 126 which carried plates from other buses when pictured as they were then unregistered.
Andrew Jarosz

MALAWI

Stagecoach Malawi, P O Box 176, Blantyre, Malawi, Central Africa.

Depots : Chichiri, Lilongwe, Makata and Mzuzu.

1	BH9601	Volvo B10M-61	Plaxton Paramount 3500 III	C46FT	1988	Ex Travellers, London, 1991
2w	BH9602	Volvo B10M-61	Plaxton Paramount 3500 III	C46FT	1988	Ex Travellers, London, 1991
3	BH9603	Volvo B10M-61	Plaxton Paramount 3500 III	C46FT	1988	Ex Travellers, London, 1991
4	BH9604	Volvo B10M-61	Plaxton Paramount 3500 III	C46FT	1988	Ex Travellers, London, 1991
5	BJ4981	Volvo B10M-61	Plaxton Paramount 3500 III	C46FT	1988	Ex Wallace Arnold, 1993
6	BJ8256	Volvo B10M-61	Plaxton Paramount 3500 III	C46FT	1988	Ex ??, 1994
7	BJ8257	Volvo B10M-61	Plaxton Paramount 3500 III	C46FT	1988	Ex ??, 1994
200	BJ5851	Mercedes-Benz 812D	PEW	B32F	1993	
201	BJ5852	Mercedes-Benz 812D	PEW	B32F	1993	
202	BJ5853	Mercedes-Benz 812D	PEW	B32F	1993	
203	BJ5854	Mercedes-Benz 812D	PEW	B32F	1993	

204-233 ERF Trailblazer 6LXB PEW B61F 1993

204	BJ6020	210	BJ6112	216	BJ6255	222	BJ6414	228	BJ6512
205	BJ6021	211	BJ6137	217	BJ6258	223	BJ6419	229	BJ6521
206	BJ6066	212	BJ6147	218	BJ6313	224	BJ6439	230	BJ6525
207	BJ6070	213	BJ6157	219	BJ6341	225	BJ6450	231	BJ6542
208	BJ6080	214	BJ6205	220	BJ6353	226	BJ6460	232	BJ6594
209	BJ6079	215	BJ6245	221	BJ6405	227	BJ6471	233	BJ6595

307	BC6557	Guy Victory J	AUT(1983)	B51F	1971

311-330 Leyland Victory J AUT* B54D 1975 *309-12 rebuilt 1984-85

311	BD2508	315	BD2515	322	BD2522	328	BD6256	330	BD6258
314	BD2514	319	BD2519	325	BD6253	329	BD6257		

338-345 Leyland Victory J AUT B55D 1978

338	BE3166	340	BE3168	343	BE5105	344	BE5106	345	BE5107
339	BE3167	341	BE5103						

346	BF363	Leyland Victory J MkII	AUT	B53D	1980
347	BF364	Leyland Victory J MkII	AUT	B55D	1981
348	BF365	Leyland Victory J MkII	AUT(1986)	B53D	1981

Number 1 in the Stagecoach Malawi fleet might look rather familiar. Registered BH9601, it was exported to Central Africa from London in 1991, one of four previously in the Trathens fleet. Now with additional protection at the front from Rhino and Zebra it is seen heading for the Capital, Blantyre.
Stagecoach Malawi

350-371 — Leyland Victory J MkII — AUT — B57D — 1985-87

350	BG150	355	BG1255	360	BG1260	364	BG7364	368	BG7368
351	BG151	356	BG1256	361	BG149	365	BG7365	369	BG7369
352	BG152	357	BG1257	362	BG7362	366	BG7366	370	BG7370
353	BG153	358	BG1258	363	BG7363	367	BG7367	371	BG7371
354	BG154	359	BG1259						

422	BG2422	Leyland Victory J MkII	AUT(1989)	B59F	1985
423	BG2423	Leyland Victory J MkII	AUT(1988)	B59F	1985
424	BG2434	Leyland Victory J MkII	AUT(1989)	B49D	1985
425	BG2435	Leyland Victory J MkII	AUT(1989)	B49D	1985

426-437 — AVM Dahmer DH825 — AUT — B59F — 1989

426	BH1886	429	BH1889	432	BH1892	434	BH1894	436	BH1896
427	BH1887	430	BH1890	433	BH1893	435	BH1895	437	BH1897
428	BH1888	431	BH1891						

438-443 — DAF TB2105 — AUT — B59F — 1989

438	BH1808	440	BH1910	441	BH1911	442	BH1912	443	BH1913
439	BH1909								

447-465 — ERF Trailblazer — PEW — B59F — 1990-92

447	BH5747	453	BH2380	456	BH2577	458	BH2451	464	BJ2713
451	BH5751	454	BH2381	457	BH2450	459	BJ2711	465	BJ3095
452	BH9333	455	BH2576						

447-489 — Volvo B10M-55 — Alexander PS — B53F — 1993

470	BJ5558	474	BJ5554	478	BJ5753	482	BJ5967	486	BJ6195
471	BJ5551	475	BJ5643	479	BJ5779	483	BJ6075	487	BJ6249
472	BJ5552	476	BJ5604	480	BJ5960	484	BJ6106	488	BJ6267
473	BJ5553	477	BJ5752	481	BJ5966	485	BJ6114	489	BJ6764

500	BJ7150	ERF SuperTrailblazer	PEW	B??F	1994

720-798 — Leyland Victory J MkII — AUT — B57F — 1981-85 *720/1 are B59F, 773 is B56F

720	BG2420	783	BF8810	788	BF8815	791	BF8978	796	BF8983
721	BG2421	784	BF8811	789	BF8975	792	BF8979	797	BF8984
773	BF2232	785	BF8812	790	BF8977	793	BF8980	798	BF8985
781	BF8808	787	BF8814						

ERF Trailblazers have been added to the Malawi fleet in recent years, including 205, BJ6021 in 1993. Promoting Lipton's Tea, and carrying a respectable load, it features a PEW locally-built body.
Stagecoach Malawi

One of the older buses working from Lilongwe is a Leyland Victory from the mid 1980s. These vehicles are being replaced by newer ERFs and Volvos. Stagecoach Malawi

800-819 — Leyland Victory J MkII — AUT B53F — 1985

800	BF8987	804	BG134	808	BG138	813	BG143	817	BG147
801	BG131	805	BG135	809	BG139	814	BG144	818	BG148
802	BG132	806	BG136	811	BG141	815	BG145	819	BG691
803	BG133	807	BG137	812	BG142	816	BG146		

826-861 — Leyland Victory J MkII — AUT — B53F — 1986-87

826	BG3826	834	BG3834	842	BG3842	849	BG3849	856	BG3856
827	BG3827	835	BG3835	843	BG3843	850	BG3850	857	BG3857
828	BG3828	836	BG3836	844	BG3844	851	BG3851	858	BG3858
829	BG3829	837	BG3837	845	BG3845	852	BG3852	859	BG3859
830	BG3830	838	BG3838	846	BG3846	854	BG3854	860	BG3860
832	BG3832	839	BG3839	847	BG3847	855	BG3855	861	BG3861
833	BG3833	841	BG3841	848	BG3848				

862-897 — ERF Trailblazer — PEW — B61F — 1991-92

862	BH5862	870	BH5870	877	BH5877	884	BH9599	891	BJ1191
863	BH5863	871	BH5871	878	BH8178	885	BJ445	892	BJ1192
864	BH5864	872	BH5872	879	BH8179	886	BJ446	893	BJ1283
865	BH5865	873	BH5873	880	BH5752	887	BJ447	894	BJ1284
866	BH5866	874	BH5874	881	BH9596	888	BJ448	895	BJ1285
867	BH5867	875	BH5875	882	BH9597	889	BJ1193	896	BJ1286
868	BH5868	876	BH5876	883	BH9598	890	BJ1194	897	BJ1287
869	BH5869								

898-949

		ERF Trailblazer		PEW B61F		1992			
898	BJ1604	**909**	BJ2063	**920**	BJ3247	**930**	BJ3600	**940**	BJ4044
899	BJ1605	**910**	BJ2064	**921**	BJ3246	**931**	BJ3604	**941**	BJ4064
900	BJ1606	**911**	BJ2065	**922**	BJ3354	**932**	BJ3673	**942**	BJ4151
901	BJ1754	**912**	BJ2331	**923**	BJ3373	**933**	BJ3674	**943**	BJ4161
902	BJ1755	**913**	BJ2332	**924**	BJ3387	**934**	BJ3675	**944**	BJ4212
903	BJ1756	**914**	BJ2333	**925**	BJ3402	**935**	BJ3857	**945**	BJ4213
904	BJ1974	**915**	BJ3095	**926**	BJ3403	**936**	BJ3858	**946**	BJ4301
905	BJ1975	**916**	BJ3136	**927**	BJ3461	**937**	BJ3872	**947**	BJ4358
906	BJ1976	**917**	BJ3203	**928**	BJ3519	**938**	BJ3971	**948**	BJ4394
907	BJ2061	**918**	BJ3244	**929**	BJ3521	**939**	BJ3997	**949**	BJ4438
908	BJ2062	**919**	BJ3245						

		ERF Trailblazer		PEW		B47F	1993		
950	BJ5517								

951-960

		ERF Trailblazer		PEW		B59F	1990-92		
951	BH5748	**953**	BF5750	**955**	BJ2715	**957**	BJ3094	**959**	BH5745
952	BH5749	**954**	BJ2712	**956**	BJ2710	**958**	BH5744	**960**	BH5746

1002-1056

		Daimler CVG6LX-34		Metsec		H52/33D	1971-72 Ex KMB, Hong Kong, 1989-90		
1002	BH2628	**1025**	BH5125	**1036**	BH5836	**1045**	BH5845	**1052**	BH6752
1013	BH2639	**1027**	BH5127	**1039**	BH5839	**1047**	BH5847	**1053**	BH6753
1014	BH2640	**1029**	BH5129	**1040**	BH5840	**1048**	BH5848	**1054**	BH6754
1015	BH2641	**1030**	BH5130	**1041**	BH5841	**1049**	BH5849	**1055**	BH6755
1016	BH2642	**1034**	BH5134	**1044**	BH5844	**1050**	BH5850	**1056**	BH6756
1019	BH2645								

2001-2010

		Dennis Dragon DDA1811		Duple-Metsec		H67/41F	1992		
2001	BJ3701	**2003**	BJ4302	**2005**	BJ4397	**2007**	BJ4575	**2009**	BJ4618
2002	BJ4153	**2004**	BJ4370	**2006**	BJ4505	**2008**	BJ4590	**2010**	BJ4915

Not many Stagecoach buses operate with trailers, but working the Blantyre to Lilongwe service is Leyland Victory 902, BJ1755, complete with freight trailer.
Stagecoach Malawi

133

STAGECOACH WELLINGTON

Wellington City Transport Ltd, 45 Onepu Road, Kilbirnie, P O Box 14 070, Wellington, New Zealand.

141-170

				MAN SL202		Coachwork International	B40D	1986-89		
141	NF2109	147	NH2755	153	NL9414	159	NL9540	165	NZ8003
142	NF2117	148	NI5642	154	NL9420	160	NL9566	166	NZ8266
143	NH2634	149	NI5704	155	NL9466	161	OB1550	167	OG8397
144	NH2652	150	NL5718	156	NL9460	162	NT9387	168	OG8398
145	NH2754	151	NL9377	157	NL9461	163	PA6879	169	OG8399
146	NH2756	152	NL9393	158	NL9531	164	NZ8004	170	OG8551

171-180

				MAN 16200		Coachwork International	B40D	1989-91		
171	ON525	173	PL5272	175	PL5274	177	PL5823	179	PP5206
172	PL5003	174	PL5273	176	PL5822	178	PL5824	180	PP5205

181	PP5219	MAN 16400	Coachwork International	B40D	1991

201-233

				Volvo B58-61 Trolleybus		Hawke Coachwork	B40D	1980-81		
201	KA9102	207	JY5832	213	KA9184	220	KA7235	226	KD7487
202	KA9108	208	JY5831	214	KA9185	221	KD7490	227	KH4274
203	PE8106	209	KA9103	216	KA9192	222	KD7488	229	KH4358
204	JM7127	210	KA9109	217	NA87	223	KD7485	232	KJ8245
205	JM7125	211	KA9110	218	KA7233	224	KD7486	233	KJ8244
206	JY6549	212	KA9111	219	KA7234	225	KH4273		

234-254

				Volvo B58-61 Trolleybus		Hawke Coachwork	B40D	1984-85		
234	LQ2643	239	MB7635	243	ME9235	247	MJ2016	251	MJ2168
235	LW6465	240	MB7638	244	ME9236	248	MJ2015	252	MJ2169
236	MA8821	241	MB7636	245	ME2504	249	MJ2014	253	MJ2171
237	MA5210	242	MB7637	246	MJ2012	250	MJ2013	254	MJ2172
238	MA5209								

255-268

				Volvo B58-61 Trolleybus		Hawke Coachwork	B40D	1986		
255	MO1322	258	SC2911	261	MS1706	264	MS1703	267	MS1812
256	MO1321	259	MO1397	262	MS1705	265	MS1814	268	MS1815
257	MO1391	260	MS1707	263	MS1704	266	MS1813		

270	MC6399	Hino AC140	Micanta	C23F	1985
290	PD1036	Renault S75	Coachwork International	B23F	1990
292	PD1038	Renault S75	Coachwork International	B23F	1990
293	PE5096	Renault S75	Coachwork International	B23F	1990

401-416

				Leyland Leopard PSU3C/2R		Hawke Coachwork	B40D	1976-77		
401	HZ2712	404	FL349	408	HQ3899	411	HQ3939	415	IL4461
402	HI1974	405	FL350	409	HQ3907	413	IL4518	416	IK7801
403	GA6806	406	HE2656	410	PW8450	414	IK7802		

418-480

				Leyland Leopard PSU3E/2R		Hawke Coachwork	B40D	1978-79 479/80 ex Goldstar, Frankton, 1992		
418	IU9433	434	IX7763	446	JC2570	458	JF1914	470	JA1197
420	IU9431	435	IU9931	447	JD184	459	IX3806	471	JA2261
421	IX7733	436	IU9932	448	JD183	460	IX3814	472	JC2505
422	IX7732	437	IU9929	449	JD182	461	IX3815	473	NR3918
423	IX3304	438	JC2431	450	JD196	462	IX7767	474	JD181
425	IX3781	439	JC2430	451	JD197	463	IX7766	475	JC2520
426	IX3660	440	JA1187	452	JF1903	464	IU9930	476	JD199
427	IX3783	441	JA1185	453	JF1909	465	IU9928	477	JF1902
430	IX3808	442	JA1198	454	JF1908	466	KP7998	478	JF1912
431	IX3817	443	JC2506	455	JF1910	467	JA1188	479	IX3303
432	PA6877	444	JC2568	456	JF1911	468	LH1322	480	IX7734
433	IX7765	445	JC2569	457	JF1913	469	JA1184		

The cover picture shows the one of the latest batch of MAN 11.190s for this New Zealand fleet. The bodywork on all twenty of the batch is by Designline. First to arrive is 501, SS5537, seen here just prior to its entry into service. *Stagecoach New Zealand*

Eastbourne Buses was acquired by Stagecoach during 1994. Not on the English south coast, but in the vicinity of Wellington in New Zealand. Below is a picture of one of the acquired fleet, not yet in corporate livery. *Stagecoach New Zealand*

| 481 | LA5234 | Leyland Leopard PSU3E/2R | New Zealand Motor Bodies | B44D | 1983 | Ex Invercargill, 1992 |

501-520   MAN 11.190 HOCL   Designline   B40D   1994-95

501	SS5537	505	SX7725	509	SY1641	513	TA2667	517
502	SS5538	506	SW4400	510	SY1631	514	TA2691	518
503	ST7109	507	SW4435	511	SY5917	515		519
504	SX7724	508	SW4436	512	SZ5918	516		520

521-580   MAN 11.190 HOCL   Designline   B40D   1995

521		533		545		557		569
522		534		546		558		570
523		535		547		559		571
524		536		548		560		572
525		537		549		561		573
526		538		550		562		574
527		539		551		563		575
528		540		552		564		576
529		541		553		565		577
530		542		554		566		578
531		543		555		567		579
532		544		556		568		580

Cityline Lower Hutt:

| 5907 | 1055IC | Hino BG300 | Emslie | C41F | 1980 |

6890-7242   Hino RK176   Coachwork International   B47D*   1985-88   *6890 is B45D

| 6890 | MI8415 | 7232 | NA7350 | 7233 | NA7351 | 7239 | NA7361 | 7242 | NL7824 |
| 7193 | NA6078 | | | | | | | | |

7255-7556   Hino RK177   Coachwork International   B47D   1988-89

7255	NL7823	7267	NL7793	7534	NX9507	7543	OE4212	7549	OG5328
7256	NL7790	7271	NL8273	7535	NX9508	7545	OE7913	7551	OG5327
7259	NL7797	7278	NX9487	7540	OB4215	7546	OE7916	7555	OG5343
7263	NL7791	7532	NX9510	7542	OB4213	7548	OE7917	7556	OG5344
7264	NL7792	7533	NX9509						

7601-7608   Mercedes-Benz L608D   Alexander   DP19F   1986   Ex Stagecoach South, 1994

| 7601 | SN7472 | 7603 | ST9430 | 7606 | SX6692 | 7607 | SZ205 | 7608 | TA7124 |
| 7602 | ST9425 | 7605 | SX6698 | | | | | | |

Cityline Hutt Valley:

| 5908 | 1056IC | Hino BG300 | Emslie | C41F | 1980 |

7197-7252   Hino RK176   Coachwork International   B47D*   1987-88   *7197-7200 are B45D

7197	NA6060	7231	NA7352	7244	NL7825	7247	NL7828	7250	NL7831
7198	NA6947	7236	NA7357	7245	NL7826	7248	NL7829	7251	NA7832
7200	NA6945	7237	NA7358	7246	NL7827	7249	NL7830	7252	NA7833
7201	NK8507	7238	NA7359						

7253-7554   Hino RK177   Coachwork International   B47D   1988-89

7253	NA7834	7266	NL8272	7273	NL8267	7536	NX9516	7544	OB4214
7258	NL7796	7268	NL8264	7274	NL8268	7537	NX9517	7547	OB7912
7260	NL7799	7269	NL8265	7276	NX9485	7538	OB4297	7553	OG5341
7261	NL7794	7270	NL8266	7279	NX9488	7539	OB4208	7554	OG5342
7265	NL7798								

Cityline Auckland:

7611-7615		Mercedes-Benz L608D		Alexander		DP19F	1986	Ex Stagecoach South, 1994	
7611	SZ8591	**7612**	SZ8592	**7613**	TA7462	**7614**	TA7468	**7615**	SZ8598

Eastbourne Bus Company:

1	FL4297	Ford R226		B49F	1976
2	NA4281	Isuzu MR113		B28F	1987
3	FL4281	Ford R192		B41F	1973
4	NA4279	Isuzu MR113		B28F	1987
5	NA3943	Isuzu MR113		B28F	1987
6	SK700	Isuzu ECR570		B45F	1986
7	FL4279	Ford R192		B41F	1972
8	NY58	Isuzu ECR570		B46F	1988
9	MQ8716	Isuzu ECR		B50F	1986
10	JR48	Ford R1114	Hess	B49F	1980
11	ON223	Isuzu ECR570		B46D	1989
12	PT2685	Hino RG197		B37F	1991
13	JR47	Ford R1114	Hess	B49F	1980
14	IN2551	Ford R226		B49F	1977
15	JZ7041	Ford R1114	Hess	B49F	1981
16	OB1552	Isuzu ECR570		B50F	1988
17	JR2616	Mercedes-Benz 0303		B42D	1980
18	JW8024	Mercedes-Benz 0303		B42D	1980
19	LE4641	Hino BX341		B49F	1983
20	MC609	Isuzu ECR570		B50F	1985

The Kelburn Cable Car is one of the best known tourist attractions in Wellington, New Zealand. The Cable Car carries around 1 million passengers per annum, one third are commuters, one third travelling to the University and one third visitors. From the top station there is a superb view of downtown Wellington and the harbour. It is operated by Harbour City Cable Car Ltd, a joint venture between Stagecoach Wellington and local tourist company, East and West. *Stagecoach International*

Index to British vehicles listed in the 1995 Stagecoach Bus Handbook

1JVK	Busways	9258VC	Midland Red	A213FHN	Cleveland
2JVK	Busways	9492SC	Bluebird	A214MCK	Ribble
13CLT	Western Scottish	9737VC	Midland Red	A227MDD	Red & White
49CLT	Selkent	9984PG	Midland Red	A243YGF	Grimsby Cleethorpes
83CBD	United Counties	A7GGT	Midland Red	A314XWG	East Midland
109DRM	Cumberland	A8GGT	Midland Red	A315XWG	East Midland
126ASV	Bluebird	A35XBO	Midland Red	A316XWG	East Midland
127ASV	Bluebird	A36XBO	Midland Red	A317XWG	East Midland
128ASV	Bluebird	A37XBO	Midland Red	A318XWG	East Midland
145CLT	Bluebird	A39XHE	East Midland	A319YWJ	East Midland
147YFM	Bluebird	A40XHE	Bluebird	A320YWJ	East Midland
230HUE	Midland Red	A41XHE	East Midland	A321YWJ	East Midland
331HWD	Midland Red	A42XHE	East Midland	A322AKU	East Midland
400DCD	Coastline	A43XHE	East Midland	A323AKU	East Midland
403DCD	Hampshire Bus	A44FRS	Bluebird	A324AKU	East Midland
405DCD	Coastline	A44XHE	East Midland	A325AKU	East Midland
406DCD	Hampshire Bus	A45FRS	Bluebird	A353ASF	Bluebird
407DCD	Hampshire Bus	A46FRS	Bluebird	A541HAC	Red & White
409DCD	Coastline	A47FRS	Bluebird	A542HAC	Midland Red
410DCD	Hampshire Bus	A65THX	Selkent	A543HAC	Midland Red
411DCD	Coastline	A66THX	Selkent	A544HAC	Midland Red
415DCD	Coastline	A67THX	Selkent	A545HAC	Midland Red
416DCD	Coastline	A71GEE	Grimsby Cleethorpes	A546HAC	Midland Red
417DCD	Coastline	A72GEE	Grimsby Cleethorpes	A547HAC	Midland Red
418DCD	Coastline	A73GEE	Grimsby Cleethorpes	A548HAC	Red & White
419DCD	South Coast Buses	A74GEE	Grimsby Cleethorpes	A549HAC	Red & White
420DCD	Hampshire Bus	A75NAC	Midland Red	A603THV	Selkent
420GAC	Midland Red	A76NAC	Midland Red	A607THV	Selkent
424DCD	Coastline	A76THX	Selkent	A613THV	Selkent
461CLT	East London	A77THX	Selkent	A625THV	Selkent
467WYA	Cheltenham & Gloucester	A102DAO	Cumberland	A626THV	East London
468CLT	East London	A108TRP	United Counties	A627THV	Selkent
485CLT	East London	A109TRP	United Counties	A628THV	Selkent
490CLT	Bluebird	A110TRP	United Counties	A629THV	Selkent
491GAC	Midland Red	A111TRP	United Counties	A630THV	Selkent
491JVX	Busways	A112TRP	United Counties	A631THV	Selkent
495FFJ	Coastline	A113TRP	United Counties	A632THV	Selkent
498FYB	Midland Red	A114TRP	United Counties	A634THV	Selkent
511OHU	Cheltenham & Gloucester	A116ESA	Bluebird	A635THV	Selkent
515CLT	Selkent	A117ESA	Bluebird	A636THV	Selkent
527CLT	East London	A118ESA	Bluebird	A645THV	Selkent
552OHU	Midland Red	A121GSA	Bluebird	A648THV	Selkent
552UTE	Busways	A121XWB	Bluebird	A650THV	East London
644HKX	Busways	A122GSA	Bluebird	A652THV	Selkent
647DYE	United Counties	A123GSA	Bluebird	A663WSU	Bluebird
685DYE	United Counties	A124GSA	Bluebird	A728ANH	United Counties
703DYE	Western Scottish	A125GSA	Bluebird	A729ANH	United Counties
803DYE	Western Scottish	A126GSA	Bluebird	A769SUL	East London
813VPU	Busways	A127GSA	Bluebird	A784SUL	East London
837XHW	Hartlepool	A138MRN	Ribble	A789SUL	East London
866NHT	Bluebird	A142MRN	Ribble	A802SUL	East London
896HOD	Coastline	A143MRN	Ribble	A819SUL	East London
927GTA	Ribble	A145MRN	Ribble	A823SUL	Selkent
1412NE	Bluebird	A150LFR	Ribble	A824SUL	Selkent
3063VC	Midland Red	A156OFR	Ribble	A825SUL	Selkent
3273AC	Midland Red	A157OFR	Ribble	A826SUL	East London
4012VC	Midland Red	A158OFR	Ribble	A827SUL	East London
4585SC	Bluebird	A159OFR	Ribble	A828SUL	Selkent
4828VC	Midland Red	A209FHN	Cleveland	A829SUL	Selkent
6253VC	Midland Red	A211FHN	Cleveland	A830SUL	Selkent
6804VC	Midland Red	A212FHN	Cleveland	A832SUL	East London

A833SUL	East London	AAE650V	Cheltenham & Gloucester	ARP607X	United Counties
A834SUL	Selkent	AAE651V	Cheltenham & Gloucester	ARP608X	United Counties
A837SUL	Selkent	AAE659V	Cheltenham & Gloucester	ARP609X	United Counties
A838SUL	Selkent	AAE660V	Cheltenham & Gloucester	ARP610X	United Counties
A840SUL	East London	AAE665V	Cheltenham & Gloucester	ARP611X	United Counties
A841SUL	Selkent	AAL516A	Red & White	ASA22T	Western Scottish
A842SUL	Selkent	AAL518A	Red & White	ASA24T	Western Scottish
A843SUL	Selkent	AAL538A	Red & White	ASA26T	Western Scottish
A845SUL	Selkent	AAL544A	Red & White	ASA27T	Western Scottish
A846SUL	East London	AAL575A	Red & White	ASA33T	Western Scottish
A847SUL	Selkent	AAP647T	Coastline	ASD825T	Western Scottish
A848SUL	Selkent	AAP648T	South Coast Buses	ASD826T	Western Scottish
A848VML	Midland Red	AAP649T	Stagecoach South	ASD827T	Western Scottish
A849SUL	East London	AAP660T	South Coast Buses	ASD829T	Western Scottish
A850SUL	Selkent	AAP662T	Stagecoach South	ASD831T	Western Scottish
A854SUL	Selkent	AAP668T	South Coast Buses	ASD832T	Western Scottish
A855SUL	Selkent	AAP670T	Coastline	ASD833T	Western Scottish
A856SUL	Selkent	AAP671T	South Coast Buses	ASD834T	Western Scottish
A857SUL	Selkent	AAP672T	Coastline	ASD835T	Western Scottish
A858SUL	Selkent	AAX450A	Red & White	ASD836T	Western Scottish
A859SUL	Selkent	AAX451A	Red & White	ASD837T	Western Scottish
A866SUL	Selkent	AAX465A	Red & White	ASD842T	Western Scottish
A867SUL	East London	AAX466A	Red & White	ASD843T	Western Scottish
A868SUL	Selkent	AAX488A	Red & White	ASD844T	Western Scottish
A871KDF	Cheltenham & Gloucester	AAX489A	Red & White	AUP713S	Midland Red
A873SUL	East London	AAX515A	Red & White	AVK134V	Busways
A874SUL	Selkent	AAX516A	Red & White	AVK135V	Busways
A876SUL	East London	AAX529A	Red & White	AVK136V	Busways
A877SUL	Selkent	AAX589A	Bluebird	AVK137V	Busways
A880SUL	Selkent	AAX600A	Bluebird	AVK138V	Busways
A881SUL	Selkent	AAX601A	Bluebird	AVK139V	Busways
A882SUL	Selkent	AAX631A	Bluebird	AVK140V	Busways
A883SUL	Selkent	AET181T	Midland Red	AVK141V	Busways
A885SUL	Selkent	AET182T	Hants & Surrey	AVK142V	Busways
A902SUL	East London	AET185T	Red & White	AVK143V	Busways
A905SUL	East London	AET186T	South Coast Buses	AVK144V	Busways
A918SYE	Selkent	AET187T	Coastline	AVK145V	Busways
A921SUL	East London	AFY192X	Midland Red	AVK146V	Busways
A922SYE	East London	AHH201T	Busways	AVK147V	Busways
A925SYE	Selkent	AHH206T	Ribble	AVK148V	Busways
A926SYE	Selkent	AHH208T	Ribble	AVK149V	Busways
A935SYE	East London	AHH209T	Ribble	AVK150V	Busways
A940XGG	Busways	AHN388T	Busways	AVK151V	Busways
A941XGG	Busways	AHN389T	Busways	AVK152V	Busways
A942XGG	Busways	AHN390T	Busways	AVK153V	Busways
A944SYE	East London	AHN397T	Cleveland	AVK154V	Busways
A945SYE	East London	AIB4053	Midland Red	AVK155V	Busways
A949SYE	East London	AKG162A	Bluebird	AVK156V	Busways
A950SYE	Selkent	AKG197A	Red & White	AVK157V	Busways
A951SYE	Selkent	AKG214A	Red & White	AVK158V	Busways
A953SYE	East London	AKG232A	Bluebird	AVK159V	Busways
A960SYE	East London	AKG271A	Red & White	AVK160V	Busways
A961SYE	Selkent	AKG296A	Red & White	AVK161V	Busways
A965SYE	East London	ALD968B	Bluebird	AVK162V	Busways
A970SYE	East London	ANA211T	Western Scottish	AVK163V	Busways
A975OST	Ribble	ARN888Y	Ribble	AVK164V	Busways
A976SYE	Selkent	ARN889Y	Ribble	AVK165V	Busways
A977OST	Ribble	ARN890Y	Ribble	AVK166V	Busways
A978OST	Ribble	ARN891Y	Ribble	AVK167V	Busways
A978SYE	Selkent	ARN892Y	Cheltenham & Gloucester	AVK168V	Busways
A979OST	Ribble	ARN893Y	Ribble	AVK169V	Busways
A988SYE	Selkent	ARN894Y	Ribble	AVK170V	Busways
A996SYE	Selkent	ARP601X	United Counties	AVK171V	Busways
A999SYE	Selkent	ARP602X	United Counties	AVK172V	Busways
AAE644V	Cheltenham & Gloucester	ARP604X	United Counties	AVK173V	Busways
AAE648V	Cheltenham & Gloucester	ARP605X	United Counties	AVK174V	Busways
AAE649V	Cheltenham & Gloucester	ARP606X	United Counties	AVK175V	Busways

AVK176V	Busways	B121WUV	Selkent	BCW823V	Ribble
AVK177V	Busways	B122WUV	Selkent	BCW824V	Ribble
AVK178V	Busways	B124WUV	Selkent	BCW825V	Ribble
AVK179V	Busways	B125WUV	Selkent	BCW826V	Ribble
AVK180V	Busways	B151WRN	Cumberland	BCW827V	South Coast Buses
AVK181V	Busways	B152TRN	Ribble	BFV221Y	Ribble
AVK182V	Busways	B152WRN	Ribble	BFV222Y	Ribble
AVK183V	Busways	B153WRN	Cumberland	BFW136W	Grimsby Cleethorpes
AYJ89T	HS	B154WRN	Cumberland	BHO441V	Grimsby Cleethorpes
AYJ91T	Hampshire Bus	B158WRN	Ribble	BHY996V	Cheltenham & Gloucester
AYJ92T	Hampshire Bus	B162WRN	Cumberland	BHY997V	Cheltenham & Gloucester
AYJ94T	Hants & Surrey	B214OAJ	Cleveland	BHY998V	Cheltenham & Gloucester
AYJ95T	South Coast Buses	B215OAJ	Cleveland	BIW4977	Midland Red
AYJ97T	South Coast Buses	B216OAJ	Cleveland	BJG671V	East Kent
AYJ98T	Stagecoach South	B217OAJ	Cleveland	BJG672V	East Kent
AYJ100T	Hampshire Bus	B218OAJ	Cleveland	BJG673V	East Kent
AYJ101T	South Coast Buses	B348LSO	Bluebird	BJG674V	East Kent
AYJ102T	South Coast Buses	B349LSO	Bluebird	BJG675V	East Kent
AYJ103T	South Coast Buses	B350LSO	Bluebird	BJV103L	Grimsby Cleethorpes
AYJ104T	Hampshire Bus	B351LSO	Bluebird	BKE849T	South Coast Buses
AYJ105T	South Coast Buses	B352LSO	Bluebird	BKE850T	South Coast Buses
AYJ107T	South Coast Buses	B353LSO	Bluebird	BKE851T	South Coast Buses
B27PAJ	Hartlepool	B354LSO	Bluebird	BKE858T	South Coast Buses
B28PAJ	Hartlepool	B355LSO	Bluebird	BKE859T	Hants & Surrey
B29PAJ	Hartlepool	B356LSO	Bluebird	BKE860T	Stagecoach South
B30PAJ	Hartlepool	B357LSO	Bluebird	BKE862T	South Coast Buses
B31PAJ	Hartlepool	B358LSO	Bluebird	BKR837Y	Stagecoach South
B32PAJ	Hartlepool	B359LSO	Bluebird	BNC936T	Western Scottish
B43MAO	Cumberland	B360LSO	Bluebird	BOU6V	Cheltenham & Gloucester
B49DWE	East Midland	B625DWF	East Midland	BPT903S	Red & White
B52DWE	East Midland	B626DWF	East Midland	BPY402T	Cleveland
B53DWJ	East Midland	B627DWF	East Midland	BPY403T	Cleveland
B54DWJ	East Midland	B628DWF	East Midland	BSD851T	Western Scottish
B60WKH	Kingston upon Hull	B629DWF	East Midland	BSD852T	Western Scottish
B79WUV	Selkent	B630DWF	East Midland	BSD853T	Western Scottish
B81WUV	Selkent	B631DWF	East Midland	BSD856T	Western Scottish
B83WUV	Selkent	B632DWF	East Midland	BSD858T	Western Scottish
B84WUV	Selkent	B633DWF	East Midland	BSD859T	Western Scottish
B89WUV	Selkent	B764DEG	Western Scottish	BSD860T	Western Scottish
B91WUV	Selkent	B875GSG	Bluebird	BSD862T	Western Scottish
B92WUV	Selkent	B891UAS	Ribble	BSD863T	Western Scottish
B93WUV	Selkent	B892UAS	Ribble	BSD864T	Western Scottish
B96WUV	Selkent	B893UAS	Ribble	BSJ895T	Western Scottish
B97WUV	Selkent	B894UAS	Ribble	BSJ896T	Western Scottish
B99WUV	Selkent	B895UAS	Ribble	BSJ917T	Western Scottish
B100WUV	Selkent	B896UAS	Ribble	BSJ930T	Western Scottish
B101WUV	Selkent	B897UAS	Ribble	BSJ931T	Western Scottish
B103HAO	Cumberland	B898UAS	Ribble	BSK744	Bluebird
B103WUV	Selkent	B899UAS	Ribble	BSK756	Bluebird
B105HAO	Cumberland	B900WRN	Ribble	BTU33W	Hartlepool
B106HAO	Cumberland	B910ODU	Midland Red	BUH203V	Red & White
B106UAT	Kingston upon Hull	B911ODU	Midland Red	BUH207V	Red & White
B106WUV	Selkent	B912ODU	Midland Red	BUH210V	Red & White
B107UAT	Kingston upon Hull	B960ODU	Midland Red	BUH211V	Red & White
B108UAT	Kingston upon Hull	B961ODU	Midland Red	BUH212V	Red & White
B108WUV	Selkent	B979EGG	Western Scottish	BUH214V	Red & White
B109UAT	Kingston upon Hull	B981EGG	Western Scottish	BUH232V	Red & White
B110UAT	Kingston upon Hull	B985EGG	Western Scottish	BUH237V	Red & White
B110WUV	Selkent	B986EGG	Western Scottish	BUT24Y	Kingston upon Hull
B112WUV	Selkent	B987EGG	Western Scottish	BUT25Y	Kingston upon Hull
B113WUV	Selkent	BAU178T	United Counties	BVP771V	Midland Red
B114WUV	Selkent	BAU179T	United Counties	BVP772V	Midland Red
B115WUV	Selkent	BAU180T	Stagecoach South	BVP791V	Midland Red
B116WUV	Selkent	BCS865T	Western Scottish	BVP801V	Midland Red
B117WUV	Selkent	BCS869T	Western Scottish	BVP808V	Midland Red
B118WUV	Selkent	BCS870T	Western Scottish	BVP816V	Midland Red
B119WUV	Selkent	BCS871T	Western Scottish	BVP817V	Midland Red

BVP818V	Midland Red	C112CHM	Selkent	C467SSO	Bluebird
BYJ919Y	Hampshire Bus	C113CAT	Kingston upon Hull	C468SSO	Bluebird
C23CHM	Selkent	C113HUH	Red & White	C469SSO	Bluebird
C28CHM	Selkent	C114CHM	Selkent	C470SSO	Bluebird
C29CHM	Selkent	C115CHM	Selkent	C471BHY	Red & White
C30CHM	Selkent	C116CHM	Selkent	C474BHY	Red & White
C42CHM	Selkent	C117CHM	Selkent	C501DYM	Selkent
C43CHM	Selkent	C118CHM	Selkent	C505DYM	Selkent
C43CHM	Selkent	C118HUH	Red & White	C514BFB	Red & White
C44CHM	Selkent	C119CHM	Selkent	C516BFB	Midland Red
C51CHM	Selkent	C120CHM	Selkent	C544RAO	Cumberland
C53CHM	Selkent	C120PNV	United Counties	C557TUT	Red & White
C53FDV	Midland Red	C121CHM	Selkent	C591SHC	Cheltenham & Gloucester
C54CHM	Selkent	C121PNV	United Counties	C593SHC	Red & White
C55CHM	Selkent	C122CAT	Kingston upon Hull	C594SHC	Cheltenham & Gloucester
C57CHM	Selkent	C122CHM	Selkent	C595SHC	Red & White
C60CHM	Selkent	C122PNV	United Counties	C596SHC	Red & White
C61CHM	Selkent	C123CAT	Kingston upon Hull	C601LFT	Busways
C62CHM	Selkent	C124CAT	Kingston upon Hull	C602LFT	Busways
C64CHM	Selkent	C125CAT	Kingston upon Hull	C603LFT	Busways
C67CHM	Selkent	C126CAT	Kingston upon Hull	C604LFT	Busways
C68CHM	Selkent	C127CAT	Kingston upon Hull	C605LFT	Busways
C69CHM	Selkent	C128CAT	Kingston upon Hull	C606LFT	Busways
C70CHM	Selkent	C129CAT	Kingston upon Hull	C608LFT	Busways
C71CHM	Selkent	C131CAT	Kingston upon Hull	C609LFT	Busways
C72CHM	Selkent	C170ECK	Ribble	C610LFT	Busways
C73CHM	Selkent	C171ECK	Ribble	C611LFT	Busways
C74CHM	Selkent	C172ECK	Ribble	C612LFT	Busways
C75CHM	Selkent	C173ECK	Ribble	C613LFT	Busways
C76CHM	Selkent	C174ECK	Ribble	C614LFT	Busways
C77CHM	Selkent	C175ECK	Cumberland	C615LFT	Busways
C80CHM	Selkent	C176ECK	Cumberland	C616LFT	Busways
C81CHM	Selkent	C177ECK	Cumberland	C617SFH	Cheltenham & Gloucester
C82CHM	Selkent	C178ECK	Ribble	C618LFT	Busways
C83CHM	Selkent	C179ECK	Ribble	C618SFH	Midland Red
C84PRP	South Coast Buses	C219WAJ	Cleveland	C619LFT	Busways
C86CHM	Selkent	C220WAJ	Cleveland	C619SFH	Midland Red
C87CHM	Selkent	C221WAJ	Cleveland	C620LFT	Busways
C91CHM	Selkent	C222WAJ	Cleveland	C620SFH	Midland Red
C92CHM	Selkent	C293MEG	Red & White	C621LFT	Busways
C94CHM	Selkent	C294MEG	Red & White	C621SFH	Cheltenham & Gloucester
C97CHM	Selkent	C316OFL	Red & White	C622LFT	Busways
C98CHM	Selkent	C318OFL	Red & White	C622SFH	Midland Red
C101HKG	Red & White	C326HWJ	East Midland	C623LFT	Busways
C101KDS	Western Scottish	C327HWJ	East Midland	C623SFH	Midland Red
C102HKG	Midland Red	C328HWJ	East Midland	C624LFT	Busways
C103CHM	Selkent	C329HWJ	East Midland	C624SFH	Midland Red
C103HKG	Red & White	C330HWJ	East Midland	C625LFT	Busways
C104CHM	Selkent	C331HWJ	East Midland	C625SFH	Midland Red
C104KDS	Western Scottish	C332HWJ	East Midland	C626LFT	Busways
C105CHM	Selkent	C333HWJ	East Midland	C626SFH	Cheltenham & Gloucester
C105HKG	Midland Red	C334HWJ	East Midland	C627LFT	Busways
C105KDS	Western Scottish	C335HWJ	East Midland	C627SFH	Midland Red
C106CHM	Selkent	C336HWJ	East Midland	C628LFT	Busways
C106HKG	Red & White	C345GFJ	Midland Red	C628SFH	Midland Red
C106KDS	Western Scottish	C351GFJ	Red & White	C629LFT	Busways
C107CHM	Selkent	C352GFJ	Midland Red	C629SFH	Midland Red
C107HKG	Red & White	C362GFJ	Red & White	C630LFT	Busways
C108CHM	Selkent	C364GFJ	Red & White	C631LFT	Busways
C108HKG	Red & White	C382SAO	Cumberland	C631SFH	Cheltenham & Gloucester
C109CHM	Selkent	C383SAO	Cumberland	C632LFT	Busways
C110CHM	Selkent	C434BHY	Red & White	C632SFH	Cheltenham & Gloucester
C111CAT	Kingston upon Hull	C461SSO	Bluebird	C633LFT	Busways
C111CHM	Selkent	C462SSO	Bluebird	C633SFH	Cheltenham & Gloucester
C111HKG	Red & White	C463SSO	Bluebird	C634LFT	Busways
C111JCS	Bluebird	C466BHY	Red & White		
C112CAT	Kingston upon Hull	C466SSO	Bluebird		

Reg	Operator	Reg	Operator	Reg	Operator
C634SFH	Midland Red	C709FKE	Midland Red	CJJ676W	East Kent
C635LFT	Busways	C710FKE	Midland Red	CJJ677W	East Kent
C635SFH	Midland Red	C711FKE	Midland Red	CJJ678W	East Kent
C636LFT	Busways	C712FKE	Hants & Surrey	CJJ679W	East Kent
C636SFH	Cheltenham & Gloucester	C713FKE	Midland Red	CMJ447T	Busways
C637LFT	Busways	C714FKE	Midland Red	CMJ450T	Busways
C637SFH	Cheltenham & Gloucester	C715FKE	Midland Red	CPO98W	South Coast Buses
C638LFT	Busways	C716FKE	Midland Red	CPO99W	South Coast Buses
C638SFH	Midland Red	C717FKE	Midland Red	CPO100W	South Coast Buses
C639LFT	Busways	C718FKE	Midland Red	CPY705T	Cleveland
C639SFH	Cheltenham & Gloucester	C719FKE	Midland Red	CRS60T	Bluebird
C640LFT	Busways	C720FKE	Midland Red	CRS61T	Bluebird
C640SFH	Cheltenham & Gloucester	C721FKE	Midland Red	CRS62T	Bluebird
C641LFT	Busways	C722FKE	Midland Red	CRS63T	Bluebird
C641SFH	Cheltenham & Gloucester	C724FKE	Midland Red	CRS68T	Bluebird
C642LFT	Busways	C729JJO	Midland Red	CRS69T	Bluebird
C642SFH	Cheltenham & Gloucester	C742HKK	East Kent	CRS70T	Bluebird
C643LFT	Busways	C800SDY	South Coast Buses	CRS71T	Bluebird
C643SFH	Cheltenham & Gloucester	C802KBT	Western Scottish	CRS73T	Bluebird
C644LFT	Busways	C807BYY	Selkent	CRS74T	Bluebird
C644SFH	Cheltenham & Gloucester	C808SDY	Red & White	CSO386Y	Bluebird
C645LFT	Busways	C809BYY	Selkent	CSO387Y	Busways
C645SFH	Cheltenham & Gloucester	C810BYY	Selkent	CSO388Y	Busways
C646LFT	Busways	C811BYY	Selkent	CSO389Y	Busways
C646SFH	Midland Red	C812BYY	Selkent	CSU920	Bluebird
C647LFT	Busways	C815BYY	Selkent	CSU921	Bluebird
C647SFH	Midland Red	C818BYY	Selkent	CSU922	Bluebird
C648LFT	Busways	C819BYY	Selkent	CSU923	Bluebird
C649LFT	Busways	C820SDY	Red & White	CSV219	Midland Red
C649XDF	Cheltenham & Gloucester	C901HWF	Bluebird	CUL80V	East London
C650LFT	Busways	C902HWF	Red & White	CUL130V	Selkent
C650XDF	Cheltenham & Gloucester	C904LEW	Midland Red	CUL137V	Selkent
C651LFT	Busways	C962XVC	Midland Red	CUL140V	East London
C651XDF	Cheltenham & Gloucester	C963XVC	Midland Red	CUL142V	Selkent
C652LFT	Busways	C964XVC	Midland Red	CUL163V	Selkent
C652XDF	Cheltenham & Gloucester	CBB476V	Busways	CUL168V	Selkent
C653LFT	Busways	CBB477V	Busways	CUL169V	Selkent
C653XDF	Cheltenham & Gloucester	CBD902T	United Counties	CUL175V	East London
C654LFT	Busways	CBD903T	United Counties	CUL179V	Selkent
C654XDF	Cheltenham & Gloucester	CBV2S	Cumberland	CUL180V	Selkent
C655LFT	Busways	CBV6S	Red & White	CUL189V	Selkent
C655XDF	Cheltenham & Gloucester	CBV8S	Red & White	CUL190V	Selkent
C656LFT	Busways	CBV11S	Midland Red	CUL193V	East London
C656XDF	Cheltenham & Gloucester	CBV16S	Midland Red	CUL197V	East London
C657LFT	Busways	CBV20S	Midland Red	CUL198V	Selkent
C657XDF	Cheltenham & Gloucester	CBV21S	Ribble	CUL208V	Selkent
C658LFT	Busways	CBV776S	Hampshire Bus	CUL209V	Selkent
C658XDF	Cheltenham & Gloucester	CBV780S	Midland Red	CUL214V	East London
C659LFT	Busways	CBV783S	Midland Red	CUL215V	Selkent
C659XDF	Cheltenham & Gloucester	CBV784S	Stagecoach South	CUL222V	East London
C660LFT	Busways	CBV798S	Stagecoach South	CUL223V	East London
C660XDF	Cheltenham & Gloucester	CCS459T	Western Scottish	CUL224V	Selkent
C661LFT	Busways	CD7045	Coastline	CUL225V	Selkent
C661XDF	Cheltenham & Gloucester	CDG213Y	Midland Red	CUV272C	East London
C662LFT	Busways	CEO720W	Ribble	CUV286C	East London
C662XDF	Cheltenham & Gloucester	CEO721W	Ribble	CUV300C	East London
C663LFT	Busways	CEO722W	Ribble	CUV303C	East London
C664LFT	Busways	CEO723W	Ribble	CUV311C	East London
C665LFT	Busways	CHH210T	Ribble	CVN400T	Cleveland
C701FKE	Stagecoach South	CHH211T	Ribble	CYJ492Y	Red & White
C701RSS	Bluebird	CHH214T	Ribble	CYJ493Y	Red & White
C702FKE	Midland Red	CHH389X	Cheltenham & Gloucester	D22WNH	United Counties
C703FKE	Midland Red	CJH117V	Hampshire Bus	D26BVV	United Counties
C705FKE	Midland Red	CJH119V	Hants & Surrey	D27PVS	Bluebird
C706FKE	Midland Red	CJH120V	Hants & Surrey	D33UAO	Busways
C707FKE	Midland Red	CJH142V	Hants & Surrey	D34KAX	Midland Red
C708FKE	Midland Red	CJH145V	Hants & Surrey	D34UAO	Cumberland

D35KAX	Midland Red	D228UHC	South Coast Buses	D406TFT	Busways
D35UAO	Cumberland	D229NCS	Western Scottish	D407TFT	Busways
D36UAO	Cumberland	D230NCS	Western Scottish	D408TFT	Busways
D37UAO	Cumberland	D230UHC	South Coast Buses	D409TFT	Busways
D38UAO	Cumberland	D230VCD	East Kent	D410TFT	Busways
D39UAO	Cumberland	D231NCS	Western Scottish	D411TFT	Busways
D40UAO	Cumberland	D231VCD	East Kent	D412TFT	Busways
D41UAO	Cumberland	D232NCS	Western Scottish	D413TFT	Busways
D42UAO	Cumberland	D233NCS	Western Scottish	D414TFT	Busways
D43KAX	Midland Red	D234NCS	Western Scottish	D415TFT	Busways
D43UAO	Cumberland	D235NCS	Western Scottish	D416TFT	Busways
D44UAO	Cumberland	D236NCS	Western Scottish	D417TFT	Busways
D45KAX	Midland Red	D237NCS	Western Scottish	D418TFT	Busways
D45UAO	Cumberland	D238NCS	Western Scottish	D419TFT	Busways
D46UAO	Cumberland	D239NCS	Western Scottish	D420TFT	Busways
D47KAX	Midland Red	D240NCS	Western Scottish	D435RYS	Bluebird
D48KAX	Midland Red	D241NCS	Western Scottish	D436RYS	Bluebird
D94EKV	Western Scottish	D242NCS	Western Scottish	D457CKV	Midland Red
D107NUS	Western Scottish	D243NCS	Western Scottish	D458CKV	Midland Red
D108NUS	Western Scottish	D244NCS	Western Scottish	D460CKV	Midland Red
D109NDW	Red & White	D245NCS	Western Scottish	D461CKV	Midland Red
D109NUS	Western Scottish	D246NCS	Western Scottish	D462CKV	Midland Red
D110NUS	Western Scottish	D247NCS	Western Scottish	D464CKV	Midland Red
D111NUS	Western Scottish	D248NCS	Western Scottish	D467CKV	Midland Red
D112NUS	Western Scottish	D249NCS	Western Scottish	D469WPM	Hants & Surrey
D113NUS	Western Scottish	D250NCS	Western Scottish	D470WPM	Hants & Surrey
D114NUS	Western Scottish	D251NCS	Western Scottish	D471WPM	Hants & Surrey
D115NUS	Western Scottish	D252NCS	Western Scottish	D473WPM	Hants & Surrey
D116NUS	Western Scottish	D253NCS	Western Scottish	D475CKV	Midland Red
D117NUS	Western Scottish	D254NCS	Western Scottish	D476CKV	Midland Red
D118NUS	Western Scottish	D255NCS	Western Scottish	D476PON	East London
D121NUS	Western Scottish	D256NCS	Western Scottish	D476WPM	Hants & Surrey
D122NUS	Western Scottish	D257NCS	Western Scottish	D478CKV	Midland Red
D123FYM	Selkent	D258NCS	Western Scottish	D482CKV	Midland Red
D123NUS	Western Scottish	D259NCS	Western Scottish	D501RCK	Ribble
D124FYM	Selkent	D260NCS	Western Scottish	D502RCK	Ribble
D124NUS	Western Scottish	D271OOJ	Midland Red	D503RCK	Cumberland
D125FYM	Selkent	D273OOJ	Midland Red	D504RCK	Cumberland
D126FYM	Selkent	D301SDS	Western Scottish	D505RCK	Ribble
D127FYM	Selkent	D302SDS	Western Scottish	D506RCK	Ribble
D128FYM	Selkent	D303SDS	Western Scottish	D507RCK	Ribble
D128NUS	Western Scottish	D304SDS	Western Scottish	D508RCK	Ribble
D129FYM	Selkent	D305SDS	Western Scottish	D510RCK	Ribble
D129NUS	Western Scottish	D306SDS	Western Scottish	D511RCK	Cumberland
D130FYM	Selkent	D307SDS	Western Scottish	D512RCK	Ribble
D130NUS	Western Scottish	D309SDS	Western Scottish	D513RCK	Ribble
D131FYM	Selkent	D313WPE	Midland Red	D514RCK	Cumberland
D132FYM	Selkent	D314WPE	Midland Red	D515RCK	Ribble
D133FYM	Selkent	D315WPE	Midland Red	D516RCK	Ribble
D134FYM	Selkent	D320WPE	Midland Red	D518RCK	Cumberland
D136FYM	Selkent	D321WPE	Midland Red	D519RCK	Cumberland
D136NUS	Western Scottish	D322MNC	Bluebird	D520RCK	Cumberland
D137FYM	Selkent	D380XRS	Cumberland	D521RCK	Ribble
D141FYM	Selkent	D381XRS	Cumberland	D522FYL	Selkent
D142FYM	Selkent	D383XRS	United Counties	D522RCK	Cumberland
D144FYM	Selkent	D384XAO	Cumberland	D523KSE	Bluebird
D145FYM	Selkent	D385XRS	Bluebird	D523RCK	Busways
D167TRA	Western Scottish	D386XRS	Bluebird	D524RCK	Ribble
D211VEV	East Kent	D387XRS	Bluebird	D525RCK	Cumberland
D222NCS	Western Scottish	D388XRS	Bluebird	D526RCK	Busways
D223NCS	Western Scottish	D389XRS	Bluebird	D527RCK	Ribble
D224NCS	Western Scottish	D401TFT	Busways	D528RCK	Cumberland
D225NCS	Western Scottish	D402TFT	Busways	D529RCK	Cumberland
D226NCS	Western Scottish	D403TFT	Busways	D530RCK	Cumberland
D226VCD	East Kent	D404TFT	Busways	D531RCK	Cumberland
D227NCS	Western Scottish	D405TFT	Busways	D533RCK	Cumberland
D228NCS	Western Scottish	D406FRV	United Counties	D534RCK	Cumberland

D535RCK	Busways	D856CKV	Midland Red	DSD943V	Western Scottish
D536RCK	Ribble	D857CKV	Midland Red	DSD944V	Western Scottish
D537RCK	Ribble	D858CKV	Midland Red	DSD945V	Western Scottish
D538RCK	Busways	D859CKV	Midland Red	DSD947V	Western Scottish
D539RCK	Cumberland	D859FOT	United Counties	DSD948V	Western Scottish
D540RCK	Red & White	D860CKV	Midland Red	DSD949V	Western Scottish
D541RCK	Ribble	D861CKV	Midland Red	DSD950V	Western Scottish
D542RCK	Ribble	D862CKV	Midland Red	DSD951V	Western Scottish
D543RCK	Busways	D863CKV	Midland Red	DSD952V	Western Scottish
D544RCK	Red & White	D882CKV	Midland Red	DSD953V	Western Scottish
D545RCK	Ribble	D883CKV	Midland Red	DSD954V	Western Scottish
D546RCK	Ribble	D884CKV	Midland Red	DSD955V	Western Scottish
D547RCK	Cumberland	D885CKV	Midland Red	DSD956V	Western Scottish
D548RCK	Ribble	D886CKV	Midland Red	DSD957V	Western Scottish
D549RCK	Ribble	D887CKV	Midland Red	DSD960V	Western Scottish
D550RCK	Ribble	D888CKV	Midland Red	DSD962V	Western Scottish
D551RCK	Ribble	D917GRU	Western Scottish	DSD964V	Western Scottish
D552RCK	Ribble	D918GRU	Western Scottish	DSD970V	Western Scottish
D553RCK	Manchester	D935EBP	Coastline	DSD972V	Western Scottish
D554RCK	Ribble	D938ECR	United Counties	DSD973V	Western Scottish
D555RCK	Ribble	D948UDY	Red & White	DSD974V	Western Scottish
D556RCK	Ribble	D950UDY	Red & White	DSD975V	Western Scottish
D557RCK	Cumberland	DAK201V	Red & White	DSD976V	Western Scottish
D558RCK	Cumberland	DBV23W	Midland Red	DSD977V	Western Scottish
D559RCK	Cumberland	DBV24W	Cumberland	DSD978V	Western Scottish
D560RCK	Cumberland	DBV25W	Coastline	DSD979V	Western Scottish
D561RCK	Cumberland	DBV26W	Red & White	DSD980V	Western Scottish
D562RCK	Ribble	DBV29W	Coastline	DSD981V	Western Scottish
D563RCK	Ribble	DBV30W	Ribble	DSD982V	Western Scottish
D564RCK	Ribble	DBV31W	Midland Red	DSD983V	Western Scottish
D601MKH	Kingston upon Hull	DBV32W	Cumberland	DSD984V	Western Scottish
D602MKH	Kingston upon Hull	DBV100W	Ribble	DSV943	Cumberland
D603MKH	Kingston upon Hull	DBV131Y	Ribble	DTL548T	Busways
D604MKH	Busways	DBV132Y	Ribble	DWF22V	East Midland
D605MKH	Kingston upon Hull	DBV134Y	Cumberland	DWF23V	East Midland
D606MKH	Busways	DBV137Y	Ribble	DWF24V	East Midland
D607MKH	Busways	DBV828W	Ribble	DWF25V	East Midland
D608MKH	Kingston upon Hull	DBV829W	Ribble	DWF26V	East Midland
D609MKH	Kingston upon Hull	DBV830W	Ribble	DWF188V	Bluebird
D610BCK	United Counties	DBV831W	Ribble	DWF189V	Midland Red
D611MKH	Kingston upon Hull	DBV832W	Ribble	DWF190V	Bluebird
D612MKH	Kingston upon Hull	DBV833W	Ribble	DWF191V	Bluebird
D613BCK	United Counties	DBV834W	Ribble	DWF193V	Bluebird
D613MKH	Kingston upon Hull	DBV835W	Ribble	DWF194V	Midland Red
D614MKH	Kingston upon Hull	DBV836W	Ribble	DWF195V	Midland Red
D615MKH	Kingston upon Hull	DBV837W	Ribble	DWF197V	Midland Red
D616BCK	United Counties	DBV838W	Ribble	E45HFE	Grimsby Cleethorpes
D619BCK	United Counties	DBV839W	Ribble	E46HFE	Grimsby Cleethorpes
D672SHH	Ribble	DBV840W	Ribble	E47CHH	Cumberland
D724YBV	United Counties	DBV841W	Ribble	E47HFE	Grimsby Cleethorpes
D725YBV	United Counties	DBV842W	Ribble	E48CHH	Cumberland
D726YBV	United Counties	DBV843W	Ribble	E48HFE	Grimsby Cleethorpes
D728YBV	United Counties	DDM24X	Midland Red	E49CHH	Cumberland
D729YBV	United Counties	DDM31X	Midland Red	E49HFE	Grimsby Cleethorpes
D731YBV	United Counties	DDW432V	Red & White	E50CHH	Cumberland
D735OOG	Midland Red	DDW433V	Red & White	E50HFE	Grimsby Cleethorpes
D735YBV	United Counties	DDW434V	Red & White	E51HFE	Grimsby Cleethorpes
D736OOG	Midland Red	DGS625	Bluebird	E52WAG	Kingston upon Hull
D755JUB	Midland Red	DHW350W	Cheltenham & Gloucester	E56HFE	Grimsby Cleethorpes
D762JUB	Midland Red	DHW352W	Cheltenham & Gloucester	E57HFE	Grimsby Cleethorpes
D771MUR	United Counties	DRU6T	Hampshire Bus	E58HFE	Grimsby Cleethorpes
D799USB	Western Scottish	DSD934V	Western Scottish	E65BVS	Coastline
D851CKV	Midland Red	DSD935V	Western Scottish	E77PUH	Midland Red
D852CKV	Midland Red	DSD936V	Western Scottish	E95OUH	Midland Red
D853CKV	Midland Red	DSD937V	Western Scottish	E96OUH	Red & White
D854CKV	Midland Red	DSD940V	Western Scottish	E97OUH	Red & White
D855CKV	Midland Red	DSD942V	Western Scottish	E99OUH	Midland Red

The 1995 Stagecoach Bus Handbook

Reg	Operator	Reg	Operator	Reg	Operator
E100OUH	Red & White	E324JVN	Cleveland	E631BVK	Busways
E113RBO	Red & White	E333LHN	Cleveland	E632BVK	Busways
E114SDW	Red & White	E364YGB	Bluebird	E633BVK	Busways
E115RAX	Red & White	E421AFT	Busways	E634BVK	Busways
E115SDW	Red & White	E422AFT	Busways	E634DCK	Western Scottish
E122RAX	Red & White	E423AFT	Busways	E635BVK	Busways
E127KYW	Selkent	E424AFT	Busways	E636BVK	Busways
E130ORP	United Counties	E425AFT	Busways	E636DCK	Western Scottish
E131ORP	United Counties	E426AFT	Busways	E637BVK	Busways
E132ORP	United Counties	E427AFT	Busways	E637DCK	Western Scottish
E132SAT	Kingston upon Hull	E428AFT	Busways	E638BVK	Busways
E133ORP	United Counties	E429AFT	Busways	E638YUS	Western Scottish
E133SAT	Kingston upon Hull	E430AFT	Busways	E639BVK	Busways
E134ORP	United Counties	E431AFT	Busways	E640BVK	Busways
E134SAT	Kingston upon Hull	E432AFT	Busways	E640DCK	Western Scottish
E135SAT	Kingston upon Hull	E433AFT	Busways	E641KYW	East London
E136SAT	Kingston upon Hull	E433YHL	Midland Red	E642KYW	East London
E137SAT	Kingston upon Hull	E434AFT	Busways	E643DCK	Western Scottish
E138SAT	Kingston upon Hull	E435AFT	Busways	E643KYW	East London
E139SAT	Kingston upon Hull	E436AFT	Busways	E644DCK	Western Scottish
E140SAT	Kingston upon Hull	E437AFT	Busways	E644KYW	East London
E141SAT	Kingston upon Hull	E438AFT	Busways	E645KYW	East London
E142BKH	Kingston upon Hull	E439AFT	Busways	E646DCK	Western Scottish
E143BKH	Kingston upon Hull	E440AFT	Busways	E646KYW	East London
E144BKH	Kingston upon Hull	E441AFT	Busways	E647KYW	East London
E145BKH	Kingston upon Hull	E442AFT	Busways	E648KCX	Bluebird
E146BKH	Kingston upon Hull	E443AFT	Busways	E648KYW	East London
E146KYW	Selkent	E444AFT	Busways	E649KYW	East London
E147BKH	Kingston upon Hull	E445AFT	Busways	E650KYW	East London
E148BKH	Kingston upon Hull	E446AFT	Busways	E663JAD	Cheltenham & Gloucester
E149BKH	Kingston upon Hull	E447AFT	Busways	E664JAD	Cheltenham & Gloucester
E150BKH	Kingston upon Hull	E448AFT	Busways	E665JAD	Cheltenham & Gloucester
E151BKH	Kingston upon Hull	E449AFT	Busways	E666JAD	Cheltenham & Gloucester
E151UKR	East Kent	E450AFT	Busways	E667JAD	Cheltenham & Gloucester
E152UKR	East Kent	E451AFT	Busways	E668JAD	Cheltenham & Gloucester
E153UKR	East Kent	E452AFT	Busways	E669JAD	Cheltenham & Gloucester
E154UKR	East Kent	E453AFT	Busways	E670JDG	Cheltenham & Gloucester
E155CGJ	East London	E454AFT	Busways	E671JDG	Cheltenham & Gloucester
E155UKR	East Kent	E455AFT	Busways	E672KDG	Cheltenham & Gloucester
E156UKR	East Kent	E456AFT	Busways	E673KDG	Cheltenham & Gloucester
E157UKR	East Kent	E457AFT	Busways	E674KDG	Cheltenham & Gloucester
E158RNY	Red & White	E458AFT	Busways	E675KDG	Cheltenham & Gloucester
E158UKR	East Kent	E459AFT	Busways	E676KDG	Cheltenham & Gloucester
E159UKR	East Kent	E460AFT	Busways	E705LYU	East London
E160UKR	East Kent	E481DAU	East Midland	E706LYU	East London
E161UKR	East Kent	E510PVV	Cumberland	E709MFR	Cumberland
E162UKR	East Kent	E511PVV	Cumberland	E712LYU	East London
E163UKR	East Kent	E512PVV	Cumberland	E713LYU	East London
E164UKR	East Kent	E580TKJ	East Kent	E714LYU	East London
E165UKR	East Kent	E581TKJ	East Kent	E721BVO	East Midland
E166UKR	East Kent	E582TKJ	East Kent	E746SKR	East Kent
E167UKR	East Kent	E583TKJ	East Kent	E747SKR	East Kent
E168UKR	East Kent	E584TKJ	East Kent	E748SKR	East Kent
E169UKR	East Kent	E585TKJ	East Kent	E749SKR	East Kent
E170UKR	East Kent	E586TKJ	East Kent	E750SKR	East Kent
E201EPB	Hants & Surrey	E587TKJ	East Kent	E751SKR	East Kent
E202EPB	Coastline	E621BVK	Busways	E752SKR	East Kent
E203EPB	Coastline	E622BVK	Busways	E753SKR	East Kent
E204EPB	Hants & Surrey	E623BVK	Busways	E754UKR	East Kent
E233JRF	Hampshire Bus	E624BVK	Busways	E755UKR	East Kent
E275BRG	Red & White	E625BVK	Busways	E842KAS	Bluebird
E291TAX	Red & White	E626BVK	Busways	E849AAO	Western Scottish
E292TAX	Red & White	E627BVK	Busways	E854UKR	East Kent
E293TAX	Red & White	E628BVK	Busways	E855UKR	East Kent
E294TAX	Red & White	E629BVK	Busways	E864RCS	Western Scottish
E295TAX	Red & White	E630BVK	Busways	E865RCS	Western Scottish
E317BRM	Cumberland	E630KCX	Midland Red	E866RCS	Western Scottish

E867RCS	Western Scottish	EHU383K	Busways	EYE250V	Selkent
E880DRA	East Midland	EJR104W	Busways	F21PSL	Hampshire Bus
E889HHP	Midland Red	EJR105W	Busways	F22PSL	Hampshire Bus
E896SDW	Red & White	EJR106W	Busways	F23PSL	Hampshire Bus
E897SDW	Red & White	EJR107W	Busways	F24HGG	East London
E898SDW	Red & White	EJR108W	Busways	F25PSL	Hampshire Bus
E899SDW	Red & White	EJR109W	Busways	F26PSL	Hampshire Bus
E901KYR	Busways	EJR110W	Busways	F32CWY	East London
E905KYR	Busways	EJR111W	Busways	F50CWY	East London
E906KYR	Busways	EJR112W	Busways	F53EAT	Kingston upon Hull
E907KYR	Busways	EJR113W	Busways	F55EAT	Kingston upon Hull
E908KYR	Busways	EJR114W	Busways	F57AVV	United Counties
E909KYR	Busways	EJR115W	Busways	F58AVV	United Counties
E910KYR	Busways	EJR117W	Busways	F59AVV	United Counties
E911KYR	Busways	EJR118W	Busways	F60AVV	United Counties
E912KYR	Busways	EJR119W	Busways	F61AVV	Coastline
E914KYR	Busways	EJR121W	Busways	F62AVV	Hampshire Bus
E915KYR	Busways	EJR122W	Busways	F71FKK	East Kent
E917KYR	Busways	EJR123W	Busways	F71LAL	Midland Red
E918KYR	Busways	EJV31Y	Grimsby Cleethorpes	F72FKK	East Kent
E919KYR	Busways	EJV32Y	Grimsby Cleethorpes	F73FKK	East Kent
E920KYR	Busways	EJV33Y	Grimsby Cleethorpes	F74DCW	Red & White
E921KYR	Busways	EJV34Y	Grimsby Cleethorpes	F74FKK	East Kent
E922KYR	Busways	EKW614V	East Midland	F75FKK	East Kent
E923KYR	Busways	EKW615V	East Midland	F75TFU	Grimsby Cleethorpes
E924KYR	Busways	EKW616V	East Midland	F76TFU	Grimsby Cleethorpes
E925KYR	Busways	ELJ208V	Hampshire Bus	F77HAU	Bluebird
E927KYR	Busways	ELJ209V	Midland Red	F77TFU	Grimsby Cleethorpes
E927PBE	Grimsby Cleethorpes	ELJ212V	Hampshire Bus	F78TFU	Grimsby Cleethorpes
E928PBE	Grimsby Cleethorpes	ELJ213V	South Coast Buses	F101HVK	Busways
E929PBE	Grimsby Cleethorpes	EMB365S	Midland Red	F102HVK	Busways
E929UBO	Red & White	ENJ909V	South Coast Buses	F103HVK	Busways
E930PBE	Grimsby Cleethorpes	ENJ910V	South Coast Buses	F104HVK	Busways
E930UBO	Red & White	ENJ911V	South Coast Buses	F105HVK	Busways
E931UBO	Red & White	ENJ912V	South Coast Buses	F106HVK	Busways
E932UBO	Red & White	ENJ913V	South Coast Buses	F106YVP	East London
E947BHS	Bluebird	ENJ914V	South Coast Buses	F107HVK	Busways
E986AHH	Cumberland	ENJ915V	South Coast Buses	F108HVK	Busways
E992MSE	Bluebird	ENJ916V	South Coast Buses	F109HVK	Busways
EAP973V	South Coast Buses	ENJ917V	South Coast Buses	F109YVP	East London
EAP977V	Hampshire Bus	ENJ918V	South Coast Buses	F110HVK	Busways
EAP978V	Coastline	EPW516K	Busways	F110NES	United Counties
EAP980V	Hampshire Bus	ERV115W	South Coast Buses	F110YVP	East London
EAP982V	Hampshire Bus	ERV116W	South Coast Buses	F111HVK	Busways
EAP983V	East Kent	ERV117W	South Coast Buses	F111YVP	East London
EAP984V	Coastline	ERV118W	South Coast Buses	F112HVK	Busways
EAP985V	Coastline	ERV251D	Cumberland	F112YVP	East London
EAP985V	Coastline	ESU263	Busways	F113HVK	Busways
EAP986V	Coastline	EWE202V	East Midland	F113YVP	East London
EAP987V	Coastline	EWE203V	East Midland	F114HVK	Busways
EAP988V	South Coast Buses	EWE205V	East Midland	F114YVP	East London
EAP990V	Coastline	EWE206V	East Midland	F115HVK	Busways
EAP991V	Coastline	EWS740W	Cheltenham & Gloucester	F116HVK	Busways
EAP992V	Coastline	EWS743W	Cheltenham & Gloucester	F117HVK	Busways
EAP996V	Coastline	EWS746W	Cheltenham & Gloucester	F118HVK	Busways
ECS876V	Western Scottish	EWS748W	Cheltenham & Gloucester	F118YVP	East London
ECS877V	Western Scottish	EWS751W	Cheltenham & Gloucester	F119HVK	Busways
ECS878V	Western Scottish	EYE229V	Selkent	F119YVP	East London
ECS879V	Western Scottish	EYE230V	East London	F120HVK	Busways
ECS880V	Western Scottish	EYE233V	Selkent	F120YVP	East London
ECS882V	Western Scottish	EYE236V	Selkent	F121HVK	Busways
ECS883V	Western Scottish	EYE237V	Selkent	F121YVP	East London
ECS885V	Western Scottish	EYE238V	Selkent	F122HVK	Busways
ECS887V	Western Scottish	EYE240V	Selkent	F123HVK	Busways
ECU201E	Busways	EYE244V	Selkent	F124HVK	Busways
EDS50A	Bluebird	EYE246V	East London	F125HVK	Busways
EFU935Y	Grimsby Cleethorpes	EYE248V	East London	F125YVP	East London

Reg	Operator	Reg	Operator	Reg	Operator
F126YVP	East London	F494NTR	Busways	F701BAT	Kingston upon Hull
F128YVP	East London	F495NTR	Busways	F702BAT	Kingston upon Hull
F130YVP	East London	F496NTR	Busways	F703BAT	Kingston upon Hull
F131YVP	East London	F561HPP	Coastline	F704BAT	Kingston upon Hull
F132YVP	East London	F562HPP	Coastline	F705BAT	Kingston upon Hull
F135SPX	Ribble	F563HPP	Coastline	F706CAG	Kingston upon Hull
F135URP	United Counties	F564HPP	Coastline	F761EKM	East Kent
F136SPX	Ribble	F601MSL	Hampshire Bus	F762EKM	East Kent
F137SPX	Ribble	F601UVN	Cleveland	F763EKM	East Kent
F152HAT	Kingston upon Hull	F602MSL	Hampshire Bus	F764EKM	East Kent
F153HAT	Kingston upon Hull	F602UVN	Cleveland	F765EKM	East Kent
F154HAT	Kingston upon Hull	F603MSL	Hampshire Bus	F766EKM	East Kent
F155HAT	Kingston upon Hull	F603UVN	Cleveland	F767EKM	East Kent
F156FWY	East London	F604MSL	Hampshire Bus	F771EKM	East Kent
F156HAT	Kingston upon Hull	F604UVN	Cleveland	F772EKM	East Kent
F157HAT	Kingston upon Hull	F605MSL	Hampshire Bus	F773EKM	East Kent
F160FWY	East London	F605UVN	Cleveland	F774EKM	East Kent
F164XCS	Bluebird	F606MSL	Hampshire Bus	F775EKM	East Kent
F165FWY	East London	F606UVN	Cleveland	F781KKP	East Kent
F166FWY	East London	F607UVN	Cleveland	F782KKP	East Kent
F169FWY	East London	F608UVN	Cleveland	F803FAO	Cumberland
F170FWY	East London	F609UVN	Cleveland	F804FAO	Cumberland
F171FWY	East London	F609XMS	Selkent	F805FAO	Cumberland
F172FWY	East London	F610UVN	Cleveland	F806FAO	Cumberland
F173FWY	East London	F614XMS	Selkent	F807FAO	Cumberland
F174FWY	East London	F615XMS	Selkent	F808FAO	Cumberland
F175FWY	East London	F616XMS	Selkent	F809FAO	Cumberland
F176FWY	East London	F617XMS	Selkent	F810FAO	Cumberland
F177FWY	East London	F619XMS	Selkent	F811FAO	Cumberland
F178FWY	East London	F620MSL	United Counties	F846TLU	Midland Red
F179FWY	East London	F620XMS	Selkent	F862FWB	Bluebird
F180FWY	East London	F621MSL	United Counties	F864PAC	Midland Red
F197YDA	East London	F621XMS	Selkent	F865PAC	Midland Red
F201FHH	Cumberland	F622MSL	United Counties	F866PAC	Midland Red
F202FHH	Cumberland	F623MSL	United Counties	F867PAC	Midland Red
F202YKG	Red & White	F624MSL	United Counties	F868PAC	Midland Red
F251JRM	Cumberland	F624XMS	Selkent	F871UAC	Midland Red
F252JRM	Cumberland	F625MSL	United Counties	F872UAC	Midland Red
F253KAO	Cumberland	F625XMS	Selkent	F901JRG	Busways
F301MYJ	South Coast Buses	F626MSL	United Counties	F902JRG	Busways
F302MYJ	South Coast Buses	F627MSL	United Counties	F903JRG	Busways
F303MYJ	South Coast Buses	F628MSL	United Counties	F904JRG	Busways
F304MYJ	Coastline	F629MSL	United Counties	F905JRG	Busways
F305MYJ	Coastline	F629XMS	Selkent	F906JRG	Busways
F306MYJ	Coastline	F630MSL	United Counties	F907JRG	Busways
F307MYJ	Coastline	F630XMS	Selkent	F908JRG	Busways
F308MYJ	Coastline	F631MSL	United Counties	F909JRG	Busways
F309MYJ	Coastline	F631XMS	Selkent	F910JRG	Busways
F311DET	Cheltenham & Gloucester	F632MSL	United Counties	F911JRG	Busways
F334JHS	Western Scottish	F633MSL	United Counties	F912JRG	Busways
F335JHS	Western Scottish	F634MSP	United Counties	F912YWY	East London
F335SPY	Cleveland	F635YRP	United Counties	F913JRG	Busways
F336JHS	Western Scottish	F636YRP	United Counties	F913YWY	East London
F336VEF	Cleveland	F637OHD	Bluebird	F914JRG	Busways
F337VEF	Cleveland	F637YRP	United Counties	F915JRG	Busways
F338VEF	Cleveland	F638YRP	United Counties	F916JRG	Busways
F339VEF	Cleveland	F641XMS	Selkent	F917JRG	Busways
F340VEF	Cleveland	F651KNL	Busways	F918JRG	Busways
F341VEF	Cleveland	F653KNL	Busways	F919JRG	Busways
F342VEF	Cleveland	F654KNL	Busways	F920JRG	Busways
F343VEF	Cleveland	F658KNL	Busways	F958HTO	Red & White
F344VEF	Cleveland	F659KNL	Busways	FAO417V	United Counties
F345VEF	Cleveland	F660PWK	Midland Red	FAO418V	United Counties
F394DHL	Selkent	F661KNL	Busways	FAO419V	United Counties
F491NTR	United Counties	F661PWK	Midland Red	FAO420V	Cumberland
F492NTR	United Counties	F677PDF	Cheltenham & Gloucester	FAO421V	Cumberland
F493NTR	United Counties	F695OPA	Hants & Surrey	FAO422V	Cumberland

FAO423V	Cumberland	G37SSR	Hampshire Bus	G190PAO	Ribble
FAO424V	Cumberland	G37TGW	Selkent	G191PAO	Ribble
FAO425V	Cumberland	G38SSR	Hampshire Bus	G192PAO	Ribble
FAO426V	Cumberland	G38TGW	Selkent	G193PAO	Bluebird
FAO427V	Cumberland	G39SSR	Hampshire Bus	G194PAO	Bluebird
FAO428V	Cumberland	G39TGW	Selkent	G195PAO	Bluebird
FAO429V	Cumberland	G40SSR	United Counties	G196PAO	Bluebird
FCY284W	Western Scottish	G40TGW	Selkent	G197PAO	Bluebird
FCY286W	Western Scottish	G41SSR	United Counties	G198PAO	Bluebird
FCY294W	Western Scottish	G42SSR	Hampshire Bus	G199PAO	Bluebird
FDV784V	Ribble	G43SSR	Hampshire Bus	G200PAO	Bluebird
FDV799V	Cumberland	G56SAG	Kingston upon Hull	G201PAO	Bluebird
FDV809V	United Counties	G61JVV	United Counties	G202PAO	Bluebird
FDV810V	Bluebird	G62JVV	United Counties	G203PAO	Bluebird
FDV811V	United Counties	G63JVV	United Counties	G210SSL	Hampshire Bus
FDV812V	United Counties	G64JVV	United Counties	G211SSL	Hampshire Bus
FDV813V	Ribble	G65JVV	United Counties	G212SSL	Hampshire Bus
FDV816V	Bluebird	G66JVV	United Counties	G213SSL	Hampshire Bus
FDV817V	Ribble	G67LVV	United Counties	G214SSL	Hampshire Bus
FDV818V	Hampshire Bus	G71APO	Hampshire Bus	G251TSL	Bluebird
FDV819V	Bluebird	G72APO	Hampshire Bus	G252TSL	Bluebird
FDV820V	Midland Red	G73APO	Hampshire Bus	G253TSL	Bluebird
FDV822V	Midland Red	G79VFW	Grimsby Cleethorpes	G254TSL	Bluebird
FDV829V	Coastline	G80VFW	Grimsby Cleethorpes	G255TSL	Bluebird
FDV830V	Coastline	G81VFW	Grimsby Cleethorpes	G256TSL	Bluebird
FDV831V	Coastline	G86KUB	East London	G257TSL	Bluebird
FDV832V	United Counties	G91KUB	East London	G258TSL	Bluebird
FDV833V	Ribble	G91VMM	South Coast Buses	G259TSL	Bluebird
FDV834V	Hampshire Bus	G92VMM	South Coast Buses	G260TSL	Bluebird
FDV835V	United Counties	G95SKR	East Kent	G261TSL	Bluebird
FDV838V	United Counties	G96SKR	East Kent	G262EHD	Western Scottish
FDV839V	Hampshire Bus	G97SKR	East Kent	G262TSL	Bluebird
FDV840V	Bluebird	G98SKR	East Kent	G263TSL	Cumberland
FES831W	Bluebird	G101AAD	Cheltenham & Gloucester	G264TSL	Cumberland
FPR62V	Hants & Surrey	G102AAD	Cheltenham & Gloucester	G265TSL	Cumberland
FRP908T	United Counties	G103AAD	Cheltenham & Gloucester	G266TSL	Cumberland
FRP909T	United Counties	G104AAD	Cheltenham & Gloucester	G267TSL	Cumberland
FRP910T	United Counties	G105AAD	Cheltenham & Gloucester	G268TSL	Cumberland
FRP911T	United Counties	G105KUB	East London	G269TSL	Cumberland
FRP912T	United Counties	G106KUB	East London	G270TSL	Bluebird
FSL61W	Hartlepool	G107KUB	East London	G271TSL	Bluebird
FSL62W	Hartlepool	G108CEH	Busways	G272TSL	Bluebird
FSU737	Western Scottish	G113SKX	Busways	G273TSL	Bluebird
FSU739	Western Scottish	G115OGA	Midland Red	G274TSL	Bluebird
FYX824W	Busways	G119KUB	East London	G275TSL	Bluebird
G21CSG	Red & White	G178PAO	Cumberland	G276TSL	Bluebird
G22CSG	Busways	G179PAO	Ribble	G277TSL	Bluebird
G23CSG	Busways	G180JHG	Ribble	G278TSL	Bluebird
G24CSG	Red & White	G180PAO	Ribble	G279TSL	Bluebird
G26XBK	Midland Red	G181JHG	Ribble	G282TSL	Bluebird
G27PSR	United Counties	G181PAO	Ribble	G283TSL	Bluebird
G28PSR	United Counties	G182JHG	Ribble	G284TSL	Bluebird
G29PSR	United Counties	G182PAO	Ribble	G285TSL	Bluebird
G30PSR	Hampshire Bus	G183JHG	Ribble	G286TSL	Bluebird
G30TGW	Selkent	G183PAO	Ribble	G287TSL	Bluebird
G31PSR	United Counties	G184JHG	Ribble	G288TSL	Bluebird
G31TGW	Selkent	G184PAO	Ribble	G289TSL	Bluebird
G32PSR	United Counties	G185JHG	Ribble	G290TSL	Bluebird
G32TGW	Selkent	G185PAO	Ribble	G291TSL	Bluebird
G33SSR	United Counties	G186JHG	Ribble	G292TSL	Bluebird
G33TGW	Selkent	G186PAO	Ribble	G293TSL	Cumberland
G34PSR	Coastline	G187JHG	Ribble	G294TSL	Cumberland
G34TGW	Selkent	G187PAO	Ribble	G295TSL	Cumberland
G35PSR	East Kent	G188JHG	Ribble	G296TSL	Cumberland
G35TGW	Selkent	G188PAO	Ribble	G297TSL	Cumberland
G36SSR	Hampshire Bus	G189JHG	Ribble	G298TSL	Cumberland
G36TGW	Selkent	G189PAO	Ribble	G299TSL	Cumberland

The 1995 Stagecoach Bus Handbook

G300TSL	Cumberland	G649EVV	United Counties	G925TCU	Busways	
G301WHP	Midland Red	G665PHH	Ribble	G926TCU	Busways	
G302WHP	Midland Red	G679AAD	Cheltenham & Gloucester	G974ARV	South Coast Buses	
G303WHP	Midland Red	G680AAD	Cheltenham & Gloucester	G975ARV	South Coast Buses	
G339KKW	East Midland	G681AAD	Cheltenham & Gloucester	G976ARV	Hampshire Bus	
G340KKW	East Midland	G682AAD	Cheltenham & Gloucester	G977ARV	Hampshire Bus	
G341KKW	East Midland	G683AAD	Cheltenham & Gloucester	G978ARV	Hampshire Bus	
G342KKW	East Midland	G684AAD	Cheltenham & Gloucester	GAJ125V	Cleveland	
G343KKW	East Midland	G684KNW	East London	GAJ126V	Cleveland	
G386PNV	Bluebird	G701TCD	Coastline	GAJ127V	Cleveland	
G387PNV	Bluebird	G702TCD	Coastline	GAJ128V	Cleveland	
G418RYJ	Coastline	G703TCD	Coastline	GAJ129V	Cleveland	
G419RYJ	Coastline	G704TCD	Coastline	GAJ130V	Cleveland	
G420RYJ	Coastline	G705TCD	East Kent	GAJ131V	Cleveland	
G421RYJ	Coastline	G706TCD	East Kent	GAJ132V	Cleveland	
G422RYJ	Coastline	G707TCD	East Kent	GAJ133V	Cleveland	
G446VKK	East Kent	G708TCD	Coastline	GAJ134V	Cleveland	
G447VKK	East Kent	G709TCD	Coastline	GAJ135V	Cleveland	
G491RKK	East Kent	G710TCD	Coastline	GAJ136V	Cleveland	
G492RKK	East Kent	G801JRH	Kingston upon Hull	GCS33V	Western Scottish	
G493RKK	East Kent	G802JRH	Kingston upon Hull	GCS37V	Western Scottish	
G494RKK	East Kent	G803JRH	Kingston upon Hull	GCS38V	Western Scottish	
G528LWU	Midland Red	G804JRH	Kingston upon Hull	GCS41V	Western Scottish	
G529LWU	Midland Red	G805JRH	Kingston upon Hull	GCS45V	Western Scottish	
G530LWU	Midland Red	G806JRH	Kingston upon Hull	GCS47V	Western Scottish	
G531LWU	Midland Red	G807LAG	Kingston upon Hull	GCS48V	Western Scottish	
G532LWU	Midland Red	G807RTS	Hampshire Bus	GCS49V	Western Scottish	
G533LWU	Cheltenham & Gloucester	G808LAG	Kingston upon Hull	GCS51V	Western Scottish	
G534LWU	Cheltenham & Gloucester	G808RTS	Hampshire Bus	GCS53V	Western Scottish	
G535LWU	Midland Red	G809RTS	Coastline	GCS57V	Western Scottish	
G546LWU	Cheltenham & Gloucester	G820KWF	East Midland	GCS58V	Western Scottish	
G547LWU	Cheltenham & Gloucester	G821KWF	East Midland	GCS60V	Western Scottish	
G548LWU	Cheltenham & Gloucester	G822KWF	East Midland	GCS61V	Western Scottish	
G566PRM	Ribble	G823KWF	East Midland	GCS62V	Western Scottish	
G567PRM	Ribble	G824KWF	East Midland	GCS65V	Western Scottish	
G568PRM	Ribble	G825KWF	East Midland	GCS69V	Western Scottish	
G569PRM	Ribble	G825VGA	Western Scottish	GCW461S	Ribble	
G570PRM	Ribble	G826KWF	East Midland	GEF185N	Hartlepool	
G571PRM	Ribble	G827KWF	East Midland	GEF186N	Hartlepool	
G572PRM	Ribble	G831VGA	Western Scottish	GEF187N	Hartlepool	
G573PRM	Ribble	G864BPD	Hants & Surrey	GEF188N	Hartlepool	
G574FSD	Western Scottish	G901PKK	East Kent	GEF189N	Hartlepool	
G574PRM	Ribble	G902PKK	East Kent	GEF190N	Hartlepool	
G575PRM	Ribble	G903PKK	East Kent	GEF191N	Hartlepool	
G576PRM	Ribble	G904PKK	East Kent	GFN546N	Stagecoach South	
G577PRM	Ribble	G905PKK	East Kent	GFN552N	East Kent	
G578PRM	Ribble	G906PKK	East Kent	GFR101W	Ribble	
G611GEF	Cleveland	G907PKK	East Kent	GGM80W	Hants & Surrey	
G612GEF	Cleveland	G908PKK	East Kent	GGM81W	Hants & Surrey	
G613GEF	Cleveland	G910KWF	Coastline	GGM82W	Hants & Surrey	
G614GEF	Cleveland	G911KWF	East Kent	GGM85W	Hants & Surrey	
G615GEF	Cleveland	G912KWF	Red & White	GGM86W	Hampshire Bus	
G616GEF	Cleveland	G913KWF	East Kent	GGM105W	Hants & Surrey	
G617GEF	Cleveland	G914KWF	East Kent	GHB146N	Red & White	
G618GEF	Cleveland	G915KWF	East Midland	GHB148N	Red & White	
G619GEF	Cleveland	G916KWF	East Midland	GHV102N	Selkent	
G620GEF	Cleveland	G917KWF	East Kent	GHV948N	Selkent	
G639EVV	United Counties	G919KWF	Red & White	GLJ467N	Stagecoach South	
G640EVV	United Counties	G920KWF	Red & White	GMS285S	Western Scottish	
G641EVV	United Counties	G921KWF	East Kent	GMS292S	Western Scottish	
G642EVV	United Counties	G921TCU	Busways	GNF6V	Cheltenham & Gloucester	
G643EVV	United Counties	G922KWF	East Kent	GNF8V	Cheltenham & Gloucester	
G644EVV	United Counties	G922TCU	Busways	GNF9V	Cheltenham & Gloucester	
G645EVV	United Counties	G923KWF	East Kent	GNF10V	Cheltenham & Gloucester	
G646EVV	United Counties	G923TCU	Busways	GNF11V	Cheltenham & Gloucester	
G647EVV	United Counties	G924KWF	Red & White	GOL406N	Cheltenham & Gloucester	
G648EVV	United Counties	G924TCU	Busways	GOL412N	Midland Red	

Reg	Operator	Reg	Operator	Reg	Operator
GOL413N	Midland Red	H144UUA	Selkent	H435EFT	Busways
GOL426N	Midland Red	H145UUA	Selkent	H436EFT	Busways
GPJ894N	Hants & Surrey	H146UUA	Selkent	H437EFT	Busways
GRM625V	Cumberland	H147UUA	Selkent	H482BEE	Grimsby Cleethorpes
GRP794L	United Counties	H148UUA	Selkent	H483BEE	Grimsby Cleethorpes
GRS343E	Bluebird	H149CVU	Ribble	H484BEE	Grimsby Cleethorpes
GSO1V	Bluebird	H149UUA	Selkent	H485BEE	Grimsby Cleethorpes
GSO2V	United Counties	H150CVU	Ribble	H495MRW	Midland Red
GSO6V	United Counties	H150UUA	Selkent	H556TUG	Red & White
GSO7V	United Counties	H151UUA	Selkent	H564WWR	Selkent
GSO8V	East Midland	H152UUA	Selkent	H642GRO	East London
GSO89V	Bluebird	H153UUA	Selkent	H650VVV	United Counties
GSO90V	Bluebird	H154UUA	Selkent	H651VVV	United Counties
GSO91V	Bluebird	H160WWT	Selkent	H652VVV	United Counties
GSO92V	Bluebird	H161WWT	Selkent	H653VVV	United Counties
GSO93V	Bluebird	H162WWT	Selkent	H654VVV	United Counties
GSO94V	Bluebird	H163WWT	Selkent	H667BNL	Busways
GSO95V	Bluebird	H165WWT	Selkent	H668BNL	Busways
GSU950	Western Scottish	H166WWT	Selkent	H669BNL	Busways
GTX738W	Red & White	H167WWT	Selkent	H670BNL	Busways
GTX742W	Red & White	H168WWT	Selkent	H671BNL	Busways
GTX743W	Red & White	H169WWT	Selkent	H672BNL	Busways
GTX744W	Red & White	H170WWT	Selkent	H673BNL	Busways
GTX746W	Midland Red	H171WWT	Selkent	H674BNL	Busways
GTX747W	Red & White	H172WWT	Selkent	H675BNL	Busways
GTX748W	Red & White	H173WWT	Selkent	H676BNL	Busways
GTX750W	Red & White	H174WWT	Selkent	H679BTP	Hampshire Bus
GTX753W	Red & White	H175WWT	Selkent	H680BTP	Hampshire Bus
GTX754W	Midland Red	H176WWT	Selkent	H801BKK	East Kent
GWE617V	East Midland	H191WFR	Ribble	H802BKK	East Kent
GWE618V	East Midland	H192WFR	Ribble	H803BKK	East Kent
GWE619V	East Midland	H193WFR	Ribble	H804BKK	East Kent
GYE252W	East London	H194WFR	Ribble	H805BKK	East Kent
GYE252W	East London	H195WFR	Ribble	H806BKK	East Kent
GYE254W	East London	H196WFR	Ribble	H807BKK	East Kent
GYE261W	East London	H197WFR	Ribble	H808BKK	East Kent
GYE262W	East London	H201XKH	Cleveland	H809BKK	East Kent
GYE263W	East London	H301PAX	Red & White	H809WKH	Kingston upon Hull
GYE264W	East London	H344SWA	East Midland	H810BKK	East Kent
GYE266W	East London	H345SWA	East Midland	H810WKH	Kingston upon Hull
GYE267W	Selkent	H346SWA	East Midland	H811WKH	Kingston upon Hull
GYE268W	East London	H347SWA	East Midland	H812WKH	Kingston upon Hull
GYE270W	East London	H348SWA	East Midland	H813WKH	Kingston upon Hull
GYE272W	East London	H370PNY	Red & White	H814WKH	Kingston upon Hull
GYE273W	East London	H401DMJ	Busways	H815CBP	Hampshire Bus
GYJ919V	Hampshire Bus	H401MRW	Midland Red	H815WKH	Kingston upon Hull
GYJ920V	Coastline	H402MRW	Midland Red	H816CBP	Hampshire Bus
GYJ921V	Hampshire Bus	H403MRW	Midland Red	H816WKH	Kingston upon Hull
GYJ922V	Coastline	H404MRW	Midland Red	H817CBP	Hampshire Bus
H71XKH	Kingston upon Hull	H406MRW	Midland Red	H818CBP	Hampshire Bus
H101EKR	East Kent	H421BNL	Busways	H819CBP	Hampshire Bus
H102EKR	East Kent	H422BNL	Busways	H882LOX	Selkent
H103EKR	East Kent	H423BNL	Busways	H883LOX	Selkent
H104EKR	East Kent	H424BNL	Busways	H885LOX	Selkent
H112SAO	Cumberland	H425BNL	Busways	H912XGA	Midland Red
H113SAO	Cumberland	H426BNL	Busways	HBD914T	United Counties
H114SAO	Cumberland	H427BNL	Busways	HBD915T	United Counties
H115SAO	Cumberland	H428BNL	Busways	HBD916T	United Counties
H116SAO	Cumberland	H428EFT	Busways	HBD917T	United Counties
H117SAO	Cumberland	H429BNL	Busways	HBD919T	United Counties
H118SAO	Cumberland	H429EFT	Busways	HCS350N	Western Scottish
H119SAO	Cumberland	H430BNL	Busways	HCS817N	Midland Red
H126ACU	Busways	H430EFT	Busways	HDC416V	Cleveland
H127ACU	Busways	H431EFT	Busways	HDS566H	Western Scottish
H141UUA	Selkent	H432EFT	Busways	HDZ2601	Selkent
H142UUA	Selkent	H433EFT	Busways	HDZ2602	Selkent
H143UUA	Selkent	H434EFT	Busways	HDZ2603	Selkent

HDZ2604	Selkent	J102WSC	Selkent	J205JKH	Kingston upon Hull
HDZ2605	Selkent	J103WSC	Selkent	J206HFR	Ribble
HDZ2606	Selkent	J104WSC	Selkent	J207HFR	Ribble
HDZ2607	Selkent	J105WSC	Selkent	J208HFR	Ribble
HDZ2608	Selkent	J106WSC	Selkent	J209HFR	Ribble
HDZ2609	Selkent	J107WSC	Selkent	J210HFR	Ribble
HDZ2610	Selkent	J108WSC	Selkent	J225JJR	Busways
HDZ2611	Selkent	J109WSC	Selkent	J226JJR	Busways
HDZ2612	Selkent	J110WSC	Selkent	J227JJR	Busways
HDZ2613	Selkent	J111WSC	Selkent	J228JJR	Busways
HDZ2614	Selkent	J112LKO	East Kent	J229JJR	Busways
HDZ2615	Selkent	J112WSC	Selkent	J230JJR	Busways
HDZ2616	Selkent	J113LKO	East Kent	J230XKY	East London
HDZ8683	Hartlepool	J113WSC	Selkent	J231JJR	Busways
HEU120N	Cheltenham & Gloucester	J114LKO	East Kent	J231XKY	East London
HEU121N	Red & White	J114WSC	Selkent	J232JJR	Busways
HEU122N	Midland Red	J115LKO	East Kent	J233JJR	Busways
HFG193T	Hampshire Bus	J115WSC	Selkent	J301BRM	Western Scottish
HFG923V	Coastline	J116LKO	East Kent	J302BRM	Western Scottish
HGM335E	Bluebird	J116WSC	Selkent	J302TUH	Red & White
HHH370V	Ribble	J117LKO	East Kent	J303BRM	Western Scottish
HHH371V	Ribble	J118LKO	East Kent	J303TUH	Red & White
HHH372V	Ribble	J119LKO	East Kent	J304BRM	Western Scottish
HHH373V	Ribble	J120AAO	Cumberland	J304THP	Midland Red
HIL6075	Cheltenham & Gloucester	J120AHH	Cumberland	J304UKG	Red & White
HKE690L	Coastline	J120LKO	East Kent	J305BRM	Western Scottish
HNE252V	Bluebird	J120XHH	Bluebird	J305THP	Midland Red
HNE253V	Cumberland	J121AAO	Cumberland	J305UKG	Red & White
HNE254V	Bluebird	J121AHH	Cumberland	J306BRM	Western Scottish
HPK503N	Hants & Surrey	J121LKO	East Kent	J306UKG	Red & White
HPK505N	Hants & Surrey	J121XHH	Bluebird	J307BRM	Western Scottish
HPT86N	Red & White	J122AAO	Cumberland	J307UKG	Red & White
HPW522L	Busways	J122AHH	Cumberland	J308BRM	Western Scottish
HPY422V	Cleveland	J122XHH	Bluebird	J309BRM	Western Scottish
HPY423V	Cleveland	J123AHH	Cumberland	J310BRM	Western Scottish
HPY424V	Cleveland	J123XHH	Cumberland	J349XET	East Midland
HPY425V	Cleveland	J124AHH	Cumberland	J350XET	East Midland
HPY426V	Cleveland	J124XHH	Cumberland	J351XET	East Midland
HSK760	Bluebird	J125XHH	Cumberland	J352XET	East Midland
HTG354N	Red & White	J126XHH	Cumberland	J353XET	East Midland
HTY137W	Busways	J127XHH	Cumberland	J371BNW	Busways
HTY138W	Busways	J132HMT	East London	J372BNW	Busways
HTY139W	Busways	J133HMT	East London	J373BNW	Busways
HUD475S	Midland Red	J134HMT	East London	J374BNW	Busways
HUD479S	Midland Red	J135HMT	East London	J375BNW	Busways
HUD480S	Midland Red	J136HMT	East London	J376BNW	Busways
HUF451X	Hampshire Bus	J137HMT	East London	J377BNW	Busways
HVY132X	Western Scottish	J138HMT	East London	J378BNW	Busways
HWG207W	East Midland	J139HMT	East London	J379BNW	Busways
HWJ620W	East Midland	J140HMT	East London	J380BNW	Busways
HWJ621W	East Midland	J141HMT	East London	J401LKO	East Kent
IIL1319	Kingston upon Hull	J142HMT	East London	J402LKO	East Kent
IIL1321	Kingston upon Hull	J143HMT	East London	J403LKO	East Kent
IIL3503	Cumberland	J144HMT	East London	J407PRW	Midland Red
IIL3505	Cumberland	J145HMT	East London	J408PRW	Midland Red
IIL3507	Ribble	J196YSS	Bluebird	J409PRW	Midland Red
J8WSB	Western Scottish	J197YSS	Bluebird	J410PRW	Midland Red
J13WSB	Western Scottish	J198HFR	Ribble	J411PRW	Midland Red
J14WSB	Western Scottish	J198YSS	Bluebird	J412PRW	Midland Red
J15WSB	Western Scottish	J199HFR	Ribble	J413PRW	Midland Red
J35GCX	Bluebird	J199YSS	Bluebird	J414PRW	Midland Red
J36GCX	Bluebird	J201HFR	Ribble	J415PRW	Midland Red
J91DJV	Grimsby Cleethorpes	J202HFR	Ribble	J416PRW	Midland Red
J92DJV	Grimsby Cleethorpes	J203HFR	Ribble	J416TGM	East Kent
J93DJV	Grimsby Cleethorpes	J204HFR	Ribble	J417PRW	Midland Red
J94DJV	Grimsby Cleethorpes	J204JKH	Kingston upon Hull	J418PRW	Midland Red
J101WSC	Selkent	J205HFR	Ribble	J430HDS	United Counties

J439HDS	United Counties	J550GCD	Hampshire Bus	JAJ295N	Hartlepool
J445HDS	United Counties	J551GCD	Coastline	JAJ296N	Hartlepool
J446HDS	United Counties	J552GCD	Coastline	JAK209W	East Midland
J450HDS	United Counties	J553NGS	Busways	JAK210W	Bluebird
J455FSR	Bluebird	J620GCR	United Counties	JAK211W	East Midland
J456FSR	Bluebird	J621GCR	United Counties	JAK212W	Bluebird
J501FPS	Bluebird	J622GCR	United Counties	JCK846W	Ribble
J501GCD	South Coast Buses	J623GCR	Coastline	JCK847W	Ribble
J502FPS	Bluebird	J624GCR	Coastline	JCK848W	Ribble
J502GCD	South Coast Buses	J701KCU	Busways	JCK849W	East Kent
J503FPS	Bluebird	J701YRM	Hants & Surrey	JDZ2359	Selkent
J503GCD	South Coast Buses	J702KCU	Busways	JDZ2360	Selkent
J504FPS	Bluebird	J702YRM	Hants & Surrey	JDZ2361	Selkent
J504GCD	South Coast Buses	J703YRM	South Coast Buses	JDZ2362	Selkent
J505FPS	Bluebird	J711CYG	East London	JDZ2363	Selkent
J505GCD	South Coast Buses	J712CYG	East London	JDZ2364	Selkent
J506FPS	Bluebird	J713CYG	East London	JDZ2365	Selkent
J506GCD	South Coast Buses	J714CYG	East London	JDZ2371	Selkent
J507FPS	Bluebird	J715CYG	East London	JFR2W	Ribble
J507GCD	Coastline	J716CYG	East London	JFR3W	Ribble
J508FPS	Bluebird	J717CYG	East London	JFR4W	Ribble
J508GCD	South Coast Buses	J718CYG	East London	JFR5W	Ribble
J509FPS	Bluebird	J719CYG	East London	JFR6W	Ribble
J509GCD	South Coast Buses	J720CYG	East London	JFR7W	Ribble
J510FPS	Bluebird	J720GAP	Coastline	JFR8W	Ribble
J510GCD	South Coast Buses	J721CYG	East London	JFR9W	Ribble
J511FPS	Bluebird	J721GAP	Coastline	JFR10W	Ribble
J511GCD	South Coast Buses	J722CYG	East London	JFR11W	Ribble
J512FPS	Bluebird	J722GAP	Coastline	JFR12W	Ribble
J512GCD	South Coast Buses	J723CYG	East London	JFR13W	Ribble
J513GCD	South Coast Buses	J724CYG	East London	JFT413X	Busways
J514GCD	South Coast Buses	J725CYG	East London	JFT414X	Busways
J515GCD	South Coast Buses	J726CYG	East London	JHU899X	Cheltenham & Gloucester
J516GCD	South Coast Buses	J727CYG	East London	JHU912X	Cheltenham & Gloucester
J517GCD	South Coast Buses	J728CYG	East London	JHW103P	Cheltenham & Gloucester
J518GCD	South Coast Buses	J729CYG	East London	JJD392D	East London
J519GCD	South Coast Buses	J808WFS	United Counties	JJD399D	East London
J520GCD	South Coast Buses	J811NKK	East London	JJD402D	East London
J521GCD	South Coast Buses	J812NKK	East Kent	JJD415D	East London
J522GCD	Hants & Surrey	J813NKK	East Kent	JJD429D	East London
J523GCD	Hants & Surrey	J814NKK	East Kent	JJD435D	East London
J524GCD	Hampshire Bus	J822HMC	East London	JJD437D	East London
J525GCD	Hampshire Bus	J823HMC	East London	JJD444D	East London
J526GCD	Hampshire Bus	J824HMC	East London	JJD445D	East London
J527GCD	Hampshire Bus	J825HMC	East London	JJD450D	East London
J528GCD	Hampshire Bus	J826HMC	East London	JJD451D	East London
J529GCD	Hampshire Bus	J827HMC	East London	JJD456D	East London
J530GCD	Hampshire Bus	J828HMC	East London	JJD462D	East London
J531GCD	Hampshire Bus	J829HMC	East London	JJD470D	East London
J532GCD	Hampshire Bus	J856NKK	East Kent	JJD481D	East London
J533GCD	Hampshire Bus	J901UKV	Cleveland	JJD488D	East London
J534GCD	Hampshire Bus	J909NKP	East Kent	JJD493D	East London
J535GCD	Hampshire Bus	J917LEM	Bluebird	JJD495D	East London
J536GCD	Hampshire Bus	J919LEM	Bluebird	JJD496D	East London
J537GCD	Hampshire Bus	JAJ137W	Cleveland	JJD497D	East London
J538GCD	Hampshire Bus	JAJ138W	Cleveland	JJD541D	East London
J539GCD	Hampshire Bus	JAJ139W	Cleveland	JJD550D	East London
J540GCD	Hampshire Bus	JAJ140W	Cleveland	JJD565D	East London
J541GCD	South Coast Buses	JAJ141W	Cleveland	JJD581D	East London
J542GCD	Hampshire Bus	JAJ142W	Cleveland	JJD592D	East London
J543GCD	Hampshire Bus	JAJ143W	Cleveland	JJG890P	East Kent
J544GCD	Hampshire Bus	JAJ144W	Cleveland	JJG892P	East Kent
J545GCD	Hampshire Bus	JAJ145W	Cleveland	JJG893P	East Kent
J546GCD	Hampshire Bus	JAJ146W	Cleveland	JJG895P	East Kent
J547GCD	Hampshire Bus	JAJ292N	Hartlepool	JJG898P	East Kent
J548GCD	Hampshire Bus	JAJ293N	Hartlepool	JJG900P	East Kent
J549GCD	Hampshire Bus	JAJ294N	Hartlepool	JMW166P	Busways

JMW167P	Busways	K120XHG	Ribble	K335RCN	Busways
JMW168P	Busways	K121SRH	East London	K336RCN	Busways
JMW169P	Busways	K121XHG	Cumberland	K337RCN	Busways
JMW170P	Busways	K122SRH	East London	K341PJR	Busways
JND260V	Bluebird	K123SRH	East London	K342PJR	Busways
JNJ194V	Coastline	K124SRH	East London	K343PJR	Busways
JOU160P	Cheltenham & Gloucester	K124XHG	Ribble	K344PJR	Busways
JOX502P	Midland Red	K125SRH	East London	K345PJR	Busways
JOX503P	Midland Red	K126SRH	East London	K350ANV	United Counties
JOX504P	Midland Red	K127SRH	East London	K351ANV	United Counties
JOX505P	Midland Red	K128DAO	Cumberland	K352ANV	United Counties
JOX506P	Midland Red	K128SRH	East London	K353ANV	United Counties
JPU817	Cumberland	K129DAO	Cumberland	K354ANV	United Counties
JSA101V	Bluebird	K129SRH	East London	K354DWJ	East Midland
JSA102V	Bluebird	K130DAO	Cumberland	K355ANV	United Counties
JSA103V	Bluebird	K130SRH	East London	K355DWJ	East Midland
JSA104V	Bluebird	K131DAO	Cumberland	K356ANV	United Counties
JTF971W	Western Scottish	K131SRH	East London	K356DWJ	East Midland
JWA27W	Midland Red	K132DAO	Cumberland	K357ANV	United Counties
JWV251W	Coastline	K132SRH	East London	K357DWJ	East Midland
JWV252W	South Coast Buses	K133DAO	Cumberland	K358ANV	United Counties
JWV253W	Hampshire Bus	K133SRH	East London	K358DWJ	East Midland
JWV255W	Coastline	K134DAO	Cumberland	K359ANV	United Counties
JWV256W	Coastline	K134SRH	East London	K359DWJ	East Midland
JWV258W	Hampshire Bus	K135DAO	Cumberland	K360DWJ	East Midland
JWV266W	Hampshire Bus	K135SRH	East London	K361DWJ	East Midland
JWV267W	Coastline	K150DNV	United Counties	K362DWJ	East Midland
JWV268W	Coastline	K151DNV	United Counties	K363DWJ	East Midland
JWV269W	Hampshire Bus	K152DNV	United Counties	K420ARW	Midland Red
JWV274W	Hampshire Bus	K153DNV	United Counties	K421ARW	Midland Red
JWV275W	Coastline	K154DNV	United Counties	K422ARW	Midland Red
JWV976W	Coastline	K162FYG	Busways	K423ARW	Midland Red
K101JWJ	East Midland	K163FYG	Busways	K424ARW	Midland Red
K101XHG	Bluebird	K164FYG	Busways	K425ARW	Midland Red
K102JWJ	East Midland	K165FYG	Busways	K449YCW	Ribble
K102XHG	Bluebird	K166FYG	Busways	K450YCW	Ribble
K103JWJ	East Midland	K211SRH	East London	K508ESS	Bluebird
K103XHG	Bluebird	K235NHC	Hants & Surrey	K509ESS	Bluebird
K104JWJ	East Midland	K236NHC	Hants & Surrey	K510ESS	Bluebird
K104XHG	Bluebird	K237NHC	Coastline	K511ESS	Bluebird
K105JWJ	East Midland	K238NHC	Coastline	K515ESS	Bluebird
K105XHG	Bluebird	K239NHC	Coastline	K518ESS	Bluebird
K106JWJ	East Midland	K240NHC	Coastline	K521EFL	Selkent
K106XHG	Bluebird	K302FYG	East London	K522EFL	Selkent
K107JWJ	East Midland	K306ARW	Midland Red	K523EFL	Selkent
K107XHG	Bluebird	K308YKG	Red & White	K524EFL	Selkent
K108XHG	Bluebird	K309YKG	Red & White	K525EFL	Selkent
K109SRH	East London	K310YKG	Red & White	K526EFL	Selkent
K109XHG	Bluebird	K311YKG	Red & White	K527EFL	Selkent
K110SRH	East London	K312YKG	Red & White	K528EFL	Selkent
K110XHG	Bluebird	K313YKG	Red & White	K529EFL	Selkent
K112SRH	East London	K314YKG	Red & White	K530EFL	Selkent
K112XHG	Ribble	K315YKG	Red & White	K536RJX	Bluebird
K113SRH	East London	K316YKG	Red & White	K537RJX	Bluebird
K113XHG	Cumberland	K317YKG	Red & White	K538RJX	Bluebird
K114SRH	East London	K318YKG	Red & White	K539RJX	Bluebird
K114XHG	Cumberland	K319YKG	Red & White	K553NHC	Coastline
K115SRH	East London	K320YKG	Red & White	K554NHC	Coastline
K115XHG	Ribble	K321YKG	Red & White	K556NHC	Coastline
K116SRH	East London	K322YKG	Red & White	K557NHC	Coastline
K116XHG	Ribble	K323YKG	Red & White	K558NHC	Coastline
K117SRH	East London	K324YKG	Red & White	K559NHC	Coastline
K117XHG	Ribble	K325YKG	Red & White	K561GSA	Bluebird
K118SRH	East London	K330RCN	Busways	K561NHC	Coastline
K118XHG	Ribble	K331RCN	Busways	K562GSA	Bluebird
K119SRH	East London	K332RCN	Busways	K562NHC	Coastline
K120SRH	East London	K334RCN	Busways	K563GSA	Bluebird

Reg	Operator	Reg	Operator	Reg	Operator
K563NHC	Coastline	K631HWX	East London	K717DAO	Cumberland
K564GSA	Bluebird	K632HWX	East London	K717PCN	Busways
K564NHC	Coastline	K633HWX	East London	K718DAO	Cumberland
K565GSA	Bluebird	K634HWX	East London	K718PCN	Busways
K565NHC	Coastline	K635HWX	East London	K719DAO	Cumberland
K566GSA	Bluebird	K655NHC	Coastline	K719PCN	Busways
K566NHC	Coastline	K655UNH	United Counties	K720DAO	Cumberland
K567GSA	Bluebird	K656UNH	United Counties	K720PCN	Busways
K567NHC	Coastline	K657UNH	United Counties	K721DAO	Cumberland
K568GSA	Bluebird	K658UNH	United Counties	K721PCN	Busways
K568NHC	Coastline	K659UNH	United Counties	K722DAO	Cumberland
K569GSA	Bluebird	K660NHC	Coastline	K722PCN	Busways
K569NHC	Coastline	K660UNH	United Counties	K723DAO	Cumberland
K570GSA	Bluebird	K661UNH	United Counties	K723PNL	Busways
K570NHC	Hants & Surrey	K662UNH	United Counties	K724DAO	Cumberland
K571LTS	Bluebird	K663UNH	United Counties	K724PNL	Busways
K571NHC	Hants & Surrey	K664UNH	United Counties	K725DAO	Cumberland
K572LTS	Bluebird	K665UNH	United Counties	K725PNL	Busways
K572NHC	Hants & Surrey	K667UNH	United Counties	K726DAO	Cumberland
K573LTS	Bluebird	K668UNH	United Counties	K726PNL	Busways
K573NHC	Hants & Surrey	K669UNH	United Counties	K727DAO	Cumberland
K574LTS	Bluebird	K670UNH	United Counties	K727PNL	Busways
K574NHC	Coastline	K699ERM	Cumberland	K728DAO	Cumberland
K575LTS	Bluebird	K700DAO	Cumberland	K728PNL	Busways
K575NHC	Hants & Surrey	K701DAO	Cumberland	K729DAO	Cumberland
K576LTS	Bluebird	K701NDO	Grimsby Cleethorpes	K730DAO	Cumberland
K576NHC	Hants & Surrey	K702DAO	Cumberland	K731DAO	Cumberland
K577LTS	Bluebird	K702NDO	Grimsby Cleethorpes	K732DAO	Cumberland
K577NHC	Hants & Surrey	K703DAO	Cumberland	K733DAO	Cumberland
K578LTS	Bluebird	K703NDO	Grimsby Cleethorpes	K734DAO	Cumberland
K578NHC	Hants & Surrey	K703PCN	Busways	K735DAO	Cumberland
K579NHC	Coastline	K704ERM	Cumberland	K736DAO	Cumberland
K580NHC	Hants & Surrey	K704NDO	Grimsby Cleethorpes	K737DAO	Cumberland
K584ODY	Hants & Surrey	K704PCN	Busways	K738DAO	Cumberland
K585ODY	Hants & Surrey	K705DAO	Cumberland	K739DAO	Cumberland
K586ODY	Hants & Surrey	K705PCN	Busways	K740DAO	Cumberland
K587ODY	Hants & Surrey	K706DAO	Cumberland	K741DAO	Cumberland
K588ODY	Hants & Surrey	K706PCN	Busways	K742DAO	Cumberland
K610UFR	Ribble	K707DAO	Cumberland	K743DAO	Cumberland
K611UFR	Ribble	K707PCN	Busways	K744DAO	Cumberland
K612UFR	Ribble	K708DAO	Cumberland	K745DAO	Cumberland
K613UFR	Ribble	K708PCN	Busways	K746DAO	Cumberland
K614UFR	Ribble	K709ASC	United Counties	K748DAO	Cumberland
K615UFR	Ribble	K709DAO	Cumberland	K749DAO	Cumberland
K616UFR	Ribble	K709PCN	Busways	K750DAO	Cumberland
K617UFR	Ribble	K710ASC	United Counties	K751DAO	Cumberland
K618UFR	Ribble	K710DAO	Cumberland	K752DAO	Cumberland
K619UFR	Ribble	K710PCN	Busways	K753DAO	Cumberland
K620UFR	Ribble	K711ASC	United Counties	K754DAO	Cumberland
K621UFR	Ribble	K711DAO	Cumberland	K755DAO	Cumberland
K622UFR	Cumberland	K711PCN	Busways	K756DAO	Cumberland
K622YVN	Cleveland	K712ASC	United Counties	K757DAO	Cumberland
K623UFR	Cumberland	K712DAO	Cumberland	K758DAO	Cumberland
K623YVN	Cleveland	K712PCN	Busways	K759DAO	Cumberland
K624UFR	Ribble	K713ASC	United Counties	K760DAO	Cumberland
K624YVN	Cleveland	K713DAO	Cumberland	K761DAO	Cumberland
K625UFR	Ribble	K713PCN	Busways	K762DAO	Cumberland
K625YVN	Cleveland	K714ASC	East Kent	K763DAO	Cumberland
K626UFR	Cumberland	K714DAO	Cumberland	K764DAO	Cumberland
K626YVN	Cleveland	K714PCN	Busways	K765DAO	Cumberland
K627UFR	Ribble	K715ASC	East Kent	K766DAO	Cumberland
K627YVN	Cleveland	K715DAO	Cumberland	K767DAO	Cumberland
K628UFR	Ribble	K715PCN	Busways	K768DAO	Cumberland
K628YVN	Cleveland	K716ASC	East Kent	K769DAO	Cumberland
K629YVN	Cleveland	K716DAO	Cumberland	K770DAO	Cumberland
K630HWX	East London	K716PCN	Busways	K771DAO	Cumberland
K630YVN	Cleveland	K717ASC	East Kent	K772DAO	Cumberland

K773DAO	Cumberland	K870LMK	East London	KRS532V	Bluebird
K774DAO	Cumberland	K870ODY	Hants & Surrey	KRS540V	Western Scottish
K775DAO	Cumberland	K871GHH	Cumberland	KRS542V	Western Scottish
K776DAO	Cumberland	K871LMK	East London	KRU838W	Hampshire Bus
K777DAO	Cumberland	K871ODY	Hants & Surrey	KRU839W	Hampshire Bus
K778DAO	Cumberland	K872GHH	Cumberland	KRU840W	Hampshire Bus
K779DAO	Cumberland	K872ODY	Hants & Surrey	KRU841W	Hampshire Bus
K780DAO	Cumberland	K873GHH	Cumberland	KRU843W	United Counties
K781DAO	Cumberland	K873ODY	Hants & Surrey	KRU844W	Hampshire Bus
K782DAO	Cumberland	K874GHH	Cumberland	KRU845W	United Counties
K783DAO	Cumberland	K874ODY	Hants & Surrey	KRU846W	United Counties
K784DAO	Cumberland	K875GHH	Cumberland	KRU847W	United Counties
K785DAO	Cumberland	K875ODY	Hants & Surrey	KRU852W	United Counties
K786DAO	Cumberland	K876GHH	Cumberland	KSU454	Busways
K787DAO	Cumberland	K876ODY	Hants & Surrey	KSU455	Busways
K788DAO	Cumberland	K877GHH	Cumberland	KSU456	Busways
K789DAO	East Kent	K877ODY	Hants & Surrey	KSU457	Busways
K790DAO	East Kent	K878GHH	Cumberland	KSU458	Busways
K791DAO	East Kent	K878ODY	Hants & Surrey	KSU459	Busways
K801OMW	Cheltenham & Gloucester	K879ODY	Hants & Surrey	KSU461	Busways
K802OMW	Cheltenham & Gloucester	K880ODY	Hants & Surrey	KSU462	Busways
K821TKP	East Kent	K910TKP	East Kent	KSU463	Busways
K822TKP	East Kent	KAJ214W	Hartlepool	KSU464	Busways
K823TKP	East Kent	KAJ215W	Hartlepool	KSU465	Busways
K823TKP	East Kent	KAJ216W	Hartlepool	KSU466	Busways
K824TKP	East Kent	KAJ217W	Hartlepool	KSV460	Busways
K846LMK	East London	KAJ218W	Hartlepool	KTX242L	Busways
K847LMK	East London	KAJ219W	Hartlepool	KWA213W	East Midland
K848LMK	East London	KAJ220W	Hartlepool	KWA214W	East Midland
K849LMK	East London	KBB118D	Busways	KWA215W	East Midland
K850LMK	East London	KDW359P	Red & White	KWA216W	East Midland
K851LMK	East London	KHH374W	Ribble	KWA218W	East Midland
K852LMK	East London	KHH375W	Ribble	KWA219W	East Midland
K853LMK	East London	KHH376W	Ribble	KWA221W	East Midland
K853ODY	Hants & Surrey	KHH377W	Ribble	KWA222W	East Midland
K854LMK	East London	KHH378W	Ribble	KWA223W	East Midland
K854ODY	Hants & Surrey	KHP649N	Midland Red	KWA224W	East Midland
K855LMK	East London	KHT122P	Midland Red	KYN281X	East London
K855ODY	Hants & Surrey	KHT124P	Midland Red	KYN282X	Selkent
K856LMK	East London	KIB8140	Midland Red	KYN285X	East London
K856ODY	Hants & Surrey	KKH650	Kingston upon Hull	KYN286X	East London
K857LMK	East London	KKK888V	Hampshire Bus	KYN288X	Selkent
K857ODY	Hants & Surrey	KPA365P	South Coast Buses	KYN298X	East London
K858LMK	East London	KPA366P	Hants & Surrey	KYN305X	Selkent
K858ODY	Hants & Surrey	KPA368P	Hants & Surrey	KYN306X	East London
K859LMK	East London	KPA369P	Hants & Surrey	KYV311X	East London
K859ODY	Hants & Surrey	KPA374P	Hants & Surrey	KYV318X	East London
K860LMK	East London	KPA378P	Hants & Surrey	KYV320X	East London
K860ODY	Hants & Surrey	KPA379P	Hants & Surrey	KYV326X	East London
K861LMK	East London	KPA383P	Hants & Surrey	KYV331X	East London
K861ODY	Hants & Surrey	KPA387P	Hants & Surrey	KYV334X	East London
K862LMK	East London	KPA388P	Hants & Surrey	KYV340X	East London
K862ODY	Hants & Surrey	KPA389P	Hants & Surrey	KYV345X	Selkent
K863LMK	East London	KRM430W	Cumberland	KYV348X	Selkent
K863ODY	Hants & Surrey	KRM431W	Cumberland	KYV360X	East London
K864LMK	East London	KRM432W	Cumberland	KYV361X	Selkent
K864ODY	Hants & Surrey	KRM433W	Cumberland	KYV366X	East London
K865LMK	East London	KRM434W	Cumberland	KYV368X	Selkent
K865ODY	Hants & Surrey	KRM435W	Cumberland	KYV378X	East London
K866LMK	East London	KRM436W	Cumberland	KYV379X	East London
K866ODY	Hants & Surrey	KRM437W	Cumberland	KYV380X	East London
K867LMK	East London	KRN103T	Cumberland	KYV386X	East London
K867ODY	Hants & Surrey	KRN105T	Cumberland	KYV387X	East London
K868LMK	East London	KRN113T	Cumberland	KYV394X	East London
K868ODY	Hants & Surrey	KRN119T	Cumberland	KYV395X	East London
K869LMK	East London	KRS529V	Bluebird	KYV397X	Selkent
K869ODY	Hants & Surrey	KRS531V	Bluebird	KYV403X	East London

KYV404X	East London	KYV535X	East London	L144VRH	East London
KYV406X	East London	KYV536X	East London	L145BFV	Ribble
KYV410X	Selkent	KYV537X	East London	L145VRH	East London
KYV420X	Selkent	KYV539X	East London	L146BFV	Ribble
KYV428X	East London	KYV540X	East London	L146VRH	East London
KYV434X	East London	KYV541X	East London	L148BFV	Ribble
KYV437X	East London	KYV542X	East London	L149BFV	Ribble
KYV439X	East London	KYV543X	East London	L150BFV	Ribble
KYV441X	East London	KYV544X	East London	L151BFV	Ribble
KYV442X	Selkent	KYV545X	East London	L152BFV	Ribble
KYV444X	East London	KYV546X	East London	L153BFV	Ribble
KYV445X	East London	KYV548X	East London	L154BFV	Ribble
KYV446X	East London	KYV549X	East London	L155BFV	Ribble
KYV447X	Selkent	L26JSA	Bluebird	L155JNH	United Counties
KYV448X	East London	L27JSA	Bluebird	L156BFV	Ribble
KYV451X	Selkent	L28JSA	Bluebird	L156JNH	United Counties
KYV453X	East London	L31HHN	Cleveland	L157BFV	Ribble
KYV454X	East London	L32HHN	Cleveland	L157JNH	United Counties
KYV455X	Selkent	L33HHN	Cleveland	L158BFV	Ribble
KYV456X	East London	L34HHN	Cleveland	L158JNH	United Counties
KYV458X	East London	L35HHN	Cleveland	L159CCW	Ribble
KYV460X	East London	L36HHN	Cleveland	L159JNH	United Counties
KYV461X	East London	L37HHN	Cleveland	L160CCW	Ribble
KYV462X	East London	L81YBB	Busways	L160JNH	United Counties
KYV465X	East London	L82YBB	Busways	L161CCW	Ribble
KYV466X	East London	L83YBB	Busways	L161JNH	United Counties
KYV467X	East London	L84YBB	Busways	L162JNH	United Counties
KYV469X	East London	L101GHN	Cleveland	L188SDY	South Coast Buses
KYV470X	East London	L101JSA	Bluebird	L201YAG	Selkent
KYV471X	East London	L101SDY	Ribble	L202YAG	Selkent
KYV473X	East London	L102GHN	Cleveland	L203YAG	Selkent
KYV474X	Selkent	L102JSA	Bluebird	L204YAG	Selkent
KYV476X	East London	L102SDY	Ribble	L205YAG	Selkent
KYV480X	East London	L103GHN	Cleveland	L206YAG	Selkent
KYV486X	Selkent	L103SDY	Ribble	L207YAG	Selkent
KYV486X	East London	L104SDY	Ribble	L208PSB	Western Scottish
KYV488X	East London	L105SDY	Ribble	L208YAG	Selkent
KYV490X	East London	L106SDY	Ribble	L209YAG	Selkent
KYV492X	East London	L107SDY	Ribble	L210YAG	Selkent
KYV495X	East London	L108LHL	East Midland	L211YAG	Selkent
KYV496X	East London	L109LHL	East Midland	L212YAG	Selkent
KYV497X	East London	L110JSA	Bluebird	L237CCW	Ribble
KYV498X	East London	L119DRN	Ribble	L238CCW	Ribble
KYV500X	East London	L122DRN	Ribble	L239CCW	Ribble
KYV501X	East London	L123DRN	Cumberland	L240CCW	Ribble
KYV502X	East London	L125DRN	Ribble	L241SDY	South Coast Buses
KYV503X	East London	L125NAO	Cumberland	L242CCK	Ribble
KYV504X	East London	L126DRN	Cumberland	L242CCK	Ribble
KYV505X	East London	L126NAO	Cumberland	L242SDY	South Coast Buses
KYV506X	East London	L127DRN	Ribble	L243CCK	Ribble
KYV508X	East London	L127NAO	Cumberland	L243SDY	Coastline
KYV511X	Selkent	L128DRN	Ribble	L244CCK	Ribble
KYV512X	East London	L136VRH	East London	L244SDY	Coastline
KYV513X	East London	L137VRH	East London	L245CCK	Ribble
KYV514X	East London	L138BFV	Ribble	L245SDY	Coastline
KYV515X	East London	L138VRH	East London	L246CCK	Ribble
KYV517X	East London	L139BFV	Ribble	L246SDY	Hampshire Bus
KYV521X	East London	L139VRH	East London	L247CCK	Ribble
KYV522X	East London	L140BFV	Ribble	L247SDY	Hampshire Bus
KYV523X	Selkent	L140VRH	East London	L248CCK	Ribble
KYV525X	East London	L141BFV	Ribble	L248SDY	Hampshire Bus
KYV526X	East London	L141VRH	East London	L249CCK	Ribble
KYV527X	East London	L142BFV	Ribble	L249SDY	Hampshire Bus
KYV529X	East London	L142VRH	East London	L250CCK	Ribble
KYV531X	East London	L143BFV	Ribble	L250SDY	Hampshire Bus
KYV532X	East London	L143VRH	East London	L251CCK	Ribble
KYV533X	East London	L144BFV	Ribble	L252CCK	Ribble

Reg	Operator	Reg	Operator	Reg	Operator
L253CCK	Ribble	L343KCK	Manchester	L446LWA	East Midland
L254CCK	Ribble	L344KCK	Manchester	L447LWA	East Midland
L255CCK	Ribble	L345KCK	Stagecoach South	L448LWA	East Midland
L256CCK	Ribble	L346KCK	Coastline	L449LWA	East Midland
L270LHH	Cumberland	L347KCK	Coastline	L450LWA	East Midland
L271LHH	Cumberland	L360JBD	United Counties	L451LWA	East Midland
L272LHH	Cumberland	L361JBD	United Counties	L451YAC	Midland Red
L273LHH	Cumberland	L362JBD	United Counties	L452LWA	East Midland
L274LHH	Cumberland	L363JBD	United Counties	L452YAC	Midland Red
L275JAO	Cumberland	L364JBD	United Counties	L453LHL	East Midland
L276JAO	Cumberland	L365JBD	United Counties	L453YAC	Midland Red
L277JAO	Ribble	L366JBD	United Counties	L454YAC	Midland Red
L278JAO	Ribble	L367JBD	United Counties	L455YAC	Midland Red
L279JAO	Ribble	L368JBD	United Counties	L456YAC	Midland Red
L281JAO	Ribble	L369JBD	United Counties	L577NSB	Western Scottish
L282JAO	Cumberland	L370JBD	United Counties	L578NSB	Western Scottish
L283JAO	Ribble	L371JBD	United Counties	L579JSA	Bluebird
L301JSA	Bluebird	L372JBD	United Counties	L580JSA	Bluebird
L302JSA	Bluebird	L373JBD	United Counties	L581JSA	Bluebird
L303JSA	Bluebird	L374JBD	United Counties	L582JSA	Bluebird
L307SKV	Midland Red	L375JBD	United Counties	L583JSA	Bluebird
L308YDU	Midland Red	L376JBD	United Counties	L584JSA	Bluebird
L309YDU	Midland Red	L377JBD	United Counties	L585JSA	Bluebird
L310YDU	Midland Red	L378JBD	United Counties	L586JSA	Bluebird
L311YDU	Midland Red	L379JBD	United Counties	L587JSA	Bluebird
L312YDU	Midland Red	L380JBD	United Counties	L588JSA	Bluebird
L313YDU	Midland Red	L381NBD	United Counties	L601VCD	South Coast Buses
L314YDU	Midland Red	L382NBD	United Counties	L602VCD	South Coast Buses
L315JSA	Bluebird	L383NBD	United Counties	L603VCD	South Coast Buses
L315YDU	Midland Red	L401JBD	United Counties	L604VCD	South Coast Buses
L316JSA	Bluebird	L402JBD	United Counties	L605VCD	South Coast Buses
L316YDU	Midland Red	L403JBD	United Counties	L606TDY	South Coast Buses
L317YDU	Midland Red	L404JBD	United Counties	L607TDY	South Coast Buses
L318YDU	Midland Red	L405JBD	United Counties	L608TDY	South Coast Buses
L319YDU	Midland Red	L406JBD	United Counties	L609TDY	South Coast Buses
L320YDU	Midland Red	L407JBD	United Counties	L616TDY	South Coast Buses
L321YDU	Midland Red	L408JBD	United Counties	L617TDY	South Coast Buses
L322YDU	Midland Red	L409JBD	United Counties	L618TDY	South Coast Buses
L323YDU	Midland Red	L410JBD	United Counties	L619TDY	South Coast Buses
L324YDU	Midland Red	L411JBD	United Counties	L620TDY	South Coast Buses
L325YDU	Midland Red	L412JBD	United Counties	L621TDY	Coastline
L326CHB	Red & White	L413JBD	United Counties	L622TDY	Coastline
L326YKV	Midland Red	L414JBD	United Counties	L623TDY	Coastline
L327CHB	Red & White	L415JBD	United Counties	L624TDY	Coastline
L327YKV	Midland Red	L416JBD	United Counties	L625TDY	Coastline
L328CHB	Red & White	L417JBD	United Counties	L625TDY	Coastline
L328YKV	Midland Red	L418JBD	United Counties	L626TDY	Coastline
L329CHB	Red & White	L419JBD	United Counties	L626TDY	Coastline
L329YKV	Midland Red	L420JBD	United Counties	L627TDY	East Kent
L330CHB	Cheltenham & Gloucester	L421JBD	United Counties	L627TDY	Coastline
L330YKV	Midland Red	L422MVV	United Counties	L628TDY	Coastline
L331CHB	Red & White	L423XVV	United Counties	L629BFV	Ribble
L334FWO	Red & White	L424XVV	United Counties	L629TDY	Coastline
L335FWO	Red & White	L425XVV	United Counties	L630BFV	Ribble
L336FWO	Red & White	L426XVV	United Counties	L631BFV	Ribble
L337FWO	Red & White	L427XVV	United Counties	L632BFV	Ribble
L338FWO	Red & White	L428XVV	United Counties	L633BFV	Ribble
L338KCK	Coastline	L435LWA	East Midland	L633TDY	East Kent
L339FWO	Red & White	L436LWA	East Midland	L634BFV	Ribble
L339KCK	Manchester	L437LWA	East Midland	L634TDY	East Kent
L340FWO	Red & White	L438LWA	East Midland	L635BFV	Ribble
L340KCK	Manchester	L438LWA	East Midland	L635TDY	Coastline
L341FWO	Red & White	L440LWA	East Midland	L636BFV	Ribble
L341KCK	Manchester	L441LWA	East Midland	L637LDT	East Midland
L342FWO	Red & White	L442LWA	East Midland	L638LDT	East Midland
L342KCK	Manchester	L443LWA	East Midland	L639LDT	East Midland
L343FWO	Red & White	L445LWA	East Midland	L640LDT	East Midland

Reg	Operator	Reg	Operator	Reg	Operator
L641LDT	East Midland	L735VNL	Busways	L882LFS	Western Scottish
L642LDT	East Midland	L736LWA	East Midland	L882SDY	South Coast Buses
L643LDT	East Midland	L736VNL	Busways	L883LFS	Western Scottish
L660HKS	Ribble	L737LWA	East Midland	L883SDY	South Coast Buses
L661MSF	Ribble	L737VNL	Busways	L884SDY	South Coast Buses
L662MSF	Ribble	L738LWA	East Midland	L885SDY	South Coast Buses
L663MSF	Ribble	L738VNL	Busways	L886SDY	South Coast Buses
L664MSF	Ribble	L739LWA	East Midland	L887SDY	South Coast Buses
L665MSF	Ribble	L739VNL	Busways	LAG188V	East Midland
L667MSF	Ribble	L740LWA	East Midland	LAG189V	East Midland
L668MSF	Ribble	L740VNL	Busways	LAT506V	Kingston upon Hull
L669MSF	Ribble	L741LWA	East Midland	LAT507V	Kingston upon Hull
L671HNV	United Counties	L741VNL	Busways	LAT508V	Kingston upon Hull
L672HNV	United Counties	L742LWA	East Midland	LAT509V	Kingston upon Hull
L673HNV	United Counties	L742VNL	Busways	LAT510V	Kingston upon Hull
L674HNV	United Counties	L743LWA	East Midland	LAT511V	Kingston upon Hull
L675HNV	United Counties	L743VNL	Busways	LAT512V	Kingston upon Hull
L676HNV	United Counties	L744LWA	East Midland	LAT513V	Kingston upon Hull
L677HNV	United Counties	L744VNL	Busways	LAT514V	Kingston upon Hull
L678HNV	United Counties	L745LWA	East Midland	LAT515V	Kingston upon Hull
L679HNV	United Counties	L745VNL	Busways	LBD839P	United Counties
L680HNV	United Counties	L746LWA	East Midland	LBD920V	United Counties
L681HNV	United Counties	L746VNL	Busways	LBD921V	United Counties
L682HNV	United Counties	L748LWA	East Midland	LBD923V	United Counties
L683HNV	United Counties	L748VNL	Busways	LBN201P	Busways
L684HNV	United Counties	L749LWA	East Midland	LBN202P	Busways
L685CDD	Red & White	L749VNL	Busways	LCU112	Busways
L685JBD	United Counties	L750LWA	East Midland	LDS201A	Bluebird
L686CDD	Cheltenham & Gloucester	L750VNL	Busways	LDS210A	Bluebird
L687CDD	Cheltenham & Gloucester	L751LHL	East Midland	LDW361P	Red & White
L688CDD	Cheltenham & Gloucester	L751VNL	Busways	LDZ3145	East Kent
L689CDD	Cheltenham & Gloucester	L752VNL	Busways	LEF59H	Hartlepool
L690CDD	Cheltenham & Gloucester	L753VNL	Busways	LEF60H	Hartlepool
L691CDD	Cheltenham & Gloucester	L754VNL	Busways	LEF61H	Hartlepool
L692CDD	Cheltenham & Gloucester	L755VNL	Busways	LEF64H	Hartlepool
L693CDD	Cheltenham & Gloucester	L756VNL	Busways	LEO735Y	Ribble
L694CDD	Cheltenham & Gloucester	L757VNL	Busways	LEO736Y	Ribble
L695CDD	Cheltenham & Gloucester	L758VNL	Busways	LFB851P	Stagecoach South
L696CDD	Cheltenham & Gloucester	L759VNL	Busways	LFF875	East London
L701FWO	Red & White	L760ARG	Busways	LFJ852W	United Counties
L702FWO	Red & White	L761ARG	Busways	LFJ853W	United Counties
L703FWO	Red & White	L762ARG	Busways	LFJ854W	United Counties
L704FWO	Red & White	L763ARG	Busways	LFJ855W	United Counties
L705FWO	Red & White	L764ARG	Busways	LFJ858W	Ribble
L705HFU	Grimsby Cleethorpes	L765ARG	Busways	LFJ859W	Ribble
L706FWO	Red & White	L803XDG	Cheltenham & Gloucester	LFJ861W	Ribble
L706HFU	Grimsby Cleethorpes	L804XDG	Cheltenham & Gloucester	LFJ862W	United Counties
L707FWO	Red & White	L805XDG	Cheltenham & Gloucester	LFJ863W	United Counties
L707HFU	Grimsby Cleethorpes	L806XDG	Cheltenham & Gloucester	LFJ864W	United Counties
L708FWO	Red & White	L826BKK	East Kent	LFJ865W	United Counties
L708HFU	Grimsby Cleethorpes	L827BKK	East Kent	LFJ866W	Ribble
L709FWO	Red & White	L828BKK	East Kent	LFJ868W	United Counties
L709HFU	Grimsby Cleethorpes	L829BKK	East Kent	LFJ869W	United Counties
L710FWO	Red & White	L830BKK	East Kent	LFJ870W	Hampshire Bus
L711FWO	Red & White	L831CDG	Cheltenham & Gloucester	LFJ874W	Hampshire Bus
L712FWO	Red & White	L832CDG	Cheltenham & Gloucester	LFJ875W	Hampshire Bus
L729VNL	Busways	L833CDG	Cheltenham & Gloucester	LFJ878W	United Counties
L730VNL	Busways	L834CDG	Cheltenham & Gloucester	LFJ879W	United Counties
L731LWA	East Midland	L835CDG	Cheltenham & Gloucester	LFJ880W	Hampshire Bus
L731VNL	Busways	L836CDG	Cheltenham & Gloucester	LFJ881W	Hampshire Bus
L732LWA	East Midland	L837CDG	Cheltenham & Gloucester	LFJ882W	Ribble
L732VNL	Busways	L838CDG	Cheltenham & Gloucester	LFJ883W	Ribble
L733LWA	East Midland	L839CDG	Cheltenham & Gloucester	LFJ884W	Ribble
L733VNL	Busways	L840CDG	Cheltenham & Gloucester	LFJ885W	Ribble
L734LWA	East Midland	L841CDG	Cheltenham & Gloucester	LFR856X	Ribble
L734VNL	Busways	L842CDG	Cheltenham & Gloucester	LFR857X	Ribble
L735LWA	East Midland	L881SDY	South Coast Buses	LFR858X	Ribble

Reg	Operator	Reg	Operator	Reg	Operator
LFR859X	Ribble	M320RSO	Bluebird	M533RSO	Bluebird
LFR860X	Ribble	M321RSO	Bluebird	M533RSO	Bluebird
LFR861X	Ribble	M332DRP	United Counties	M534RSO	Bluebird
LFR862X	United Counties	M334DRP	United Counties	M536RSO	Bluebird
LFR863X	Ribble	M335DRP	United Counties	M589OSO	Bluebird
LFR864X	United Counties	M336DRP	United Counties	M590OSO	Bluebird
LFR866X	Ribble	M337DRP	United Counties	M591OSO	Bluebird
LFR868X	Ribble	M338DRP	United Counties	M592OSO	Bluebird
LFR870X	Ribble	M339DRP	United Counties	M593OSO	Bluebird
LFR871X	Ribble	M340DRP	United Counties	M594OSO	Bluebird
LFR872X	Ribble	M341DRP	United Counties	M595OSO	Bluebird
LFR873X	Ribble	M342DRP	United Counties	M596OSO	Bluebird
LFR877X	Ribble	M343DRP	United Counties	M597OSO	Bluebird
LFV205X	Ribble	M344DRP	United Counties	M598OSO	Bluebird
LFV206X	Ribble	M344JBO	Red & White	M610APN	Coastline
LHG437T	South Coast Buses	M345DRP	United Counties	M611APN	Coastline
LHG438T	South Coast Buses	M345JBO	Red & White	M612APN	Coastline
LHT724P	Midland Red	M346DRP	United Counties	M613APN	Coastline
LHT725P	Midland Red	M346JBO	Red & White	M614APN	Coastline
LJC800	Cumberland	M347DRP	United Counties	M615APN	Coastline
LJY145	Ribble	M347JBO	Red & White	M674SSX	Western Scottish
LMA411T	Midland Red	M348DRP	United Counties	M675SSX	Western Scottish
LMS160W	Western Scottish	M348JBO	Red & White	M676SSX	Western Scottish
LOA838X	Midland Red	M349DRP	United Counties	M677SSX	Western Scottish
LPF605P	Hampshire Bus	M349JBO	Red & White	M678SSX	Western Scottish
LPU452J	Busways	M350JBO	Red & White	M679SSX	Western Scottish
LSK528	Bluebird	M351JBO	Red & White	M680SSX	Western Scottish
LSK547	Bluebird	M352JBO	Red & White	M681SSX	Western Scottish
LSK548	Bluebird	M353JBO	Red & White	M697EDD	Cheltenham & Gloucester
LUA273V	Cumberland	M354JBO	Red & White	M698EDD	Cheltenham & Gloucester
LUA275V	Cumberland	M355JBO	Red & White	M699EDD	Cheltenham & Gloucester
LUP901T	Midland Red	M356JBO	Red & White	M701EDD	Cheltenham & Gloucester
LWS33Y	Cheltenham & Gloucester	M357JBO	Red & White	M702EDD	Cheltenham & Gloucester
LWS34Y	Cheltenham & Gloucester	M358JBO	Red & White	M703EDD	Cheltenham & Gloucester
LWS35Y	Cheltenham & Gloucester	M359JBO	Red & White	M718BCS	Western Scottish
LWS36Y	Cheltenham & Gloucester	M360JBO	Red & White	M719BCS	Western Scottish
LWS37Y	Cheltenham & Gloucester	M401BFG	Hampshire Bus	M720BCS	Western Scottish
LWS38Y	Cheltenham & Gloucester	M402BFG	Hampshire Bus	M721BCS	Western Scottish
LWS39Y	Cheltenham & Gloucester	M403BFG	Hampshire Bus	M722BCS	Western Scottish
LWS40Y	Cheltenham & Gloucester	M404OKM	East Kent	M723BCS	Western Scottish
LWS41Y	Cheltenham & Gloucester	M405OKM	East Kent	M724BCS	Western Scottish
M38PVN	Cleveland	M406OKM	East Kent	M725BCS	Western Scottish
M39PVN	Cleveland	M407OKM	East Kent	M726BCS	Western Scottish
M40PVN	Cleveland	M408OKM	East Kent	M727BCS	Western Scottish
M41PVN	Cleveland	M411RRN	Manchester	M732BSJ	Western Scottish
M42PVN	Cleveland	M412RRN	Manchester	M733BSJ	Western Scottish
M104PVN	Cleveland	M413RRN	Manchester	M734BSJ	Western Scottish
M105PVN	Cleveland	M414RRN	Manchester	M735BSJ	Western Scottish
M106PVN	Cleveland	M415RRN	Manchester	M736BSJ	Western Scottish
M107PVN	Cleveland	M416RRN	Manchester	M737BSJ	Western Scottish
M108PVN	Cleveland	M417RRN	Manchester	M738BSJ	Western Scottish
M160CCD	Hampshire Bus	M418RRN	Manchester	M739BSJ	Western Scottish
M161CCD	Hampshire Bus	M419RRN	Manchester	M740BSJ	Western Scottish
M162CCD	Hampshire Bus	M420RRN	Manchester	M741BSJ	Western Scottish
M163CCD	Hampshire Bus	M421RRN	Manchester	M741PRS	Busways
M164CCD	Hampshire Bus	M422RRN	Manchester	M742PRS	Busways
M164SCK	Ribble	M423BNV	United Counties	M743PRS	Busways
M165CCD	Hampshire Bus	M423RRN	Manchester	M744PRS	Busways
M165SCK	Ribble	M424RRN	Manchester	M745PRS	Busways
M166CCD	Hampshire Bus	M425RRN	Manchester	M746PRS	Busways
M201DRG	Busways	M426RRN	Manchester	M748PRS	Busways
M202DRG	Busways	M427RRN	Manchester	M749PRS	Busways
M203DRG	Busways	M430BNV	United Counties	M750PRS	Busways
M204DRG	Busways	M490BFG	Hampshire Bus	M766DRG	Busways
M317RSO	Bluebird	M530RSO	Bluebird	M767DRG	Busways
M318RSO	Bluebird	M531RSO	Bluebird	M768DRG	Busways
M319RSO	Bluebird	M532RSO	Bluebird	M769DRG	Busways

M770DRG	Busways	MTE16R	Busways	NDZ3155	East London
M771DRG	Busways	MUA872P	Cheltenham & Gloucester	NDZ3156	East London
M772BCS	Western Scottish	MUV837X	Midland Red	NDZ3157	East London
M773BCS	Western Scottish	MVK500R	Busways	NDZ3158	East London
M782PRS	Manchester	MVK507R	Busways	NDZ3159	East London
M783PRS	Manchester	MVK509R	Busways	NEL121P	Hants & Surrey
M847PRS	Busways	MVK519R	Busways	NEL121P	Hampshire Bus
M901DRG	Busways	MVK521R	Busways	NEL121P	South Coast Buses
M902DRG	Busways	MVK532R	Busways	NEO833R	Busways
M911WJK	East Kent	MVK540R	Busways	NFB602R	Cheltenham & Gloucester
M940JBO	Red & White	MVK541R	Busways	NFB603R	Cheltenham & Gloucester
M941JBO	Red & White	MVK542R	Busways	NFN81R	East Kent
M942JBO	Red & White	MVK543R	Busways	NFN82R	East Kent
M943JBO	Red & White	MVK544R	Busways	NFN83R	East Kent
M944JBO	Red & White	MVK551R	Busways	NFN84R	East Kent
M945JBO	Red & White	MVK554R	Busways	NFN86R	East Kent
M946JBO	Red & White	MVK555R	Busways	NFN87R	East Kent
M947JBO	Red & White	MVK556R	Busways	NFN88R	East Kent
M948JBO	Red & White	MVK558R	Busways	NFN89R	East Kent
M949JBO	Red & White	MVK561R	Busways	NFX667	Hampshire Bus
M950JBO	Red & White	MVK563R	Busways	NGU602P	Midland Red
M951DRG	Busways	MVK564R	Busways	NGU605P	Midland Red
M951JBO	Red & White	MVK565R	Busways	NHA256M	Western Scottish
M952DRG	Busways	MWG622X	East Midland	NHH379W	Ribble
M953DRG	Busways	MWG623X	East Midland	NHH380W	Ribble
M954DRG	Busways	MWG624X	East Midland	NHH381W	Ribble
MAO367P	Ribble	NAK28X	Midland Red	NHH382W	Cheltenham & Gloucester
MAO368P	Busways	NAK29X	Midland Red	NHL301X	East Midland
MAU145P	Midland Red	NAK30X	Midland Red	NHL302X	East Midland
MAU146P	Bluebird	NBD102Y	United Counties	NHL303X	East Midland
MBE613R	Grimsby Cleethorpes	NBD103Y	United Counties	NHL304X	East Midland
MCS138W	Western Scottish	NBD104Y	United Counties	NHL305X	East Midland
MCS139W	Western Scottish	NCW800T	Ribble	NHU670R	Cheltenham & Gloucester
MDS858V	Western Scottish	NDZ3015	East London	NHU672R	Midland Red
MDS859V	Western Scottish	NDZ3016	East London	NIB4138	Bluebird
MDS865V	Western Scottish	NDZ3017	East London	NIB5232	Bluebird
MDS866V	Western Scottish	NDZ3018	East London	NIB5233	Bluebird
MEF65J	Hartlepool	NDZ3019	East London	NIB5455	Bluebird
MEF66J	Hartlepool	NDZ3020	East London	NKG246M	Busways
MEF67J	Hartlepool	NDZ3021	East London	NLP388V	Western Scottish
MEF69J	Hartlepool	NDZ3022	East London	NLS983W	Western Scottish
MEF70J	Hartlepool	NDZ3023	East London	NLS985W	Western Scottish
MEF71J	Hartlepool	NDZ3024	East London	NLS989W	Western Scottish
MEF72J	Hartlepool	NDZ3025	East London	NML607E	East London
MFN43R	East Kent	NDZ3026	East London	NML610E	East London
MFN114R	Red & White	NDZ3133	East London	NML616E	East London
MFN115R	East Kent	NDZ3134	East London	NML624E	East London
MFN118R	East Kent	NDZ3135	East London	NML639E	East London
MFN42R	East Kent	NDZ3136	East London	NML641E	East London
MFN46R	East Kent	NDZ3137	East London	NML642E	East London
MFN946F	Coastline	NDZ3138	East London	NML657E	East London
MGR948T	Red & White	NDZ3139	East London	NMY635E	East London
MHD336L	Western Scottish	NDZ3140	East London	NMY640E	Bluebird
MHS4P	Bluebird	NDZ3141	East London	NMY640E	East London
MHS5P	Bluebird	NDZ3142	East London	NOE551R	Midland Red
MLJ917P	Hampshire Bus	NDZ3143	East London	NOE552R	Red & White
MLJ922P	Hampshire Bus	NDZ3144	East London	NOE553R	Midland Red
MOU739R	Cheltenham & Gloucester	NDZ3145	East London	NOE555R	Cheltenham & Gloucester
MRJ270W	Grimsby Cleethorpes	NDZ3146	East London	NOE568R	Midland Red
MRJ275W	Cumberland	NDZ3147	East London	NOE568R	Midland Red
MS013W	Red & White	NDZ3148	East London	NOE570R	Midland Red
MSO10W	Western Scottish	NDZ3149	East London	NOE571R	Midland Red
MSO14W	Red & White	NDZ3150	East London	NOE572R	Red & White
MSO17W	Western Scottish	NDZ3151	East London	NOE573R	Red & White
MSO18W	Western Scottish	NDZ3152	East London	NOE576R	Red & White
MSU465	United Counties	NDZ3153	East London	NOE577R	Midland Red
MSU466	South Coast Buses	NDZ3154	East London	NOE578R	Midland Red

Reg	Operator	Reg	Operator	Reg	Operator
NOE579R	Midland Red	NUW595Y	East London	NUW673Y	East London
NOE581R	Midland Red	NUW596Y	Selkent	NUW674Y	Selkent
NOE582R	Midland Red	NUW597Y	East London	NUW675Y	East London
NOE584R	Cheltenham & Gloucester	NUW598Y	East London	NWO454R	Red & White
NOE585R	Cheltenham & Gloucester	NUW600Y	East London	NWO457R	Red & White
NOE586R	Midland Red	NUW601Y	East London	NWO461R	Red & White
NOE587R	Cheltenham & Gloucester	NUW602Y	East London	NWO466R	Red & White
NOE589R	Midland Red	NUW603Y	East London	NWO468R	Red & White
NOE590R	Midland Red	NUW604Y	East London	NWO475R	Red & White
NOE602R	Midland Red	NUW605Y	East London	NWO486R	Red & White
NOE603R	Midland Red	NUW606Y	East London	NWO494R	Red & White
NOE604R	Midland Red	NUW608Y	East London	NWO500R	Red & White
NOE605R	Midland Red	NUW609Y	East London	NWS288R	Cheltenham & Gloucester
NOE606R	Midland Red	NUW610Y	East London	NWS289R	Cheltenham & Gloucester
NPA229W	Bluebird	NUW611Y	Selkent	NWS903R	Red & White
NPA230W	Midland Red	NUW613Y	East London	OCK363K	Busways
NPJ474R	Hants & Surrey	NUW614Y	East London	OCK369K	Busways
NPJ476R	Hampshire Bus	NUW615Y	East London	OCU800R	Busways
NPJ477R	Hants & Surrey	NUW616Y	Selkent	OCU801R	Busways
NPJ480R	Hants & Surrey	NUW617Y	East London	OCU802R	Busways
NPJ482R	Hants & Surrey	NUW618Y	Selkent	OCU803R	Busways
NPJ485R	Hants & Surrey	NUW619Y	East London	OCU804R	Busways
NRP580V	East Midland	NUW621Y	East London	OCU805R	Busways
NSG636A	Bluebird	NUW622Y	East London	OCU806R	Busways
NTC132Y	Cheltenham & Gloucester	NUW623Y	East London	OCU807R	Busways
NUW550Y	East London	NUW624Y	East London	OCU808R	Busways
NUW551Y	East London	NUW625Y	East London	OCU811R	Busways
NUW552Y	East London	NUW626Y	East London	OCU813R	Busways
NUW553Y	East London	NUW627Y	East London	OCU814R	Busways
NUW554Y	East London	NUW629Y	East London	OCU815R	Busways
NUW555Y	East London	NUW630Y	East London	OCU816R	Busways
NUW556Y	East London	NUW631Y	East London	OCU817R	Busways
NUW557Y	East London	NUW632Y	East London	OCU818R	Busways
NUW558Y	East London	NUW633Y	East London	OCU819R	Busways
NUW559Y	East London	NUW634Y	East London	OCU820R	Busways
NUW560Y	East London	NUW636Y	East London	OCU821R	Busways
NUW562Y	East London	NUW637Y	East London	OCU822R	Busways
NUW563Y	East London	NUW639Y	East London	OCU823R	Busways
NUW564Y	East London	NUW640Y	East London	OCU824R	Busways
NUW565Y	East London	NUW641Y	East London	OCU825R	Busways
NUW566Y	East London	NUW642Y	East London	OCY910R	Bluebird
NUW568Y	East London	NUW643Y	East London	OEF73K	Hartlepool
NUW569Y	East London	NUW644Y	East London	OEF74K	Hartlepool
NUW571Y	East London	NUW645Y	East London	OEF75K	Hartlepool
NUW572Y	East London	NUW646Y	East London	OEF76K	Hartlepool
NUW573Y	East London	NUW647Y	East London	OEF77K	Hartlepool
NUW574Y	East London	NUW648Y	East London	OEF78K	Hartlepool
NUW575Y	East London	NUW649Y	East London	OEF79K	Hartlepool
NUW576Y	East London	NUW650Y	East London	OFV14X	Ribble
NUW577Y	East London	NUW651Y	East London	OFV15X	Ribble
NUW578Y	East London	NUW652Y	East London	OFV16X	Ribble
NUW579Y	East London	NUW653Y	East London	OFV17X	Ribble
NUW580Y	East London	NUW654Y	East London	OFV18X	Ribble
NUW581Y	East London	NUW657Y	East London	OFV19X	Ribble
NUW582Y	East London	NUW658Y	East London	OFV20X	Ribble
NUW583Y	East London	NUW659Y	East London	OFV21X	Ribble
NUW584Y	East London	NUW660Y	East London	OFV22X	Ribble
NUW585Y	East London	NUW662Y	East London	OFV23X	Ribble
NUW586Y	East London	NUW663Y	East London	OHN427X	Cleveland
NUW587Y	East London	NUW664Y	East London	OHN428X	Cleveland
NUW588Y	East London	NUW665Y	East London	OHN429X	Cleveland
NUW589Y	East London	NUW666Y	East London	OHV680Y	Selkent
NUW590Y	East London	NUW668Y	East London	OHV684Y	East London
NUW591Y	East London	NUW669Y	East London	OHV686Y	East London
NUW592Y	East London	NUW670Y	East London	OHV688Y	East London
NUW593Y	East London	NUW671Y	East London	OHV691Y	East London
NUW594Y	Selkent	NUW672Y	East London	OHV697Y	East London

OHV699Y	East London	OTD825R	Busways	PVT221L	Busways
OHV700Y	Selkent	OUC42R	Midland Red	PYE841Y	Grimsby Cleethorpes
OHV702Y	East London	OUC44R	Midland Red	PYE842Y	Grimsby Cleethorpes
OHV710Y	Selkent	OVL473	Bluebird	Q275UOC	Midland Red
OHV714Y	Selkent	OVV849R	United Counties	RAH681F	Busways
OHV719Y	East London	OVV856R	United Counties	RBD397Y	United Counties
OHV721Y	Selkent	OWC720M	Busways	RCS382	Western Scottish
OHV724Y	East London	OWC722M	Busways	RCU826S	Busways
OHV728Y	Selkent	OWC723M	Busways	RCU827S	Busways
OHV729Y	East London	PCD73R	South Coast Buses	RCU828S	Busways
OHV731Y	East London	PCD78R	South Coast Buses	RCU829S	Busways
OHV738Y	East London	PCD79R	South Coast Buses	RCU830S	Busways
OHV740Y	Selkent	PCD80R	South Coast Buses	RCU831S	Busways
OHV743Y	East London	PCD82R	South Coast Buses	RCU832S	Busways
OHV744Y	East London	PCK335	Cumberland	RCU833S	Busways
OHV748Y	Selkent	PEF147X	Cleveland	RCU834S	Busways
OHV749Y	East London	PEF148X	Cleveland	RCU835S	Busways
OHV751Y	East London	PEF149X	Cleveland	RCU836S	Busways
OHV759Y	East London	PES188Y	Busways	RCU837S	Busways
OHV761Y	East London	PES189Y	Busways	RCU838S	Busways
OHV762Y	Selkent	PES190Y	Busways	RCU839S	Busways
OHV770Y	Selkent	PEU511R	Midland Red	RDZ6115	East London
OHV771Y	Selkent	PEU515R	Cheltenham & Gloucester	RDZ6116	East London
OHV772Y	Selkent	PEU516R	Midland Red	RDZ6117	East London
OHV780Y	Selkent	PFN873	East Kent	RDZ6118	East London
OHV785Y	Selkent	PHW985S	Cheltenham & Gloucester	RDZ6119	East London
OHV791Y	Selkent	PHW986S	Cheltenham & Gloucester	RDZ6120	East London
OHV797Y	Selkent	PHW987S	Cheltenham & Gloucester	RDZ6121	East London
OHV800Y	Selkent	PHW988S	Cheltenham & Gloucester	RDZ6122	East London
OHV801Y	Selkent	PHW989S	Cheltenham & Gloucester	RDZ6123	East London
OHV804Y	Selkent	PIB8019	Midland Red	RDZ6124	East London
OHV805Y	Selkent	PJI4314	East Midland	RDZ6125	East London
OHV809Y	Selkent	PJI4316	East Midland	RDZ6126	East London
OHV810Y	Selkent	PJI4317	Grimsby Cleethorpes	RDZ6127	East London
OHV812Y	Selkent	PJI4983	Cleveland	RDZ6128	East London
OHV814Y	Selkent	PJI4986	Cleveland	RDZ6129	East London
OHV815Y	Selkent	PJJ16S	East Kent	RDZ6130	East London
OIB3512	Cleveland	PJJ21S	East Kent	REU309S	Cheltenham & Gloucester
OIB3513	Cleveland	PJJ22S	East Kent	REU310S	Cheltenham & Gloucester
OIB3514	Cleveland	PJJ23S	East Kent	REU311S	Cheltenham & Gloucester
OIB3515	Cleveland	PJJ24S	South Coast Buses	RFB617S	Cheltenham & Gloucester
OIB3516	Cleveland	PJJ344S	East Kent	RFS579V	Western Scottish
OIW7024	Western Scottish	PJJ345S	East Kent	RFS582V	Western Scottish
OIW7025	Western Scottish	PJJ346S	Stagecoach South	RFS583V	Western Scottish
OJD136R	Midland Red	PKG741R	Red & White	RFS584V	Western Scottish
OJD241R	Midland Red	PRX189B	Cleveland	RHB307R	Red & White
OJL822Y	Grimsby Cleethorpes	PS2743	Grimsby Cleethorpes	RHG878X	Ribble
OJL823Y	Grimsby Cleethorpes	PS3696	Grimsby Cleethorpes	RHG879X	Ribble
OJV120S	Grimsby Cleethorpes	PSG842P	Western Scottish	RHG880X	Ribble
OJV121S	Grimsby Cleethorpes	PSO177W	Bluebird	RHG880X	Cheltenham & Gloucester
OJV122S	Grimsby Cleethorpes	PSO178W	Bluebird	RHG881X	Ribble
OJV123S	Grimsby Cleethorpes	PSO179W	Busways	RHG884X	Ribble
OJV124S	Grimsby Cleethorpes	PSU443	Grimsby Cleethorpes	RHG886X	Ribble
OLS806T	Busways	PSU764	Grimsby Cleethorpes	RJA702R	Western Scottish
OLS807T	Ribble	PSU775	Grimsby Cleethorpes	RJA801R	Western Scottish
OLS809T	Ribble	PSU787	Grimsby Cleethorpes	RJT146R	Hampshire Bus
OMS910W	Bluebird	PSU788	Grimsby Cleethorpes	RJT151R	South Coast Buses
ONH846P	Midland Red	PTF732L	Western Scottish	RJT155R	Bluebird
ONH926V	United Counties	PUK621R	Midland Red	RRM383X	Ribble
ONL645X	Busways	PUK622R	Midland Red	RRM384X	Ribble
ORY640	Cumberland	PUK623R	Midland Red	RRM385X	Ribble
OSG59V	Western Scottish	PUK624R	Midland Red	RRM386X	Ribble
OSR206R	Red & White	PUK625R	Midland Red	RRP858R	Ribble
OSR207R	Red & White	PUK626R	Midland Red	RRP862R	United Counties
OSR208R	Red & White	PUK627R	Midland Red	RRP863R	United Counties
OSR209R	Red & White	PUK628R	Midland Red	RRS46R	Bluebird
OTD824R	Busways	PUK629R	Midland Red	RRS47R	Bluebird

RRS48R	Bluebird	SCN270S	Busways	SMK723F	East London
RRS50R	Bluebird	SCN271S	Busways	SMK738F	East London
RRS53R	Bluebird	SCN273S	Busways	SMK743F	East London
RRS225X	Bluebird	SCN274S	Busways	SMK748F	East London
RRS226X	Busways	SCN275S	Busways	SMK749F	East London
RSG814V	Red & White	SCN276S	Busways	SMK760F	East London
RSG815V	Red & White	SCN277S	Busways	SNS822W	Busways
RSG822V	Red & White	SCN278S	Busways	SNS825W	Ribble
RSG824V	Red & White	SCN279S	Busways	SNS826W	Western Scottish
RSG825V	Red & White	SCN280S	Busways	SNS828W	Busways
RUF38R	Hartlepool	SCN281S	Busways	SNS831W	Ribble
RUF40R	Hartlepool	SCN282S	Busways	SNV930W	United Counties
RUT842	Cumberland	SCN283S	Busways	SNV931W	United Counties
RYK816Y	Selkent	SCN284S	Busways	SNV935W	United Counties
RYK818Y	Selkent	SCN285S	Busways	SNV936W	United Counties
RYK820Y	Selkent	SCN286S	Busways	SNV937W	United Counties
RYK821Y	Selkent	SDA651S	Midland Red	SOA664S	Midland Red
RYK822Y	Selkent	SDA715S	Midland Red	SSA2X	Bluebird
SAE751S	Cheltenham & Gloucester	SEF80L	Hartlepool	SSA3X	Bluebird
SAE752S	Cheltenham & Gloucester	SEF81L	Hartlepool	SSA4X	Bluebird
SAE754S	Cheltenham & Gloucester	SEF82L	Hartlepool	SSA5X	Bluebird
SAE755S	Cheltenham & Gloucester	SEF83L	Hartlepool	SSA6X	Bluebird
SAE756S	Cheltenham & Gloucester	SEF84L	Hartlepool	SSA7X	Bluebird
SAG516W	Kingston upon Hull	SGR555R	Red & White	SVK627G	Busways
SAG517W	Kingston upon Hull	SGS504W	Hants & Surrey	SVV586W	East Midland
SAG518W	Kingston upon Hull	SHE306Y	East Midland	SVV589W	Midland Red
SAG519W	Kingston upon Hull	SHE307Y	East Midland	SWC25K	Busways
SAG520W	Kingston upon Hull	SHE308Y	East Midland	SWC26K	Busways
SAG521W	Kingston upon Hull	SHE309Y	East Midland	SYC852	Coastline
SAG522W	Kingston upon Hull	SHE310Y	East Midland	TAE638S	Cheltenham & Gloucester
SAG523W	Kingston upon Hull	SHE311Y	East Midland	TAE639S	Cheltenham & Gloucester
SAG524W	Kingston upon Hull	SHH387X	Ribble	TAE641S	Cheltenham & Gloucester
SAG525W	Kingston upon Hull	SHH388X	Ribble	TAE642S	Cheltenham & Gloucester
SAG526W	Kingston upon Hull	SHH390X	Ribble	TAE643S	Cheltenham & Gloucester
SAG527W	Kingston upon Hull	SHH391X	Ribble	TAE644S	Cheltenham & Gloucester
SAG528W	Kingston upon Hull	SHH392X	Ribble	TBC1X	Busways
SAG529W	Kingston upon Hull	SHH393X	Ribble	TBC2X	Busways
SAG530W	Kingston upon Hull	SHH394X	Ribble	TCK200X	Ribble
SAO410R	Bluebird	SHN401R	Hartlepool	TCK212X	Ribble
SAO412R	Bluebird	SHN402R	Hartlepool	TCK841	Cumberland
SCK224X	Ribble	SHN403R	Hartlepool	TDL567K	Busways
SCK225X	Ribble	SHN404R	Hartlepool	TEL490R	Hampshire Bus
SCK226X	Ribble	SHN405R	Hartlepool	TFN982T	East Kent
SCN244S	Busways	SHN406R	Hartlepool	TFN988T	East Kent
SCN247S	Busways	SHN407R	Hartlepool	TFU59T	Grimsby Cleethorpes
SCN248S	Busways	SIB8243	East Kent	TFU60T	Grimsby Cleethorpes
SCN249S	Busways	SKG896S	Red & White	TFU61T	Grimsby Cleethorpes
SCN250S	Busways	SKG907S	Red & White	TFU62T	Grimsby Cleethorpes
SCN251S	Busways	SKG908S	Red & White	TFU63T	Grimsby Cleethorpes
SCN252S	Busways	SKG914S	Red & White	TFU64T	Grimsby Cleethorpes
SCN253S	Busways	SKG915S	Red & White	THX155S	Midland Red
SCN254S	Busways	SKG923S	Red & White	THX231S	Midland Red
SCN255S	Busways	SKL680X	East Kent	THX401S	East London
SCN256S	Busways	SKL681X	East Kent	THX402S	East London
SCN257S	Busways	SKL682X	East Kent	TNH870R	United Counties
SCN258S	Busways	SKL683X	East Kent	TNH871R	United Counties
SCN259S	Busways	SKL684X	East Kent	TNH872R	United Counties
SCN260S	Busways	SKL685X	East Kent	TNH873R	United Counties
SCN261S	Busways	SKY31Y	East Midland	TOF707S	Midland Red
SCN262S	Busways	SKY32Y	East Midland	TOF708S	Midland Red
SCN263S	Busways	SMK661F	East London	TOF709S	Midland Red
SCN264S	Busways	SMK665F	East London	TOF710S	Midland Red
SCN265S	Busways	SMK670F	East London	TOS524X	Western Scottish
SCN266S	Busways	SMK671F	East London	TOS550X	Western Scottish
SCN267S	Busways	SMK696F	East London	TOS720X	Western Scottish
SCN268S	Busways	SMK705F	East London	TPE148S	Hants & Surrey
SCN269S	Busways	SMK709F	East London	TPE149S	Hants & Surrey

Reg	Fleet	Reg	Fleet	Reg	Fleet
TPE150S	Hants & Surrey	TWS903T	Cheltenham & Gloucester	UWV618S	Cumberland
TPE156S	Hampshire Bus	TWS906T	Cheltenham & Gloucester	UWV620S	Cumberland
TPE169S	Hants & Surrey	TWS909T	Red & White	UWV621S	South Coast Buses
TPJ55S	Busways	TWS913T	Cheltenham & Gloucester	UWV622S	Ribble
TPJ60S	Busways	TWS914T	Cheltenham & Gloucester	UWV623S	South Coast Buses
TPJ62S	Busways	UCS659	Western Scottish	UWW7X	Cheltenham & Gloucester
TPJ64S	Busways	UDT312Y	East Midland	UYJ654	Bluebird
TRN469V	Ribble	UDT313Y	East Midland	VAE499T	Cheltenham & Gloucester
TRN476V	Ribble	UF4813	Coastline	VAE501T	Cheltenham & Gloucester
TRN478V	Ribble	UFG48S	South Coast Buses	VAE502T	Midland Red
TRN480V	Ribble	UFG49S	Hartlepool	VAE507T	Cheltenham & Gloucester
TRN481V	Ribble	UFG52S	Hartlepool	VBA161S	Western Scottish
TRN482V	Ribble	UFX853S	Stagecoach South	VCS376	Western Scottish
TRN484V	Ribble	UHG739R	Busways	VCS391	Western Scottish
TRN485V	Ribble	UHG757R	South Coast Buses	VCU301T	Busways
TRN802V	Ribble	UHW101T	Cheltenham & Gloucester	VCU302T	Busways
TRN805V	Busways	UIB3076	Western Scottish	VCU303T	Busways
TRN806V	Ribble	UIB3541	Western Scottish	VCU304T	Busways
TRN807V	Ribble	UIB3542	Western Scottish	VCU309T	Busways
TRN808V	Ribble	UIB3543	Western Scottish	VCU310T	Busways
TRN809V	Ribble	UKE831X	Stagecoach South	VCU312T	Busways
TRN810V	Cumberland	ULS660T	Western Scottish	VEF150Y	Cleveland
TRN811V	East Kent	ULS669T	Western Scottish	VEF151Y	Cleveland
TRN812V	Ribble	UMO180N	Hants & Surrey	VEF152Y	Cleveland
TRY118H	Busways	UNA772S	Western Scottish	VEF153Y	Cleveland
TSJ31S	Western Scottish	UNA824S	Western Scottish	VEU228T	Cheltenham & Gloucester
TSJ32S	Western Scottish	UNA840S	Western Scottish	VEU229T	Cheltenham & Gloucester
TSJ33S	Western Scottish	UNA853S	Western Scottish	VEU230T	Cheltenham & Gloucester
TSJ67S	Western Scottish	UNA863S	Western Scottish	VEU231T	Cheltenham & Gloucester
TSJ70S	Western Scottish	URF661S	Midland Red	VEU232T	Cheltenham & Gloucester
TSJ71S	Western Scottish	URF662S	Ribble	VFX984S	Hampshire Bus
TSJ76S	Western Scottish	URM801Y	Cumberland	VLF578	Cumberland
TSJ78S	Western Scottish	URM802Y	Cumberland	VLT9	Selkent
TSJ79S	Western Scottish	URP939W	United Counties	VLT14	Selkent
TSJ80S	Western Scottish	URP940W	United Counties	VLT20	Selkent
TSJ85S	Western Scottish	URP941W	United Counties	VLT37	Western Scottish
TSO12X	Bluebird	URP944W	United Counties	VLT54	Western Scottish
TSO13X	Bluebird	URP945W	United Counties	VLT73	Western Scottish
TSO14X	Bluebird	USK625	Bluebird	VLT81	Western Scottish
TSO15X	Bluebird	USV672	South Coast Buses	VLT104	Western Scottish
TSO16X	Bluebird	UTX724S	Red & White	VLT154	Western Scottish
TSO17X	Bluebird	UTX725S	Red & White	VLT206	Western Scottish
TSO20X	Bluebird	UTX726S	Red & White	VLT219	Western Scottish
TSO21X	Bluebird	UTX728S	Red & White	VLT226	Western Scottish
TSO23X	Bluebird	UVK287T	Busways	VLT245	Western Scottish
TSO24X	Bluebird	UVK288T	Busways	VLT255	United Counties
TSO29X	Bluebird	UVK289T	Busways	VLT272	Western Scottish
TSO30X	Bluebird	UVK290T	Busways	VOD593S	Cheltenham & Gloucester
TSO31X	Bluebird	UVK291T	Busways	VOD596S	Cheltenham & Gloucester
TSO32X	Bluebird	UVK292T	Busways	VOD597S	Cheltenham & Gloucester
TSU638	East Kent	UVK294T	Busways	VOD598S	Cheltenham & Gloucester
TSU639	East Kent	UVK295T	Busways	VOD604S	Hampshire Bus
TSU640	East Kent	UVK297T	Busways	VOD605S	South Coast Buses
TSU641	East Kent	UVK298T	Busways	VOD625S	South Coast Buses
TSU642	East Kent	UVK299T	Busways	VPF283S	Coastline
TSV718	Bluebird	UVK300T	Busways	VPR490S	Hampshire Bus
TSV719	Bluebird	UWP105	Hampshire Bus	VPR491S	Hampshire Bus
TSV720	Bluebird	UWV604S	Coastline	VPR492S	Hampshire Bus
TSV721	Bluebird	UWV605S	Bluebird	VRN827Y	Ribble
TSV722	Bluebird	UWV607S	Coastline	VRN828Y	Ribble
TSV778	Bluebird	UWV608S	Bluebird	VRN829Y	Ribble
TSV779	Bluebird	UWV609S	Bluebird	VRN830Y	Ribble
TSV780	Bluebird	UWV610S	Cumberland	VRR447	Cumberland
TSV781	Bluebird	UWV611S	Hants & Surrey	VSS3X	Busways
TTC532T	Cheltenham & Gloucester	UWV612S	Cumberland	VSV564	South Coast Buses
TTC787T	Busways	UWV613S	East Kent	VTV170S	Midland Red
TVC504W	Midland Red	UWV614S	Coastline	VTV171S	Hampshire Bus

VTV172S	Hampshire Bus	WLT501	Western Scottish	WYV25T	East London
VVV948W	United Counties	WLT512	United Counties	WYV26T	East London
VVV949W	United Counties	WLT526	Western Scottish	WYV27T	East London
VVV950W	United Counties	WLT528	United Counties	WYV28T	East London
VVV952W	United Counties	WLT538	Western Scottish	WYV29T	East London
VVV953W	United Counties	WLT546	Western Scottish	WYV30T	East London
VVV954W	United Counties	WLT575	Selkent	WYV31T	East London
VVV961W	United Counties	WLT613	East London	WYV32T	East London
VVV962W	United Counties	WLT682	United Counties	WYV33T	East London
VVV963W	United Counties	WLT697	Western Scottish	WYV34T	East London
VVV965W	United Counties	WLT706	Cumberland	WYV35T	East London
VVV966W	United Counties	WLT720	Western Scottish	WYV36T	East London
VVV967W	United Counties	WLT727	Western Scottish	WYV37T	East London
VWA34Y	East Midland	WLT774	Western Scottish	WYV38T	East London
VWA35Y	East Midland	WLT794	Western Scottish	WYV39T	East London
VWA36Y	East Midland	WLT809	Western Scottish	WYV40T	East London
WAO396Y	Ribble	WLT824	Cumberland	WYV49T	Selkent
WAO397Y	Busways	WLT830	Western Scottish	WYV56T	Selkent
WAO398Y	Ribble	WLT874	Western Scottish	WYV63T	East London
WAO643Y	Bluebird	WLT886	East London	WYV66T	East London
WAO645Y	Ribble	WLT890	East London	WYV79T	Selkent
WAO646Y	Ribble	WLT898	East London	WYV86T	Selkent
WAS765V	Red & White	WLT908	United Counties	WYV98T	Selkent
WAS767V	Red & White	WLT915	Western Scottish	WYV114T	Selkent
WAS768V	Western Scottish	WLT978	Western Scottish	WYV120T	Selkent
WAS771V	Western Scottish	WLT980	Cumberland	XAP636S	Coastline
WBD876S	United Counties	WPR151S	Stagecoach South	XAP644S	South Coast Buses
WCK140V	Cumberland	WPR152S	Hampshire Bus	XBO116T	Red & White
WCK213Y	Ribble	WSU293	Midland Red	XCC94V	Hartlepool
WCK215Y	Ribble	WSU450	East Kent	XDU599	East Kent
WDA1T	Red & White	WSU451	East Kent	XDV602S	Cheltenham & Gloucester
WDA2T	Red & White	WSU452	East Kent	XDV606S	Cheltenham & Gloucester
WDA5T	Red & White	WUH166T	Red & White	XFU125V	Grimsby Cleethorpes
WDA994T	Midland Red	WUH167T	Red & White	XFU126V	Grimsby Cleethorpes
WEX927S	Busways	WUH168T	Red & White	XFU127V	Grimsby Cleethorpes
WEX928S	Busways	WUH179T	Red & White	XFU128V	Grimsby Cleethorpes
WFR392V	Midland Red	WUH185T	Red & White	XFU129V	Grimsby Cleethorpes
WFS135W	Bluebird	WVM884S	Western Scottish	XFU130V	Grimsby Cleethorpes
WFS136W	Bluebird	WVM888S	Western Scottish	XGR728R	Midland Red
WFS137W	Bluebird	WVT618	Cumberland	XGS736S	Grimsby Cleethorpes
WFU465V	Grimsby Cleethorpes	WWM930W	Midland Red	XGS762X	Hants & Surrey
WFU466V	Grimsby Cleethorpes	WWM936W	Midland Red	XJJ650V	East Kent
WFU467V	Grimsby Cleethorpes	WYJ168S	Hants & Surrey	XJJ651V	East Kent
WFU468V	Grimsby Cleethorpes	WYJ168S	Hampshire Bus	XJJ652V	East Kent
WFU469V	Grimsby Cleethorpes	WYJ169S	South Coast Buses	XJJ653V	East Kent
WFU470V	Grimsby Cleethorpes	WYV3T	East London	XJJ654V	East Kent
WGA908V	Western Scottish	WYV4T	East London	XJJ655V	East Kent
WGB645W	Western Scottish	WYV5T	East London	XJJ657V	East Kent
WGB646W	Western Scottish	WYV6T	East London	XJJ658V	East Kent
WJM824T	Stagecoach South	WYV7T	East London	XJJ659V	East Kent
WJM825T	Hampshire Bus	WYV8T	East London	XJJ660V	East Kent
WJM826T	Hampshire Bus	WYV9T	East London	XJJ661V	East Kent
WJM827T	South Coast Buses	WYV10T	East London	XJJ662V	East Kent
WJM828T	Hants & Surrey	WYV11T	East London	XJJ663V	East Kent
WJM829T	Hants & Surrey	WYV12T	East London	XJJ664V	East Kent
WJM832T	Hants & Surrey	WYV13T	East London	XJJ665V	East Kent
WKO129S	Stagecoach South	WYV14T	East London	XJJ666V	East Kent
WKO130S	Stagecoach South	WYV15T	East London	XJJ667V	East Kent
WLT400	Selkent	WYV16T	East London	XJJ668V	East Kent
WLT415	Western Scottish	WYV17T	East London	XJJ669V	East Kent
WLT416	Western Scottish	WYV18T	East London	XJJ670V	East Kent
WLT439	Western Scottish	WYV19T	East London	XNV878S	United Counties
WLT441	Western Scottish	WYV20T	East London	XNV879S	United Counties
WLT444	Western Scottish	WYV21T	East London	XNV880S	United Counties
WLT447	Western Scottish	WYV22T	East London	XNV885S	United Counties
WLT465	Western Scottish	WYV23T	East London	XNV886S	United Counties
WLT491	Selkent	WYV24T	East London	XNV887S	United Counties

Reg	Operator	Reg	Operator	Reg	Operator
XNV888S	United Counties	YAY21Y	Kingston upon Hull	YRN818V	Ribble
XNV889S	United Counties	YBO16T	Midland Red	YRN819V	Ribble
XNV890S	United Counties	YBO18T	Midland Red	YRN820V	Ribble
XNV891S	United Counties	YBO144T	Red & White	YRN821V	South Coast Buses
XOV753T	Midland Red	YBO147T	Red & White	YRN822V	Ribble
XOV754T	Midland Red	YCD73T	South Coast Buses	YSD350L	Western Scottish
XOV755T	Midland Red	YCD74T	South Coast Buses	YSD818T	Western Scottish
XOV756T	Midland Red	YCD76T	South Coast Buses	YSD819T	Western Scottish
XOV760T	Midland Red	YCD77T	South Coast Buses	YSD820T	Western Scottish
XRM772Y	Bluebird	YCD82T	South Coast Buses	YSD822T	Western Scottish
XRR173S	Hampshire Bus	YCD87T	Stagecoach South	YSF98S	Bluebird
XRR175S	Ribble	YDC21Y	Hartlepool	YSF100S	Bluebird
XRR581M	Stagecoach South	YDC22Y	Hartlepool	YSO33Y	Bluebird
XSJ648T	Western Scottish	YDC23Y	Hartlepool	YSO34Y	Bluebird
XSJ651T	Western Scottish	YDC24Y	Hartlepool	YSO35Y	Bluebird
XSJ653T	Western Scottish	YDC25Y	Hartlepool	YSO36Y	Bluebird
XSJ654T	Western Scottish	YDC26Y	Hartlepool	YSO37Y	Bluebird
XSJ655T	Western Scottish	YDG616	Ribble	YSO38Y	Bluebird
XSJ656T	Western Scottish	YEL2T	Hampshire Bus	YSO39Y	Bluebird
XSJ657T	Western Scottish	YEL3T	Hampshire Bus	YSO40Y	Bluebird
XSJ658T	Western Scottish	YEL4T	Hampshire Bus	YSO41Y	Bluebird
XSJ659T	Western Scottish	YEL93Y	Coastline	YSO42Y	Bluebird
XSJ660T	Western Scottish	YEL94Y	Coastline	YSO43Y	Bluebird
XSJ661T	Western Scottish	YEU446Y	Midland Red	YSV730	Western Scottish
XSJ662T	Western Scottish	YFB972V	Cheltenham & Gloucester	YSV735	Western Scottish
XSJ665T	Western Scottish	YFB973V	Cheltenham & Gloucester	YSX932W	Red & White
XSJ666T	Western Scottish	YFS304W	Western Scottish	YSX933W	Red & White
XSJ667T	Western Scottish	YFS308W	Western Scottish	YSX934W	Red & White
XSJ668T	Western Scottish	YFS309W	Western Scottish	YSX934W	Red & White
XSJ669T	Western Scottish	YFS310W	Western Scottish	YSX935W	Red & White
XSL596A	Bluebird	YJV806	Cheltenham & Gloucester	YTS820A	Bluebird
XSU912	East Kent	YLJ332	Coastline	YVN520T	Cleveland
XVV540S	Red & White	YNA363M	Midland Red	YVN521T	Cleveland
XYK976	East Kent	YRN813V	Ribble	YVN522T	Cleveland
YAJ154Y	Cleveland	YRN814V	Ribble	YWC16L	Busways
YAJ155Y	Cleveland	YRN815V	Ribble	YWC18L	Busways
YAJ156Y	Cleveland	YRN816V	South Coast Buses	YWK3S	Midland Red
YAJ157Y	Cleveland	YRN817V	Ribble	YYS174	Western Scottish

ISBN 1 897990 22 7
Published by British Bus Publishing
The Vyne, 16 St Margaret's Drive, Wellington,
Telford, Shropshire, TF1 3PH
Fax: 01952 255669

Printed by Graphics & Print
Unit A13, Stafford Park 15
Telford, Shropshire, TF3 3BB